●●●POWER
ENGINEERING
TRAINING SYSTEMS

And

BISMARCK STATE COLLEGE

Steam Turbines and Auxiliaries

Published by PanGlobal Training Systems Ltd.
Publisher of Power Engineering Training Systems Products

Edition 1.0 July 2006

Address all inquiries to:
PanGlobal Training Systems
L400
1301 – 16 Ave. NW,
Calgary, AB
Canada
T2M 0L4
Attention: Director of Operations

This curriculum is endorsed by Bismarck State College.
This curriculum is endorsed by the American Boiler Manufacturers Association (ABMA).

First Printing – July 2006

ISNB13: 978-1-897251-82-9

Please visit our website for information on this and other products www.powerengineering.net

Any technical or editorial errors may be reported by e-mailing information to corrections@powerengineering.net or faxing suggested corrections to 1-403-284-8863

Steam Turbines and Auxiliaries

Table of Contents

UNIT 1

The Simple Steam Engine

Learning Objectives

Here is what you will be able to do when you complete each objective:

1. Define and distinguish between the terms "heat engine" and "prime mover".
2. Describe the construction and operation of a simple steam engine.

INTRODUCTION

A power engineer works with many types of energy transfer systems. These systems are designed to take a natural, and available, source of energy at one location and deliver it to another location as useful energy. If the distance is large, the energy may have to be transformed into intermediate forms along the way.

The following example will illustrate this process. Suppose we have a supply of natural gas as our energy source, and some distance away we wish to drive a large pump. There are a number of ways this can be done. Figure 1 shows a few of the more likely possibilities.

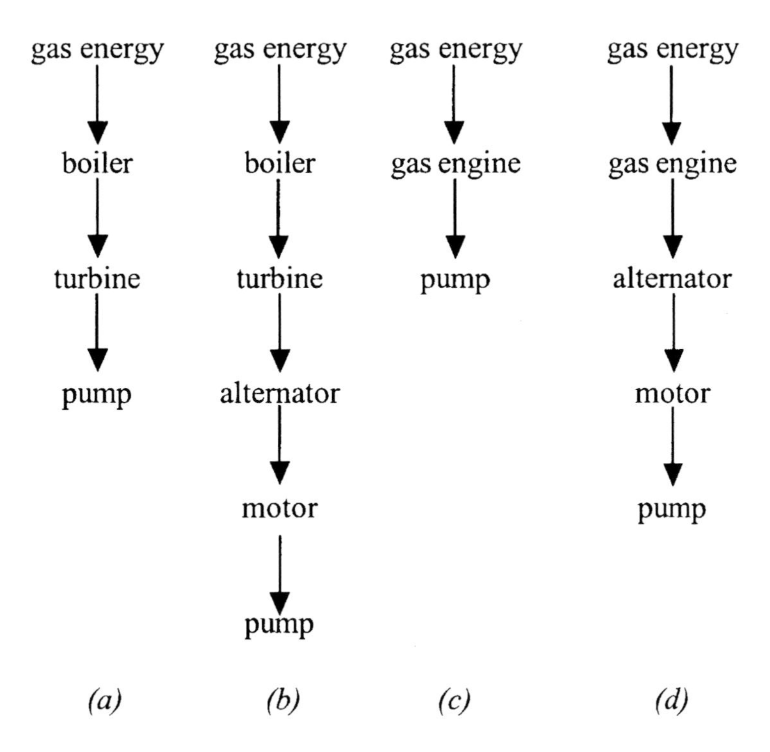

FIGURE 1

Energy Transfer

In (a) the gas energy is converted to thermal (steam) energy in the boiler, and transferred to the turbine, which converts the thermal energy into mechanical energy at the pump. In (b) the turbine drives an alternator, changing the thermal energy first to mechanical, and then electrical energy. The motor finally converts the electrical energy into mechanical energy for the pump. In (c) the gas is burned directly in an engine, changing into thermal (hot gas) energy in the cylinder, and then into mechanical energy at the pump shaft. Process (d) is similar to (b), in that an intermediate conversion to electrical energy is made.

Obviously, there are many choices for the above process. No one system is preferred over all others for all applications. The choice of which system to use will depend on many factors, such as environmental concerns, type and cost of fuel, transmission distance, equipment cost, manpower and repair costs, and system efficiency.

In order to compare such systems we need some terms of reference. This chapter will introduce some of these terms, provide an introductory survey of the major types of systems and devices used, and take a brief look at one type of device used to provide mechanical power from steam, the steam engine.

HEAT ENGINES AND PRIME MOVERS

The term "heat engine" sounds as if it refers to a single device. Actually, a heat engine is both a device (or devices) and a system, or cycle, of operations. The operating cycle uses a working fluid to convert thermal energy to mechanical energy; by heating the fluid, and then allowing it to expand under controlled conditions. For example, a gasoline engine is a heat engine. The actual device is the engine itself, the cycle of operations is called the Otto cycle (named after its inventor), and the working fluid is a mixture of air and combustion gases. By comparison, an entire steam plant is also a single heat engine. In this case there are a number of devices; the boiler, turbine, condenser, feedwater pump, and deaerator; the working fluid is water/steam, and the process is called the Rankine cycle. All of this equipment, together with the fluid and cycle, forms one big heat engine.

The term "prime mover" has a slightly different meaning. A prime mover is a single device which, either by itself or as part of an overall heat engine, converts a natural source of energy into motion. In the above two examples, the gas engine is both a heat engine and a prime mover, whereas a steam turbine, in the steam plant, is a prime mover, but not (by itself) a heat engine.

Examples of heat engines are: spark ignition engines, compression ignition (Diesel) engines, gas turbines and jet engines, and steam plants producing power. Examples of prime movers include the spark and compression ignition engines, gas turbines and jet engines, and, in addition, steam turbines, steam engines, hydraulic (water) turbines, and wind turbines (windmills). Note that electric motors are not generally considered to be prime movers, since they are neither part of a heat engine nor do they convert a natural source of energy.

Energy Sources

Although there are a number of potential energy sources, we currently use only a few for the large scale production of power. These are: solid, liquid and gaseous hydrocarbons; water power (due to gravitational potential energy of elevated water); and nuclear energy. These sources suit different types of heat engines and prime movers. One reason that steam plants are so widely used, despite their size and complexity, is because they are able to burn solid fuels such as coal and wood. In addition, their cycle of operations has the highest overall efficiency. Internal combustion engines, on the other hand, are generally restricted to using liquid or gaseous fuels.

The specific advantages and disadvantages of these devices will be covered in more detail in their respective chapters.

STEAM ENGINES

Historically, steam engines were the most important and widely used prime movers. Throughout the 20th century, however, they have been steadily losing ground to steam turbines, combustion engines, and electric motors. Today we rarely see a steam engine in service. Nevertheless, they still find use in a few specialized applications, as follows:

a. When slow rotational speed, without the use of reduction gearing, is required. Motors, turbines and combustion engines are essentially high speed devices.
b. When reversal of rotational direction, without the use of gearing, is required.
c. For driving reciprocating pumps. The piston and cylinder design of steam engines has been well suited to the simple and rugged construction of these pumps.

We will now take a quick look at steam engine construction and operation.

Construction

Figure 2 shows sectional elevations of a simple steam engine. It is a single cylinder, double-acting, vertical engine with a D-slide valve and a throttling governor.

FIGURE 2

Sectional Elevation of a Vertical Engine

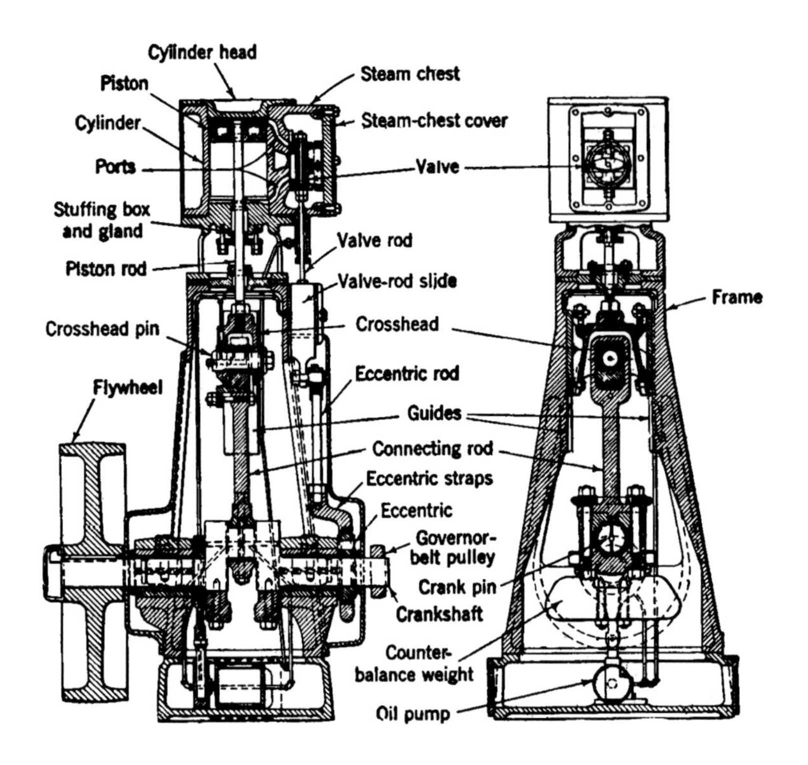

Steam from the main steam pipe is admitted by the throttle valve and passes through the governor to the steam-chest. The slide valve controls the steam admission and exhaust to and from the engine cylinder.

The valve has a reciprocating motion timed to match the motion of the piston and imparted by the valve gear. The valve gear consists of the eccentric, the eccentric rod, and the valve rod.

The steam is admitted above the piston to give a downward thrust and then below the piston to give an upward thrust. In each case the steam supply is cut off when the piston has made only part of its stroke, this may be 1/4 to 1/3 depending upon the engine load. The steam then in the cylinder maintains a thrust on the piston by expanding throughout the remainder of the stroke. Finally the slide valve opens a passage to the exhaust and allows the steam on this side of the piston to escape in preparation for the return stroke under the action of live steam on the other side of the piston.

The principle of cutting off the steam supply and allowing that in the cylinder to expand is termed "expansive" use of the steam and results in economical operation. Very few steam engines continue steam admission throughout the whole stroke. This will only be the case where reliability of operation is most important and economy is not a consideration.

Figure 3 (a) shows an engine cylinder in section with piston and steam valve shown. Figure 3 (b) illustrates an eccentric sheave; reference to Figure 2 will show its position on the engine.

FIGURE 3 (a) (b)

Engine Cylinder

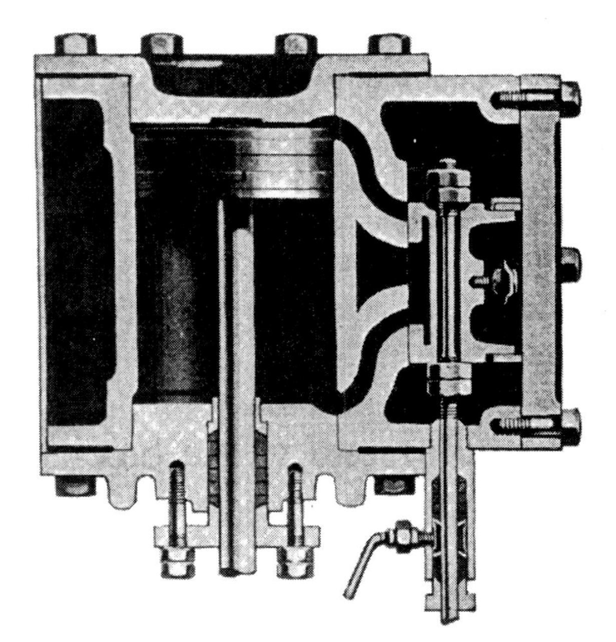

(a) Piston & Slide Valve

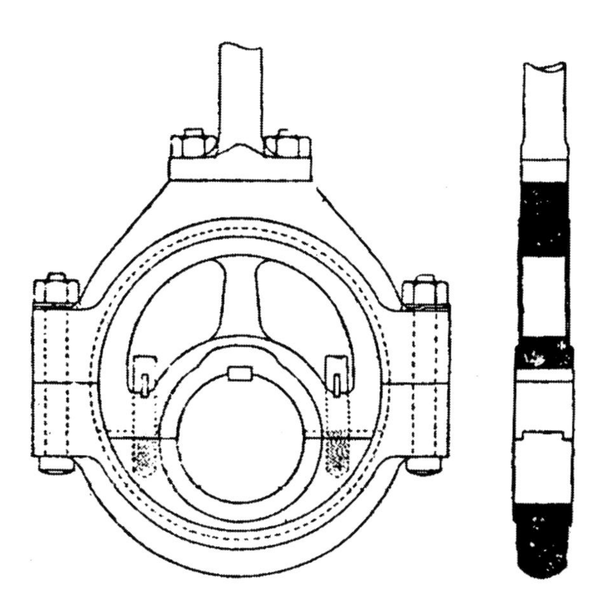

(b) Eccentric

The eccentric is a disc fixed on the crankshaft in such a way that the center of the disc is "eccentric" or "out of center" with the center of the shaft. The disc is termed the sheave of the eccentric, and is made in halves, the halves being secured by bolts and split cotters as shown. The band surrounding the sheave is called the strap. The sheave rotates inside the strap in the same way as the crank-pin rotates in the connecting rod head. The eccentric rod is attached to the strap, and the slide valve receives a reciprocating motion from it, similar to that received by the piston from the crank pin, but on a reduced scale.

As the valve moves endwise on the valve seat steam is allowed to flow through passages called steam ports into or out of the cylinder. When the piston has steam at boiler pressure on one side it is open to a lower pressure on the other side and the difference between these pressures on its two sides causes it to move along the cylinder transmitting its force through the piston rod, the connecting rod and the crank pin to the crankshaft.

The reciprocating motion of the piston is changed to a rotary motion at the crankshaft by a crank pin shrunk into a crank disc into which the end of the crankshaft is also shrunk.

The crosshead takes the angular push or pull of the connecting rod against the piston rod during the greater part of the revolution when these rods are not "in line"; the valve rod guide fulfills the same function in the case of the valve spindle and eccentric rod.

Whenever motion causes surfaces to slide or rub against each other there is friction and wear. Lubricators are provided at all such places to feed oil between the sliding surfaces and reduce the friction and wear to the lowest possible amount.

Steam must not be allowed to leak past the piston rod and valve rod where they pass out of the cylinder and valve box. A packing box filled with flexible packing is provided at each of these places. The packing is squeezed tightly into the box around the rod by a gland which is held in place by a covering nut, or studs and nuts in the cylinder body.

Drain cocks are fitted into the lowest part of the cylinder and valve box for the removal of any water caused by condensation of steam.

In most engines the admission of steam is stopped before the end of the stroke and allowed to do work by expanding during the latter part. Thus there is a greater force on the piston at the beginning than at the end of the stroke which causes the piston to move faster towards the beginning than towards the end.

While a governor is provided to take care of changes of speed due to changes of load over several revolutions, a flywheel is fitted to dampen or even-out these changes of speed caused by varying steam pressure and also to carry the engine over the dead center when no work is being done by the piston. The flywheel does this because considerable force is necessary to start it in motion or to stop it, also to increase or decrease its speed if it is already in motion.

The frame of the engines serves to hold the parts together in their relative positions and also provides a means of securing the engine solidly on its foundation.

Figure 4 shows a sectional view of a small vertical single cylinder, double-acting steam engine, with a piston type steam valve and an inertia governor in the flywheel.

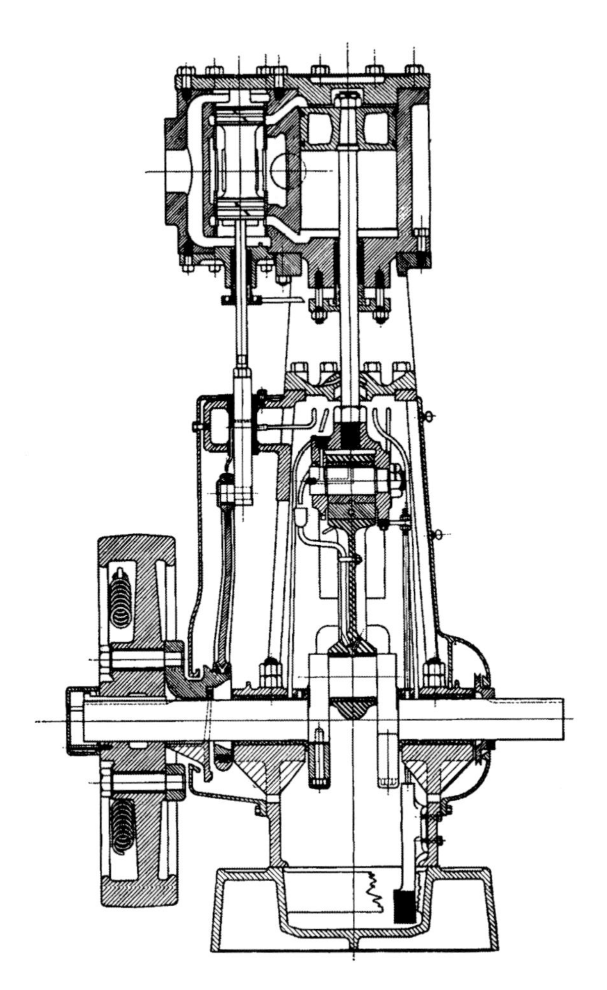

FIGURE 4

Automatic Governor

Figure 5 (a) and (b) shows a duplex reciprocating pump, driven by a steam engine.

FIGURE 5 (a) (b)

Horizontal Duplex Pump Cross-Section
(Courtesy of Worthington Corporation)

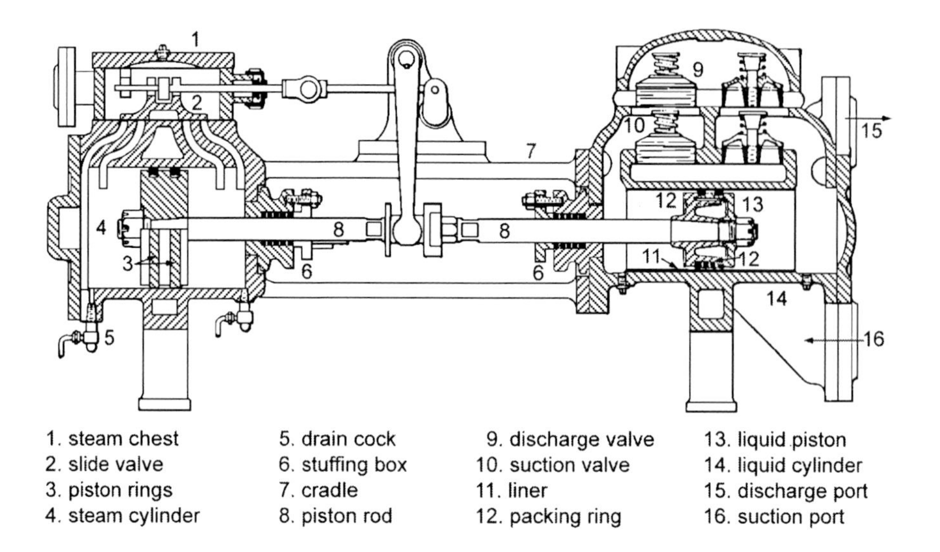

Engine Operation

1. Starting an Engine

1. See that no tools have been left around the engine where they may cause damage and that all is clear around flywheels, pulleys, armatures, or other moving parts.

2. Check the steam chest and cylinder drains to be sure they are open to clear all water from the steam chest and cylinder.

3. Open the separator drain on the steam line to empty it of water, or, if the steam separator drain is fitted with a trap, see that the trap is operating properly.

4. When water ceases to flow through the drain valves, open the stop valve slightly (cracking the valve) until steam blows freely through the drains. Some steam will be condensed in the steam line and cylinder at first and more water will flow through the drains, after the valve is cracked.

5. Never open a steam valve suddenly or any water present in the steam line will be driven violently along the pipes, causing water hammer, which may result in the fracture of pipes or fittings.

2. Inspection While Engine is Running

At regular intervals make a tour of inspection of all engines, pumps and machines. Examine all lubricators to see that they are filled and feeding properly and feel around all bearings to see if any are heating above the ordinary running temperature. This inspection should be made, say every half hour, or more often if an engine is heavily loaded, or is known to have certain bearings that have a tendency to "heat up" rapidly.

Know the sound of your engine or engines so that any change in the noise made by the engine running will give warning that something is wrong. The ability to detect any change of sound, however slight, will often lead to the detection and remedy of minor troubles that might assume serious proportions if allowed to continue without being adjusted or repaired.

UNIT 2

Steam Turbines

Learning Objectives

Here is what you will be able to do when you complete each objective:

1. Describe the principle of operation and major components of a steam turbine.
2. Describe the lubrication and sealing of steam turbine shafts.
3. Describe the construction and operation of an overspeed trip.
4. Describe the general construction of a simple type of multistage steam turbine, and an overall boiler-turbine cycle.
5. Describe how the rotational speed of a steam turbine is governed.
6. List the steps that are followed in a typical steam turbine start-up and shut-down.

INTRODUCTION

Steam turbines have been gaining in importance as prime movers since their first practical designs were proposed in the late eighteen hundreds. The introduction of turbine designs by Parsons, Curtis and De Laval laid the foundation for the development of the modern steam turbine.

The steam turbine is employed as a mechanical drive for applications covering a wide power range. It is supreme in the field of large capacity electricity generators.

Among the advantages of the steam turbine are simplicity, reliability and low maintenance costs. Space requirements for a steam turbine are much less than for a diesel or steam engine of the same power. The absence of reciprocating motion results in decreased vibration and permits lighter foundations.

Lubrication in the steam turbine is simpler than in a reciprocating engine. Furthermore since the turbine requires no cylinder lubrication it has the ability to deliver oil-free condensate or exhaust steam which is a valuable consideration where these are to be used in some industrial process.

This particular advantage allows many manufacturing industries to generate their own electrical energy cheaply as a by-product to the production of process steam.

Steam turbines may be used as prime movers for large alternators in central stations or as reliable drives for fans, pumps, and other auxiliaries located in the power plant itself, as well as industry in general.

GENERAL DESCRIPTION

The steam turbine operates through the action of a flow of steam directed by stationary nozzles or blades on to rings of rotating blades. There are basically two types of steam turbine, namely impulse and reaction, the difference being in the manner in which the steam is expanded through the turbine stages.

If all of the steam pressure drop takes place in the stationary nozzles then the turbine is known as an impulse turbine.

If on the other hand the steam pressure drops in passing through moving blades as well as the stationary nozzles or blades, the machine is called a reaction turbine.

It can be seen from the above remarks that two of the more important elements of a steam turbine are the stationary steam passages and the rotor flow passages. These, together with other essential turbine parts, are described below.

Stationary Passages

The stationary passage of an impulse turbine consists of one or more stationary nozzles. The nozzle allows steam at high pressure to expand and convert some of its thermal energy into kinetic energy so that the issuing flow of steam is at a lower pressure but traveling at high speed.

The nozzle is so positioned as to direct the flow of steam into the rotor flow passages.

Reaction turbines use stationary blades to redirect the steam into the rotor passages as it expands through the turbine stages.

Rotor Passages

Blades or buckets form the rotor flow passage and serve to change the direction of the steam received from the stationary nozzles.

Figure 1 shows the arrangement of the steam nozzles and the blade wheel or rotor of a simple impulse turbine.

FIGURE 1

Rotor and Nozzle of an Impulse Turbine

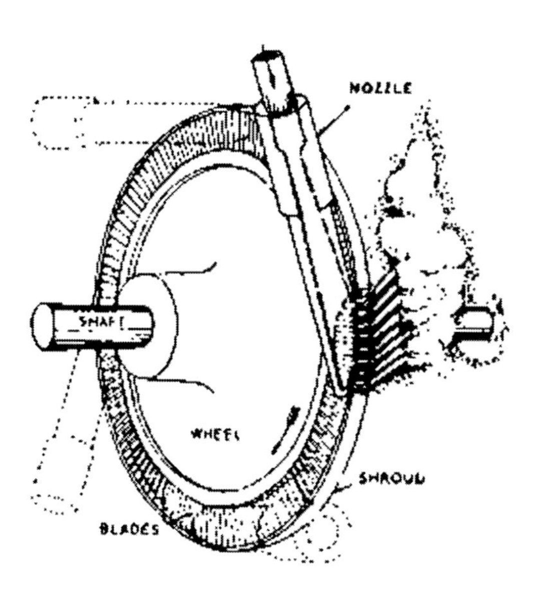

Steam emerges from the nozzle at a high velocity and strikes the blades which change its direction of flow.

Figure 2 shows the typical shape of impulse and reaction turbine blades when viewed in section.

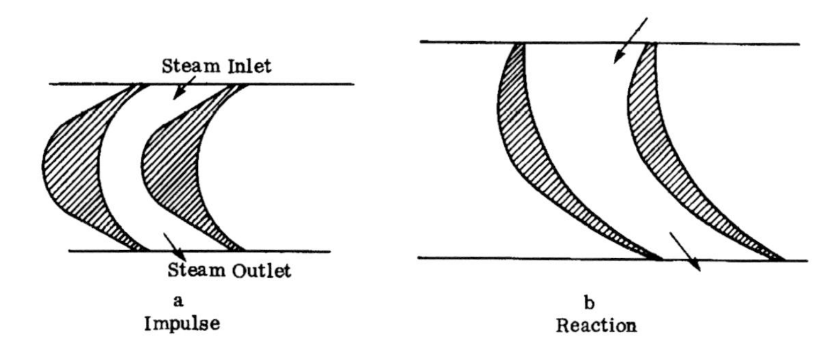

FIGURE 2

Impulse and Reaction Blades

The impulse blades are so shaped that, when fitted into a blade wheel, the space between blades does not allow any steam pressure drop in its passage through. Thus the whole of the thrust imparted by the steam on the blades derives from the change in momentum, or impulse, of the steam as it changes direction to follow the shape of the blades.

The reaction blades on the other hand are specially sized and shaped to allow a steam pressure drop. This in turn produces an increase in steam speed and causes a reaction or back thrust on the blading. The effect is very similar to that felt upon the nozzle of a fire hose when high pressure water is issuing from the jet.

Figure 3 shows an "opened up" view of a small industrial, mechanical drive turbine, manufactured by Skinner Engine Co. Dean Hill Turbine Division. These machines are built in ratings from 120 to 1200 hp. Taking steam at 610 psi and 750°F. The 120 hp turbine has a blade wheel diameter of 11 in running at 1000 to 4000 rpm.

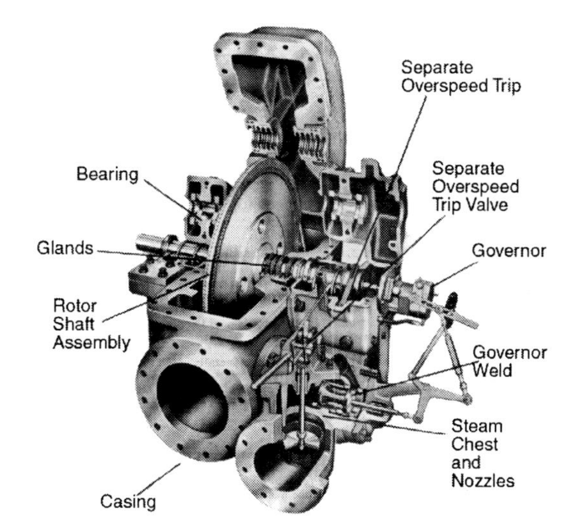

FIGURE 3

Mechanical Drive Turbine

Bearings

The bearings have a split sleeve, oil ring with a precision bored high grade babbitt. Either bearing may be removed without disturbing the wheel case cover. The governor end bearing serves as a combined thrust and journal bearing.

Glands

The glands consist of several adjacently mounted segmental carbon rings, each maintained in close contact with the shaft by a garter spring and each located in its own independent groove. This results in a negligible leakage of steam from the wheel case along the shaft.

Rotor and Shaft Assembly

The rotor consists of a carefully machined and balanced forged steel disc pressed over a key on a completely ground shaft. At the gland areas, the shaft is protected by a generous coating of stainless steel applied by the metal spray process. The shaft critical speed is well above any operating speed.

Blades

All blades are durable rolled and drawn stainless steel and are securely held in machined slots in the wheel rim by drive screws.

Shrouding

Inner and outer ends of blades are stainless steel shrouded to confine steam to the blade passage and stiffen the blades against vibration.

Casing

Type D-H Casing is Meehanite for Class 1 and 2, carbon steel for Class 3. The top half may be removed without disturbing any other part or piping connections. The casing has true center-line support. There are no internal high pressure joints; the casing is subject to exhaust pressure only. The casing has two exhaust openings so that the exhaust line may be connected at either side. The unused exhaust opening is provided with a blind flange which may be removed for wheel, blade and nozzle inspection. A sentinel warning valve is supplied.

Separate Overspeed Trip

When the steam turbine speed reaches the tripping speed (normally 10–15% over the rated speed) a spring loaded plunger held in place with snap rings, strikes the trip linkage to close the trip valve and shuts off the steam flow.

Separate Overspeed Trip Valve

The separate overspeed trip valve operates completely independently of the governor valve to shut off steam when actuated by the overspeed trip mechanism. It is a positive valve which can be tripped manually and reset with an easily accessible hand resetting device. A built-in steam strainer, removable with the trip valve cage, is incorporated in the design.

Governor

The governor is standard equipment and is hydraulically operated, directly driven from the turbine shaft, and mechanically sensing. High sensitivity keeps the linkage constantly in motion; this helps prevent the governor valve stem from sticking. There are no expensive knife edges to replace. The governor may be replaced as a unit in the field since the governor mounting is the same for all turbine frame sizes. At rest, the governor valve is closed preventing accidental startup.

Governor Valve

A Monel™ (or stainless steel) double ported, balanced floating type with renewable cage, no-resist governor valve stem bushing and stainless steel stem is used to prevent binding and friction.

Hand Speed Control

The hand speed control is located on the governor with a normal range of 10% above and 50% below the rated speed.

Steam Chest and Nozzles

An important feature is the segregation of the high pressure and high temperature steam from the wheel casing, thereby minimizing shaft misalignment resulting from expansion when in operation. The casing is subjected only to the exhaust pressure and temperature.

Figure 4 is an illustration of a General Electric Company mechanical drive turbine. These machines are built in ratings from 10-1200 hp running at speeds from 1000 to 6500 rpm. They are used to drive pumps, compressors, fans, blowers, and similar equipment.

The turbine illustrated is a single stage, velocity compounded impulse type. Two rows of blades are arranged in the one stage with a row of fixed blades between them.

FIGURE 4

Single Stage, Mechanical Drive Turbine
(Courtesy of General Electric)

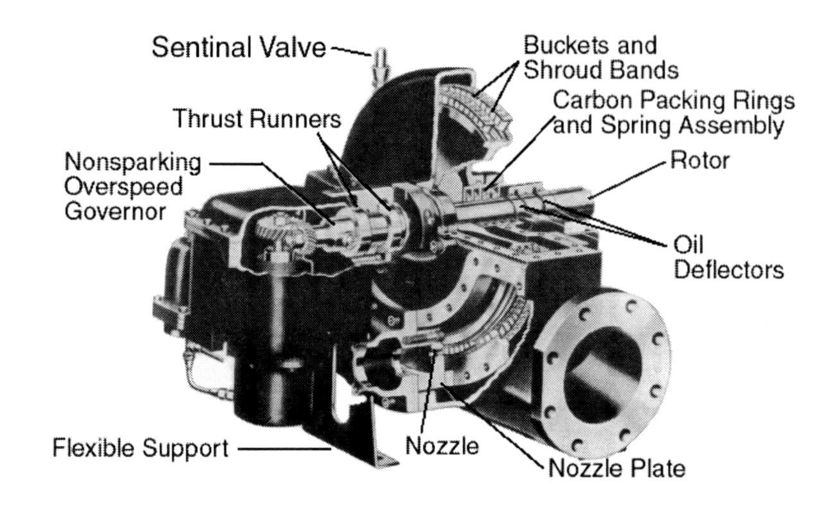

Figure 5 is a schematic drawing of the turbine governing system.

FIGURE 5

Schematic Drawing of Governing System

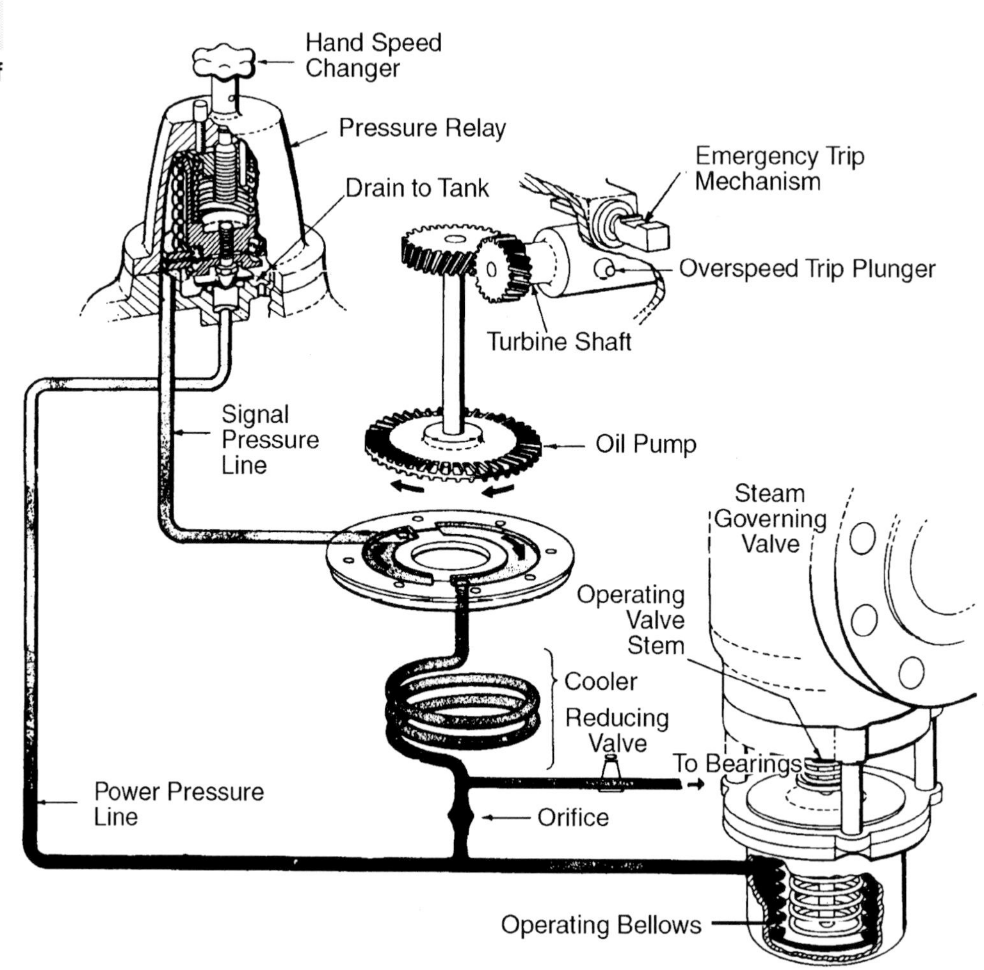

The governor oil pump, gear-driven by the turbine shaft, furnishes pressure oil through two passages to the pressure relay.

One passage leads directly to this pressure relay and provides a signal oil pressure varying with speed; the other leads through a fixed orifice to the operating bellows of the steam control valve and to the drain valve of this pressure relay.

Thus, the signal pressure and power pressure oppose each other across the drain valve, with diaphragm spring pressure normally holding the system in equilibrium. This spring compression is adjusted by the hand speed changer, and its setting determines the speed which is to be held by the turbine.

When turbine speed changes, the two opposing forces on the drain valve become unbalanced. If speed decreases, this valve opens further, more oil drains to the tank, and the pressure in the power pressure line is reduced. When speed increases, the valve opening is reduced, and pressure in the power pressure line is increased.

The operating bellows responds to these changes in pressure by opening and closing the steam admission valve through the operating valve stem. The entire system, working as a relay, is powerful, yet sensitive.

The governing valve and the trip-throttle valve are combined in the same assembly. The trip-throttle valve controls steam admission to the turbine on starting and also shuts off all steam in case of overspeeding.

After an emergency shut down it is possible to reset the combined top-throttle valve and run up the turbine again without the necessity of shutting off steam valves ahead of the turbine.

Lubrication

Lubricating oil is supplied to turbine bearings in quantities much larger than that required simply for lubrication. The purpose of this excess supply is to carry away the heat which is conducted along the shaft from the steam space and so maintain the bearings at a safe working temperature.

The lubricating oil system is sketched in Figure 6. The oil pump, gear-driven from the main turbine shaft, furnishes oil under pressure for positive bearing lubrication. From the pump, oil passes first through an oil cooler and reducing valve on the way to the bearings. This pressure oil is then fed through an opening in the top-half of the bearing shell to distribution grooves which feed the entire surface of the bearing. Grooves cut in the surface of the thrust bearings are shaped so that oil is picked up readily by the thrust runners and fed to the thrust bearing surfaces.

FIGURE 6

Schematic Diagram of Turbine Lubrication System

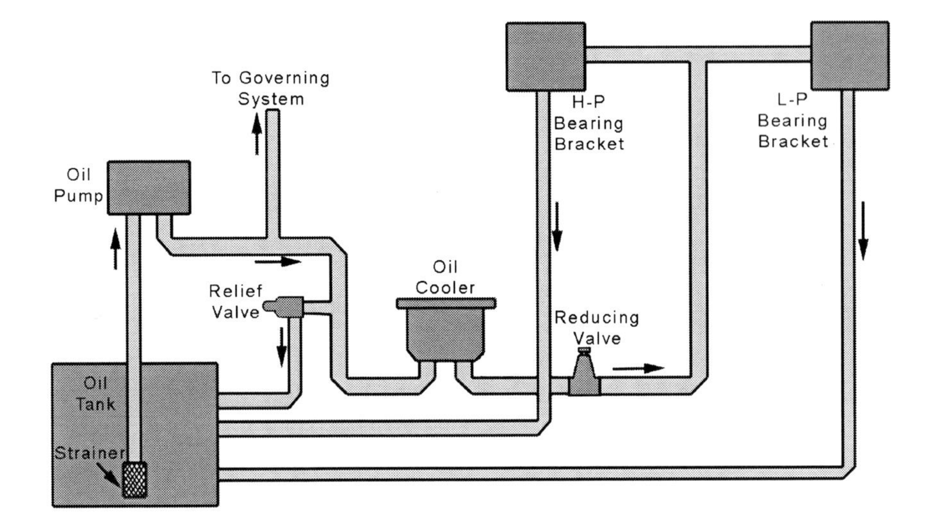

Pressure lubrication contributes to bearing life and helps assure continuous, reliable service of the turbine, with minimum maintenance. Oil level in the reservoir is checked by means of a bayonet-type gauge, or an oil sight glass.

Figure 7 shows a thrust bearing with lubricating oil grooves cut in the flanges. These are the thrust faces and they operate to locate the turbine shaft in its correct longitudinal position by rubbing against the thrust runners, or collars on the shaft.

FIGURE 7

Thrust Bearing Lubricating Oil Grooves

Also in Figure 7 are demonstrated segmental carbon packing rings for the turbine shaft steam glands. Steam-tight glands are necessary on steam turbine shafts to restrict the flow of steam from the steam space along the shaft to the atmosphere.

They may take the form of carbon rings, labyrinth, or water sealed glands. Small turbines as illustrated in the foregoing figures will generally use carbon ring glands.

1. Carbon Glands

Shaft openings at both ends of the turbine casing are sealed with packing boxes bolted to the casing. Packing boxes are integral units inserted in the casing, and split on the horizontal center-line.

To obtain an efficient shaft steam seal, carbon packing rings are assembled around the shaft in each section of the packing boxes. The carbon packing rings in the packing boxes consist of three segments with the outer surface of each ring grooved to receive a spring. Spring pressure, combined with the steam pressure, holds the packing firmly in place axially, but permits slight radial movement for automatic concentric alignment with the shaft.

The packings contain graphite, and are self-lubricating. Shafts are Monel metal sprayed at the carbon packing fit to minimize corrosive action.

2. Labyrinth Glands

High output machines, operating with high temperature, high pressure steam usually employ labyrinth type glands to prevent the escape of steam along the shaft. A labyrinth gland, as the name implies, offers a passage to the steam which is very narrow and winding.

Figure 8 shows examples of sections of labyrinth glands. In each case the clearance between turbine shaft and casing is only a very few thousandths of an inch. Consequently any steam escaping through this fine gap is immediately reduced in pressure. A number of such pressure breakdowns is sufficient to restrict the steam leakage to atmosphere of even high pressure steam to a very small amount.

Figure 8 (a) shows a section of turbine shaft with one labyrinth ring and a section of turbine casing with two labyrinth rings. Steam, in attempting to escape from the turbine steam space to atmosphere is thus forced to pass through three minute passages on its way out. Figure 8 (b) shows further examples which are variations on the basic idea illustrated in Figure 8 (a).

FIGURE 8 (a) (b)

Labyrinth Glands

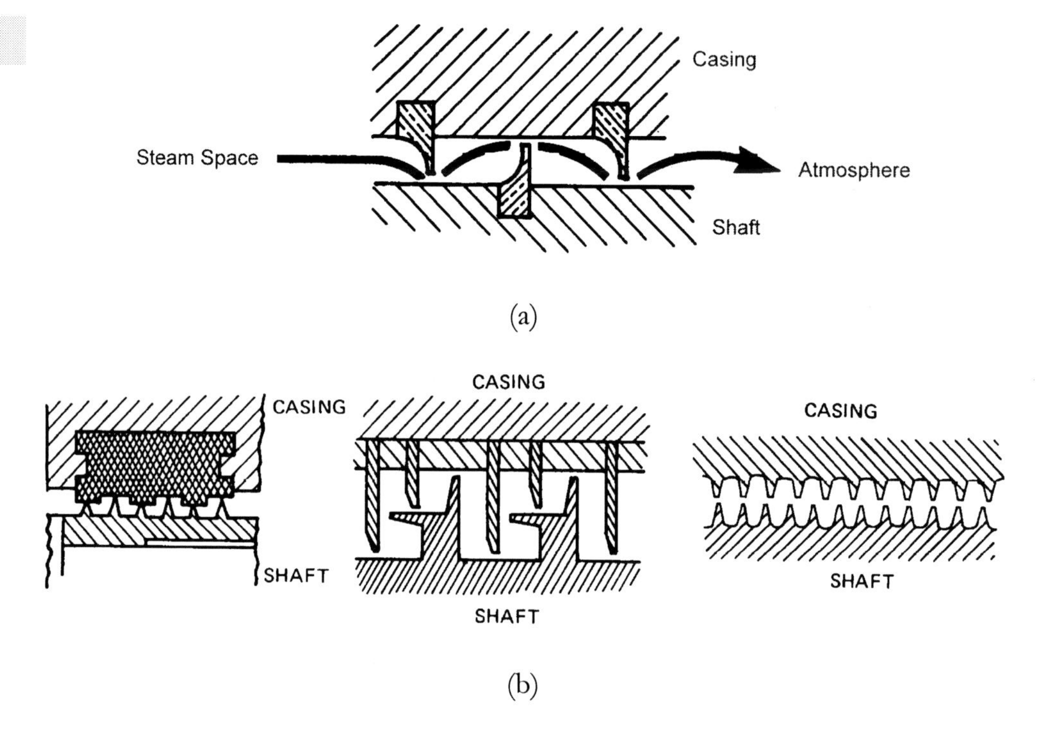

Overspeed Trips

Turbines must be protected against rotating at excessive speeds. They are designed to withstand the centrifugal forces which are present when running at all speeds up to their specified maximum. A sudden loss of load, however, can cause an unprotected machine to increase in speed to such a great extent that the centrifugal forces produced will tear the blades from the blade wheels. The final result is a complete wreck of the turbine with considerable risk of injury to operating personnel.

The overspeed trip is designed to protect the machine against these dangers. Most designs rely on centrifugal force to release some catch which, in turn, closes the steam supply valve.

Figure 9 illustrates a typical arrangement as used on a small G.E. mechanical drive turbine. Positive overspeed protection is claimed for this emergency governor. The governor consists of a spring-loaded unbalanced weight mounted in the turbine shaft, see Figure 10. If for any reason the speed increases to trip speed (usually 15 per cent above normal) centrifugal force causes the weight to move outward and trip a latch. This closes the trip-throttle valve through a direct mechanical linkage, instantly shutting off all steam to the turbine. To eliminate hazards in explosive atmospheres, the bolt is made of non-sparking material. The governor itself is totally enclosed in the main governor casing. Operating in an oil atmosphere, the probability of rusting or sticking is minimized and reliable operation is assured to provide greater safety for personnel and equipment.

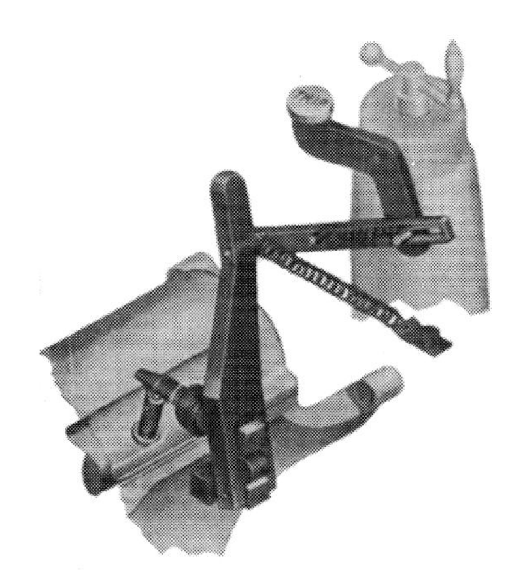

FIGURE 9

Turbine Overspeed Trip
(Courtesy of General Electric)

FIGURE 10

Turbine Shaft, Showing Trip Pin

Figure 11 shows a multi-stage impulse turbine of Terry manufacture. These machines are made in sizes of 250–450 hp running at 4000 to 6000 rpm. The first stage is velocity compounded as in Figure 4 (two rows of moving blades). The remaining three stages are pressure compounded, that is, the remaining steam pressure is broken down in steps across these three stages.

FIGURE 11

Multi-Stage Impulse Turbine
(Courtesy of the Terry Steam Turbine Company)

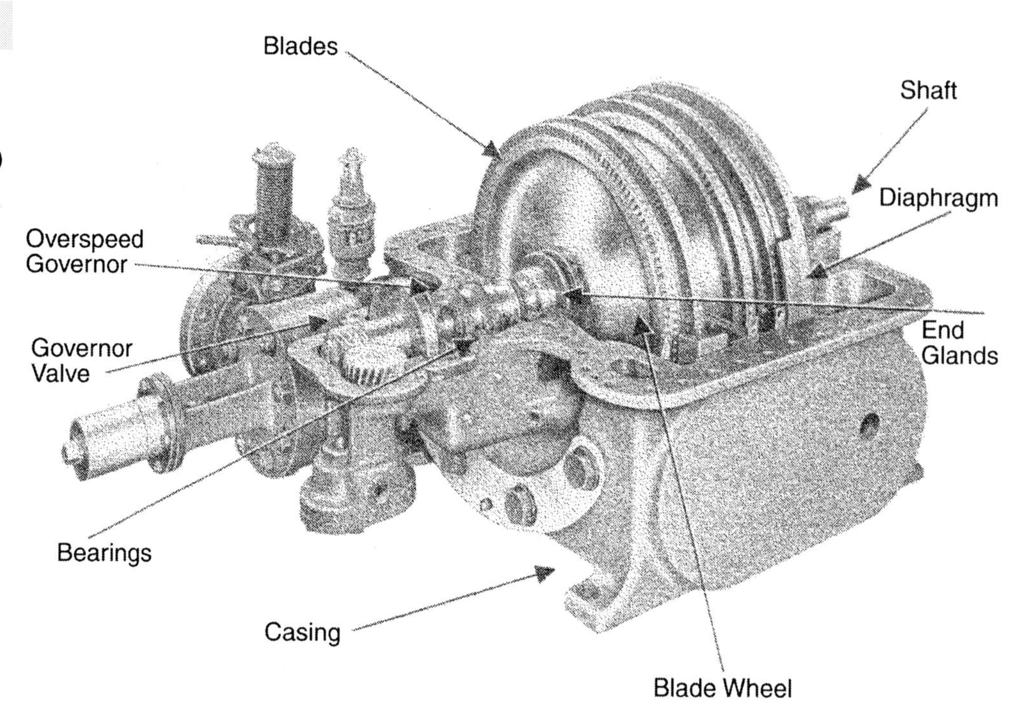

Figures 12 to 15 show some turbine parts typical of the Terry turbine of Figure 11.

Figure 12 is a turbine blade wheel complete with a ring of blades. These are the moving blades of each turbine stage.

FIGURE 12

Turbine Wheel

Figure 13 shows half of a diaphragm. These are bedded into the turbine casing and carry the fixed blades or nozzles. They form the stationary steam passages.

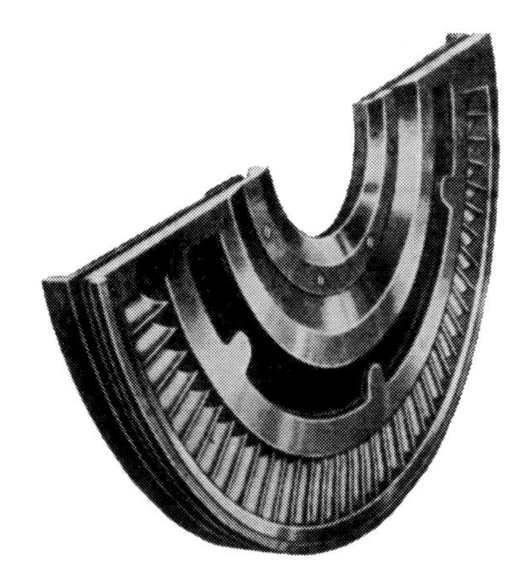

FIGURE 13
Lower Half Diaphragm

Figure 14 is a section through the outer rim of a blade wheel carrying two rows of blades and illustrates one type of blade fastening.

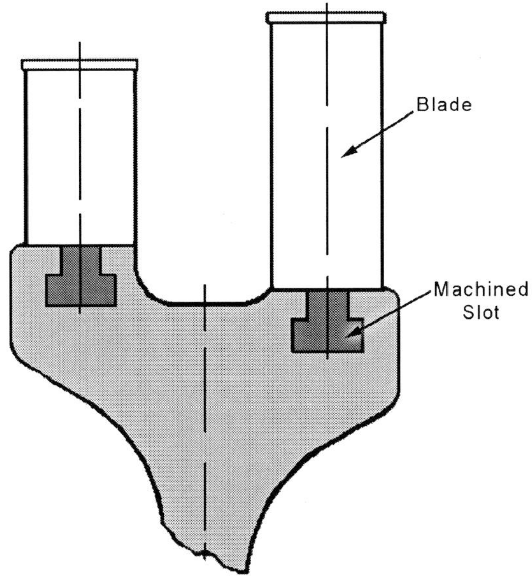

FIGURE 14
Blade Fastenings

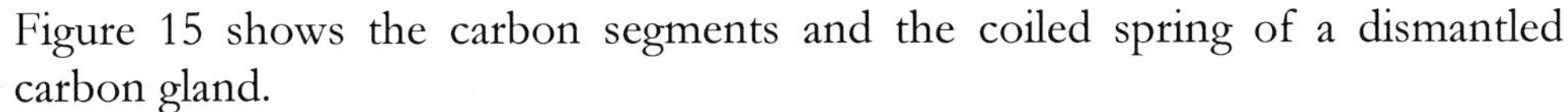

Figure 15 shows the carbon segments and the coiled spring of a dismantled carbon gland.

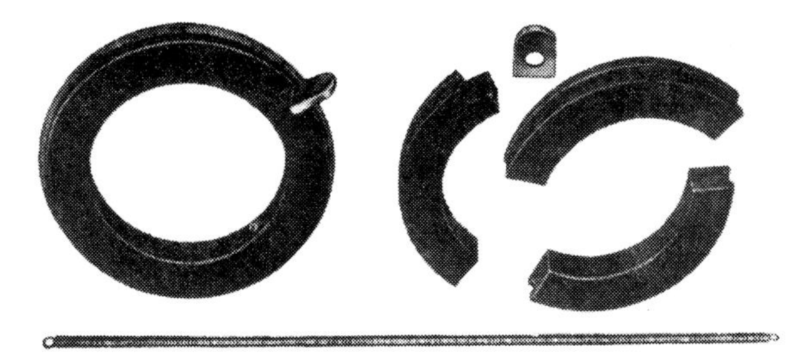

FIGURE 15
Carbon Ring End Glands

Figure 16 shows the steam cycle through a simple steam power plant and is described below.

FIGURE 16

Simple Power Plant Cycle

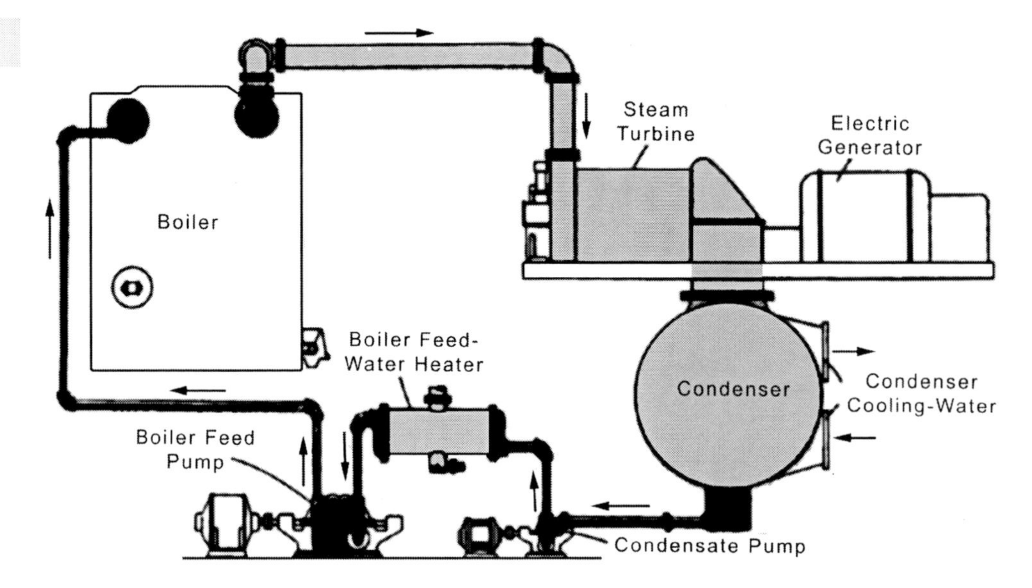

Steam, generated in the boiler at high pressure and superheated to a high temperature, flows through the turbine and so develops power to drive the electric generator. The steam is exhausted from the turbine to a condenser where cooling water transforms it back again into water. The condensate is removed from the condenser by a pump which discharges to the boiler feedwater heater and then to a boiler-feed pump. This pump raises the pressure sufficiently high to enable the water to return to the boiler and so recommence the cycle. The condenser serves two important functions. In condensing the steam a high vacuum is produced which increases the pressure drop in the turbine, thereby producing more useful work and a higher degree of power generation efficiency. It also provides a pure source of boiler feedwater, a most important consideration in all boiler operations.

The following two figures are included for interest only to show the appearance of a large output turbine in use in a central generating station.

Figure 17 shows an external view of a 100 megawatt turbo-generator. Figure 18 shows a section through the turbine. This machine is designed to operate with steam conditions of 1500 psi and 980°F at the turbine stop-valve with one stage of reheat.

FIGURE 17

100 MW Turbo-Generator
(Courtesy of Siemens Westinghouse)

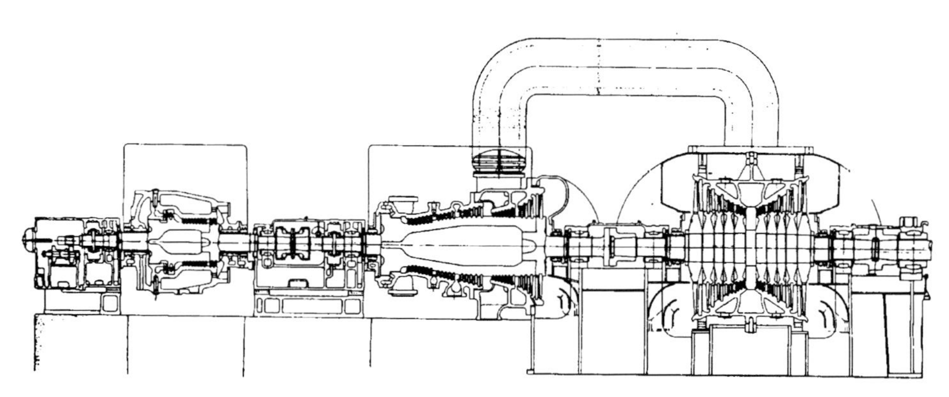

FIGURE 18

Section Through 100 MW Turbine

Turbine Governing

A turbine governor is installed in order to regulate automatically the speed and the power output and to enable changes in these to be made when required.

To regulate the speed a device is necessary which is speed sensitive and which will produce a movement corresponding to a speed change, this movement can then be used as a corrective control.

The great majority of turbine governors are of mechanical centrifugal type. The movement of a pair of revolving weights with changes of speed is applied to the turbine steam supply valve and acts either directly, or via a relay mechanism, to vary the steam supply to the turbine.

Figure 19 shows a typical pair of governor weights. They are made to revolve by the speed of the turbine shaft. An increase of speed causes them to fly outwards and to compress a spring until the increased pressure in the spring just balances the centrifugal force and the governor sleeve takes up the new position dictated by the increased speed.

FIGURE 19

Governor Weights

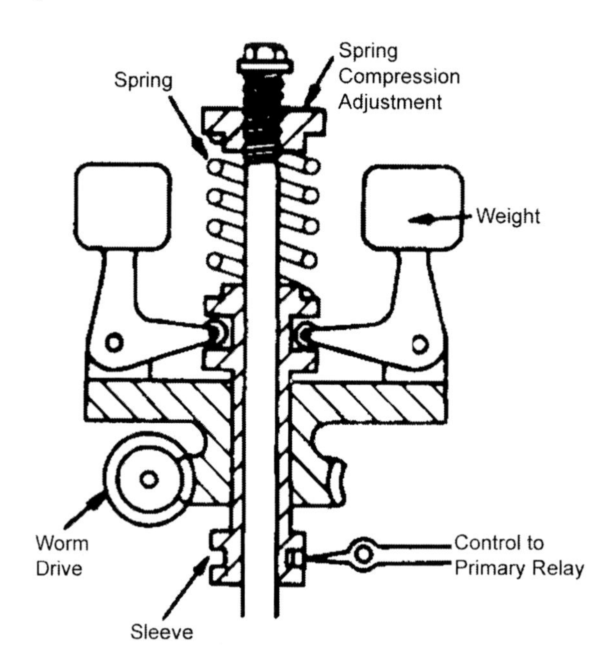

Movement of the governor sleeve can then be utilized to operate the turbine steam supply valve either directly or through a relay mechanism.

Figure 20 shows the principle. Oil pressure, exerted above or below a piston in the relay cylinder, is used to move the turbine throttle valve. The pilot valve controls the flow of this oil under pressure by covering or uncovering ports leading to the relay cylinder.

FIGURE 20

Governor Sleeve Movement

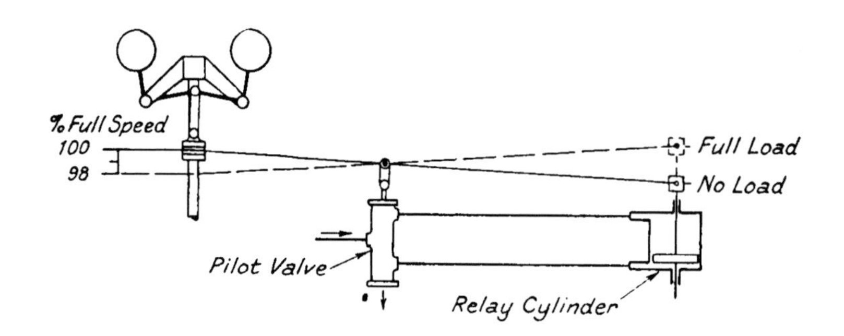

A change of turbine speed causes movement of the governor sleeve. This in turn moves the pilot valve and causes oil to flow to the relay piston. The resulting movement of the throttle valve spindle (and relay piston rod) resets the pilot valve and the throttle valve movement ceases. The whole system is then set in a new position to suit the new speed.

Reference to Figure 21 shows that a speed increase raises the governor sleeve. This raises the pilot valve, allows oil to flow above the relay piston and hence lowers the throttle valve. Lowering the throttle valve lowers the pilot valve and shuts off the oil flow to the relay piston and stops further movement.

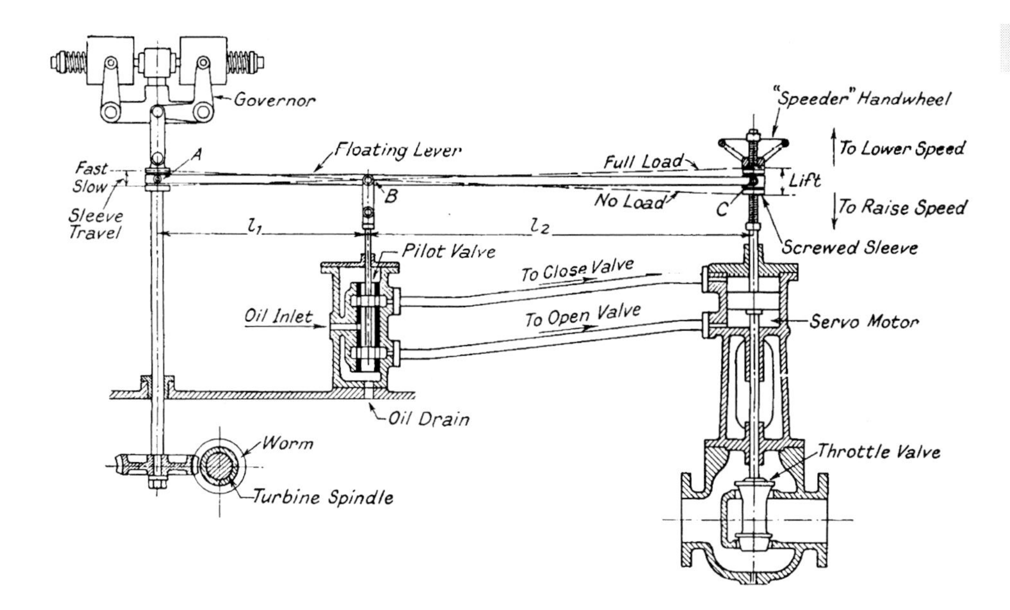

FIGURE 21

Oil Relay Governor Gear

Lowering the throttle valve also, of course, reduces the steam supply and prevents any further increase in turbine speed.

A hand control is superimposed on this equipment, named the "Speeder" handwheel, to allow adjustment of the turbine speed when running on load.

GENERAL INSTRUCTIONS FOR STARTING A STEAM TURBINE

The preceding pages have described some typical turbine designs, mostly of the small mechanical drive-type. The following instructions apply more specifically to larger turbines of the condensing type but they are included here for the assistance of those engineers who are interested in these machines.

The starting and stopping of the smaller machines will follow similar procedures except that many of the items referring to auxiliary plant will not apply.

It is hardly necessary to state that it would be impossible to give complete instructions, as machines differ so much in detail. Many manufacturers issue instruction sheets relating to their particular turbines. These should be carefully studied, and the more salient points should be noted.

The general procedure at starting is as follows:

1. Start the auxiliary oil pump. Note whether it is delivering oil to the bearings at the correct pressure.

2. Start the circulating water pump and see that it is properly primed.

3. Start the condenser air pump and keep it running slowly. Start the extraction pump.

4. Check the oil circulation to all bearings.

5. Open all the drains in preparation for warming up.

6. Open the throttle valve or throttle by-pass valve quickly to start the rotor moving. As soon as the rotor begins to turn, close the throttle valve to a point which enables the machine to run light at a speed suitable for warming up the unit. The sealing steam should now be turned on to the glands, and the speed of the air pump (or steam supply to the steam jet air ejectors where these are fitted) should be adjusted so that the vacuum is suitable for warming up purposes. This will vary from 15 to 25 in. of mercury.

7. If it is the practice to test the hand-trip gear every time the machine is started, then this should now be done. The turbine is re-started in accordance with (6) above.

8. Turn on the water supply to the oil cooler.

9. While the machine is being warmed up, attention should be given to the bearings to ensure that they are receiving an ample supply of oil.

10. When the turbine is properly heated, the throttle valve may be opened further, so as to cause a gradual increase in speed. As the machine approaches its full speed, the governor will take charge and maintain the correct speed. As the machine is gaining speed, the operator should listen for internal noises or signs of vibration. If there are obvious signs of a vibration which is not understood, the turbine should be at once shut down, and an attempt made to re-start after further warming through. If, on a second attempt to start, the vibration recurs, then, of course, it is advisable to shut down and seek the cause of the trouble.

11. As the turbine speed is increasing, the main oil pump should take charge of the oil supply to the bearings and the governor gear, and the auxiliary pump should either stop or run at a very slow speed. This should be verified.

12. If the glands are sealed hydraulically, the water may be turned on, and the steam supply shut off.

13. Close the drains and increase the vacuum to its maximum value.

14. If the turbine is running satisfactorily, the throttle valve may be opened full, and then closed half a turn to prevent it from locking. The turbine is then ready to take a load, which should be added gradually, particularly with large machines.

GENERAL INSTRUCTIONS FOR STOPPING STEAM TURBINE

If the turbine is driving an alternating current generator, then, in general, the load is first reduced by the switchboard operator by lowering the speed of the turbine in question.

1. As the load is being taken off, regulate the supply of steam to the glands to conform to the new conditions.

2. Start the auxiliary oil pump. Where the control is automatic, check its operation later as the turbine comes to rest.

3. When the order to stop the machine is received, the stop valve may be closed gradually or tripped by hand. Once a week (or at other specified intervals) the operation of the emergency governor should be checked.

4. See that the bearings are receiving a proper supply of oil while the machine is slowing down.

5. Shut off the supply of steam and water to the glands.

6. When the machine has stopped, shut off the water supply to the oil coolers and stop the auxiliary oil pump.

7. Close the steam isolating valve and open the drain between the isolating valve and stop valve. This will prevent steam from escaping past the stop valve, while the machine is standing, in the event of the isolating valve and stop valve being not quite tight.

8. Stop the condenser air and circulating water pumps.

UNIT 3

Steam Turbine Principles and Design

Learning Objectives

Here is what you will be able to do when you complete each objective:

1. Explain impulse turbine operating principles. Describe convergent and divergent nozzles, and the pressure-velocity profiles through an impulse section.

2. Explain reaction turbine operating principles and describe the pressure-velocity profiles through reaction blading.

3. Explain pressure, velocity, and pressure-velocity compounding of impulse turbines. Describe the pressure-velocity profiles and the purpose and applications of each.

4. Explain the purpose, general operating principles and arrangement for each of the following turbine types: condensing, condensing-bleeder, backpressure, extraction, topping, mixed-pressure, cross-compounded and tandem compounded.

5. Describe the designs of typical turbine casings and state the purpose and location of casing fittings, including drains and sentinel valves. Describe the designs and principles of casing/shaft seals.

6. Describe the designs and applications of disc and drum rotors. Describe methods of rotor and casing blade attachment and explain blade-sealing arrangements.

7. Explain thrust in a large turbine and describe methods to offset thrust, including thrust bearings, dummy piston, and thrust-adjusting gear.

8. Identify typical designs and components for small and large industrial turbines. Explain typical size/capacity rating specifications and explain typical applications.

IMPULSE TURBINE OPERATING PRINCIPLES

If steam at high pressure is allowed to expand through a stationary nozzle, the result will be a drop in the steam pressure and an increase in steam velocity. In fact, the steam will issue from the nozzle in the form of a high-speed jet. If this high velocity steam is applied to a properly shaped turbine blade, it will change in direction due to the shape of the blade, which is shown in Fig. 1. The effect of this change, in direction of the steam flow, will be to produce an impulse force, marked "F" in Fig. 1, on the blade, causing it to move. If the blade is attached to the rotor of a turbine, then the rotor will revolve.

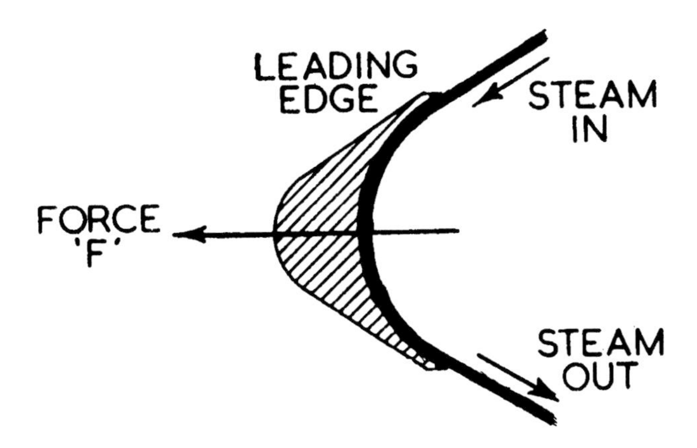

FIGURE 1

Impulse Turbine Blade Section

In Fig. 1, a force applied to the blade is developed by causing the steam to change direction of flow (Newton's 2nd Law - change of momentum). The change of momentum produces the impulse force. In an actual impulse turbine, there are a number of stationary nozzles and the moving blades are arranged completely around the rotor.

Impulse Turbine Nozzles and Buckets

Fig. 2 shows a cutaway of impulse turbine nozzles and buckets. The bucket or moving blade on the rotor converts the kinetic energy of the steam into mechanical energy, which causes a rotation of the shaft.

FIGURE 2

Impulse Turbine Nozzles And Buckets

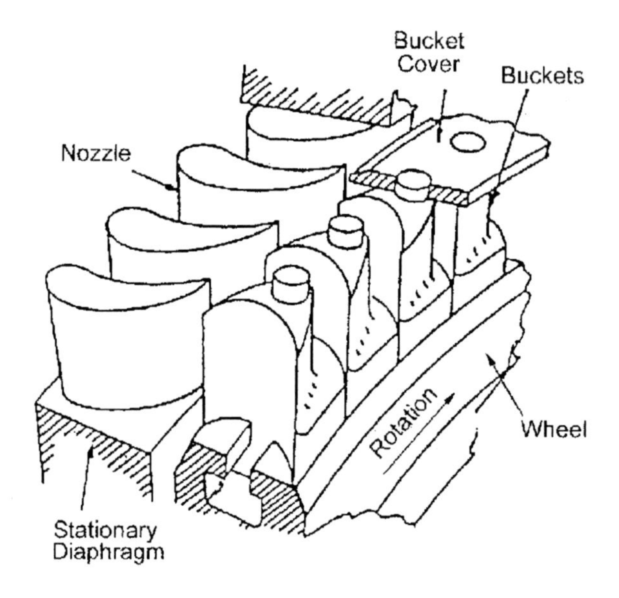

This turbine has the disadvantages of very high speed with extremely high centrifugal force, and high friction losses due to the high steam velocity.

STEAM NOZZLES

Nozzles are usually constructed of Monel metal formed over special dies. Monel metal is a high tensile strength nickel-copper alloy. Each nozzle is individually designed for proper expansion of steam at the pressure and temperature specified. Steam passages to the nozzles are outside the casing. The following two types of nozzles are used for steam turbines:

- Convergent
- Convergent-divergent

Convergent Nozzle

The convergent nozzle, as shown in Fig. 3, is used for small pressure drops. As the pressure drop across the nozzle is increased, the steam velocity also increases, but only to a specific exit pressure called the "critical pressure", which is 0.577 times the inlet pressure. With a decrease in the exit pressure to a pressure below the critical pressure, any extra energy that is added goes into the formation of eddy currents at the nozzle exit, rather than increasing steam velocity.

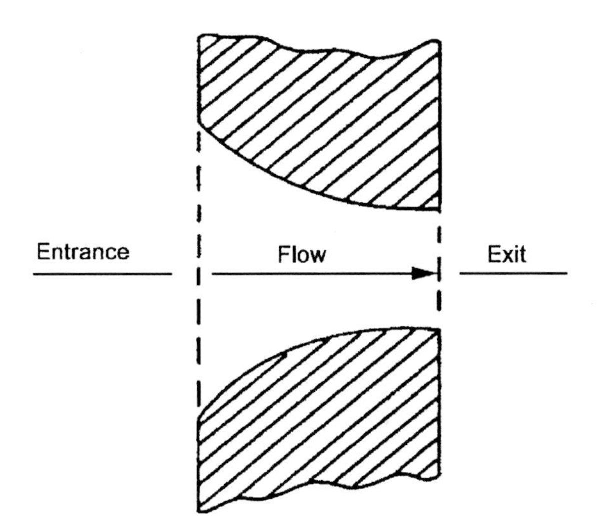

FIGURE 3

Convergent Nozzle

Convergent-Divergent Nozzle

When large pressure drops are required, a convergent-divergent nozzle, Fig. 4, is used. The pressure at the narrowest part of the nozzle, the throat of the nozzle, should be at the critical pressure. The pressure continues to drop in the divergent part of the nozzle, which is designed so it has increasing volume to match the increase in steam volume as the pressure decreases. A properly designed convergent-divergent nozzle can handle any pressure drop, to produce the calculated steam velocity, without eddy currents.

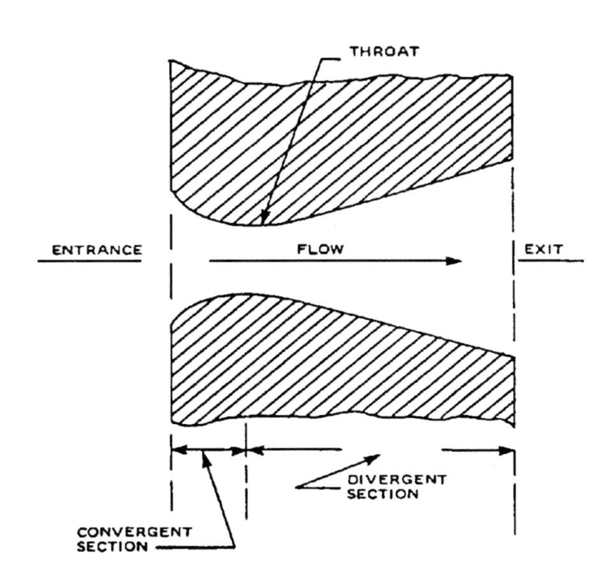

FIGURE 4

Convergent-Divergent Nozzle

IMPULSE TURBINE PRESSURE-VELOCITY PROFILE

Fig. 5 shows the nozzle and blade arrangement in a simple impulse turbine and the graph in the figure indicates how the pressure and the velocity of the steam change as the steam passes through first the stationary nozzles and then the moving blades. Note that the pressure drops and the velocity increases as the steam passes through the nozzles. Then, as the steam passes through the moving blades, the velocity drops but the pressure remains the same.

The fact that the pressure does not drop across the moving blades is the distinguishing feature of the impulse turbine. The pressure, at the inlet to the moving blades, is the same as the pressure at the outlet from the moving blades.

FIGURE 5

Impulse Turbine

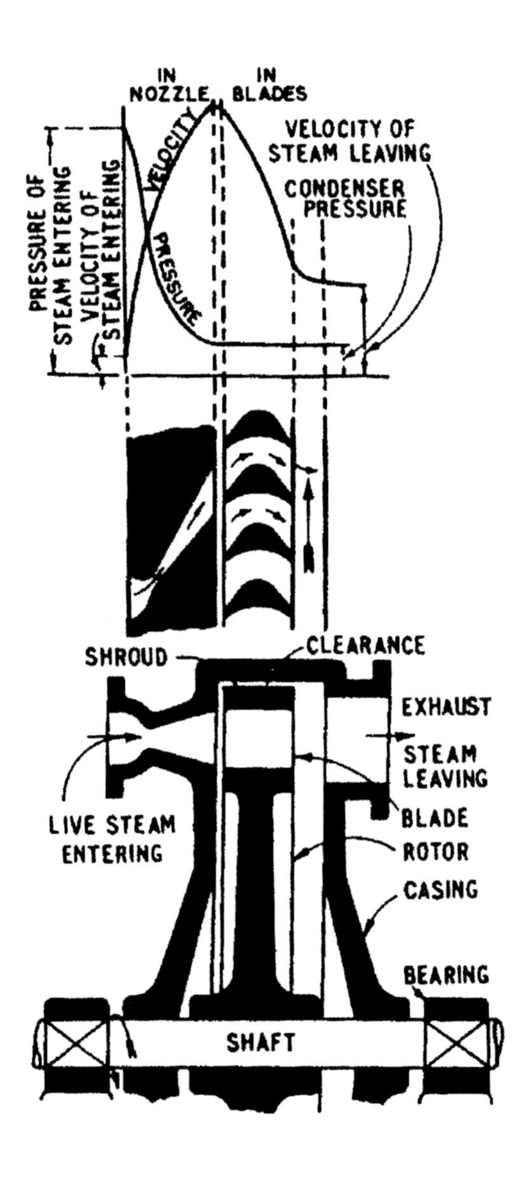

REACTION TURBINE OPERATING PRINCIPLES

If the moving blades of a turbine are shaped in such a way that the steam expands and drops in pressure as it passes through them, then a reaction will be produced which gives a force to the blades. This reaction effect can be illustrated by considering a container filled with high-pressure steam, as shown in Fig. 6. If there is not an escape opening or nozzle for the steam, then the pressure will be the same on all walls of the container and the container will remain at rest. If, however, the container has an escape opening or nozzle, then steam will expand through the opening and drop in pressure. As a result, there will be an unbalanced pressure on the wall opposite to the opening and a reaction force "R" will be produced, causing the container to move.

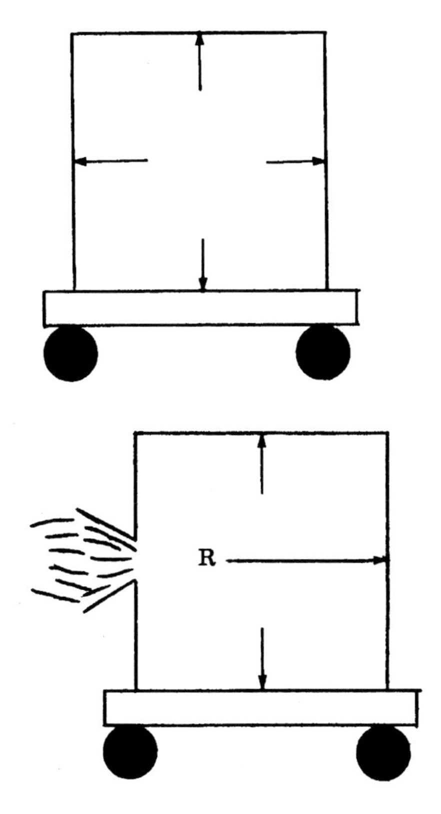

FIGURE 6

Reaction Effect

Fig. 7 shows a diagram of this principle applied to a turbine drive.

FIGURE 7

Pure Reaction Turbine

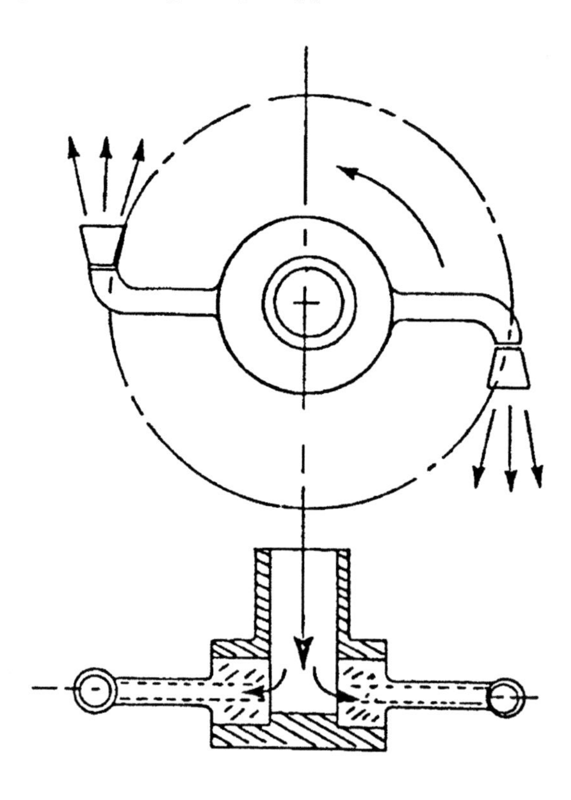

A reaction turbine has rows of stationary blades alternating with rows of moving blades. The steam expands first in the stationary blades where it gains some velocity as it drops in pressure. It then enters the moving blades where its direction of flow is changed, thus producing a force on the blades. This force is produced in accordance with Newton's Third Law of Motion, which states that every action has an equal and opposite reaction. This sequence is repeated as the steam passes through additional rows of stationary and moving blades.

Reaction Blading

Referring to Fig. 8, steam turbine reaction blading has a more rounded form than impulse blading. A reaction blade is characterized by a large entrance angle of almost 90° and a small discharge angle. The leading edge is rounded in distinction to the sharp leading edge of impulse blading, as shown in Fig. 1. The blade has a long, tapering trailing edge, with the convex side becoming straight, or nearly so.

FIGURE 8

Reaction Blade

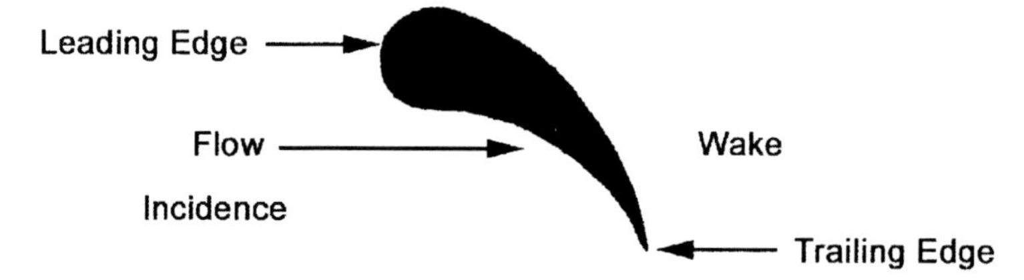

REACTION TURBINE PRESSURE-VELOCITY PROFILE

Fig. 9 shows the blade arrangement and the pressure and velocity changes of the steam in a reaction turbine. The steam pressure drops across both the stationary and the moving blades while the absolute velocity rises in the stationary blades and drops in the moving blades.

The distinguishing feature of the reaction turbine is the fact that the pressure does drop across the moving blades. In other words, there is a pressure difference between the inlet to the moving blades and the outlet from the moving blades.

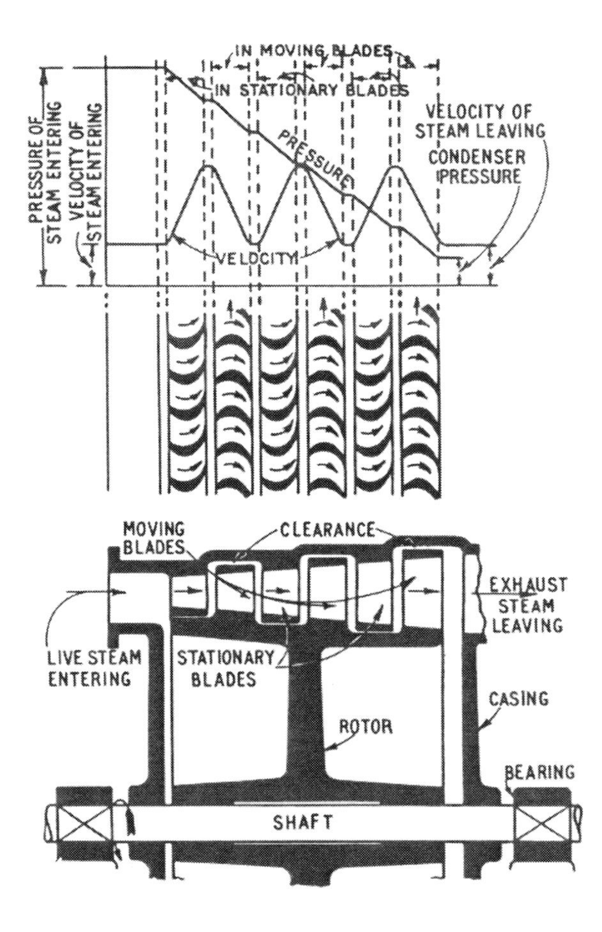

FIGURE 9

Reaction Turbine

Special Aspects of Reaction Turbines

- There is a difference in pressure across the moving blades. The steam will therefore tend to leak around the edges of the blades instead of passing through them. Blade clearances therefore must be kept to a minimum.

- Due to pressure drop across the moving blades, an unbalanced thrust will be developed upon the rotor and some arrangement must be made to balance this.

IMPULSE TURBINE STAGING

In order for the steam to give up all its kinetic energy to the moving blades in an impulse turbine, the steam should leave the moving blades at the lowest possible velocity, ideally at zero absolute velocity. This condition occurs if the blade velocity is equal to one-half the steam velocity.

If the steam is expanded from admission pressure down to the final exhaust pressure in a single set of nozzles (single stage), the velocity of the steam leaving the nozzles could be approximately 3,600 ft/s. In order to be efficient, the blade velocity would have to be about 1,800 ft/s. This would require excessively high rotational speed of the turbine rotor and failure, due to high centrifugal forces, is likely. High friction losses in the nozzles and blading would occur due to the excessively high steam velocity.

In order to reduce the steam and blade velocity, the following methods may be used:

- Pressure Compounding
- Velocity Compounding
- Pressure-Velocity Compounding

Pressure Compounding

Pressure compounding reduces the steam and blade velocity by allowing the steam pressure to drop in two or more stages. Two or more impulse turbines are used inside a single casing. A set of stationary nozzles followed by a rotor disc with blades is called a pressure-compounded stage.

The nozzle and blade arrangement for a pressure compounded impulse turbine is shown in Fig. 10. As the steam passes through the first set of nozzles, the pressure drops and the velocity increases. The steam next passes through the moving blades, where the pressure will remain near constant and the steam velocity will drop to near zero. The second set of stationary nozzles will result in a further drop in pressure and an increase in velocity of the steam. The second set of moving blades will again cause a drop in steam velocity while the pressure remains constant.

The expansion of the steam from boiler pressure to exhaust pressure is carried out in a number of stages. Thus, each stage has a set of nozzles and a row of moving blades. The rows of moving blades are separated from each other by partitions or diagrams, into which the nozzles are set.

The advantages of these types of turbines are increased efficiency due to decreased friction losses, and reduced centrifugal forces. As well, for a given rotational speed, it can be designed for a wide range of inlet steam conditions.

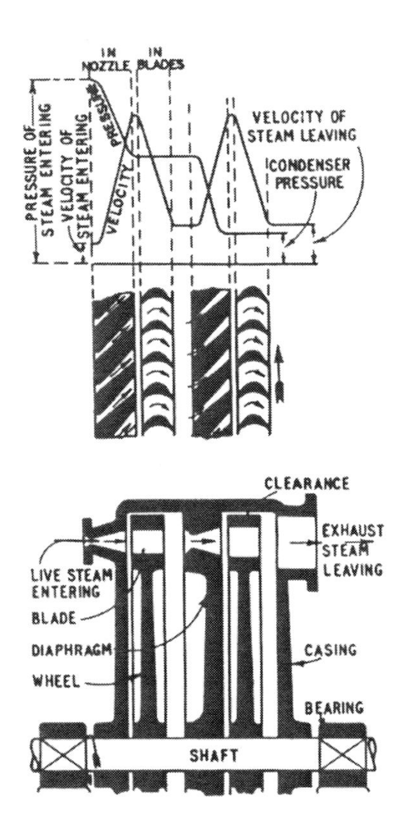

FIGURE 10

Pressure Compounded Impulse Turbine With Pressure Velocity Graph

Velocity Compounding

The velocity-compound turbine, as shown in Fig. 11, consists of a set of stationary nozzles, and a rotor with two sets of rotating blades, separated by a set of stationary blades. The total steam pressure drop occurs in the set of stationary nozzles. The first set of rotating blades reduces the steam velocity by approximately one half. The stationary blades then redirect the steam, with little loss of velocity, to the second set of rotating blades. As the steam passes through the second set of rotating blades, the velocity drops to the exit velocity. The pressure remains constant across the three sets of blades.

The result of reducing the velocity of the steam in two stages is that the speed of the rotating blades is one half the speed of the blades of a simple impulse turbine (assuming that all other factors are unchanged). The blades of the second rotating set are approximately twice the size of the first set. Since the same volume of steam passes through both sets of blades, the velocity of the steam entering the second set of blades is one half of the velocity entering the first set.

FIGURE 11

Velocity Compounded Impulse Turbine With Pressure Velocity Graph

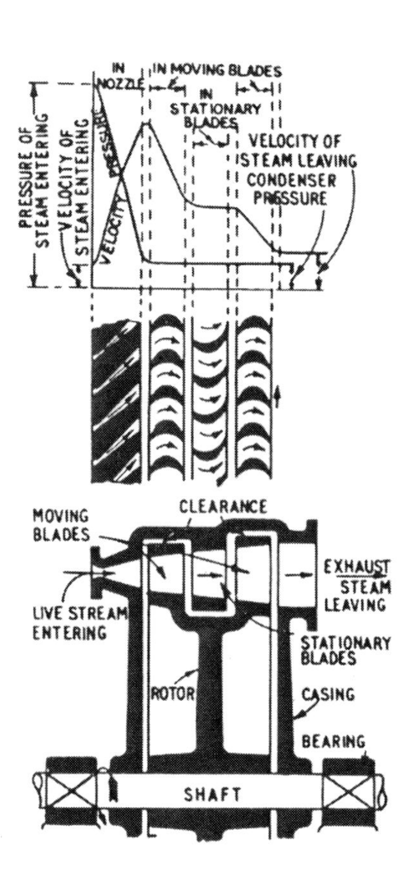

Pressure-Velocity Compounding

A pressure-velocity compounded turbine reduces the steam pressure and velocity in two or more steps. The pressure-velocity compounded impulse turbine is a number of pressure-velocity turbines, in series in a single casing, as shown in Fig. 12. As the graph shows, the pressure drop, from inlet to condenser, is divided between two sets of nozzles, with each set of nozzles supplying a velocity-compounded turbine. The pressure and velocity graphs are the same, for the two velocity compounded stages, except for the pressure drop between the stages.

The advantage of pressure-velocity compounding is that high steam pressures can be used to obtain relatively low rotational speeds.

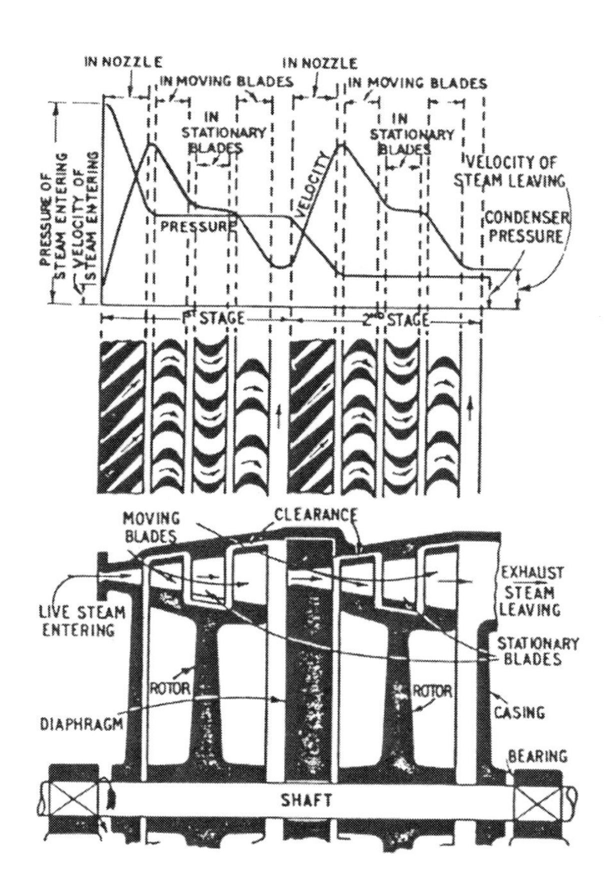

FIGURE 12

Pressure Velocity Compounded Impulse Turbine With Pressure Velocity Graph

IMPULSE TURBINE APPLICATIONS

For large impulse turbines, it is very common to have a velocity compounded first stage, followed by several pressure-compounded stages in the same casing. The design, shown in Fig. 12, is a combination of velocity compounding and pressure compounding. Each element of the pressure compounding or stage contains a complete example of velocity compounding.

The portion of the turbine, shown in Fig. 13, has one velocity and four pressure stages. The graph above the cross-section of the nozzles and blades shows how the pressure and velocity change as the steam passes through the turbine. The pressure drops as the steam expands in the nozzles but remains constant as it passes through the moving blades.

The first stage is designed for greater pressure drop than the remaining stages, therefore, the velocity of the steam leaving the first nozzle is much higher. This higher velocity can be used to produce work if it is reduced in two steps. Hence, in this stage there are usually two rows of moving blades and an intermediate row of stationary guide blades. The steam velocity decreases in both rows of moving blades and remains constant in the guide vanes.

FIGURE 13

Impulse Turbine With Velocity And Pressure Stages

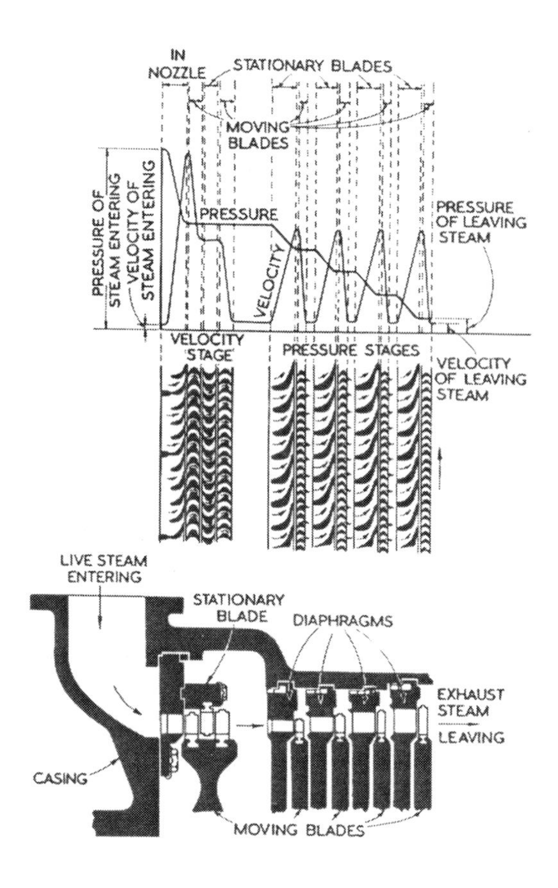

TYPES OF TURBINES

Turbines fall into two major categories, condensing and non-condensing (or back-pressure). Condensing turbines exhaust steam at pressures below atmospheric, and non-condensing turbines exhaust at or above atmospheric pressure. Four basic types of turbines are shown in Fig. 14.

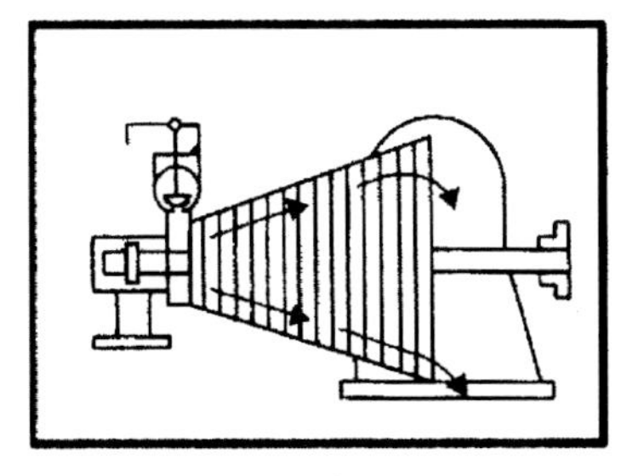

SINGLE-FLOW CONDENSING is the most widely-used type. This work-horse requires the least steam for a given power.

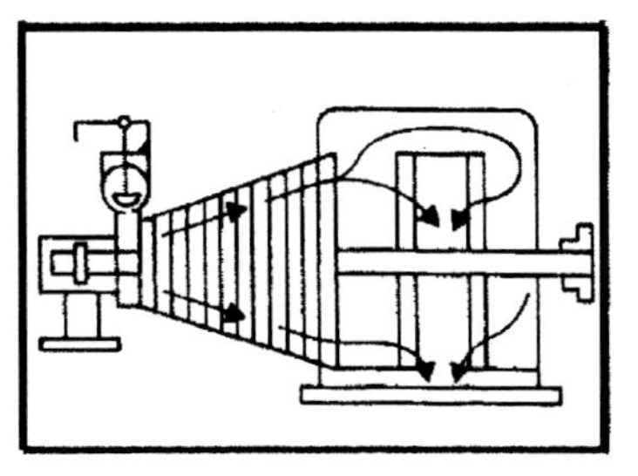

DOUBLE-FLOW CONDENSING makes possible higher powers and speeds than single-flow condensing type. This is done by double-flowing the low-pressure stage(s).

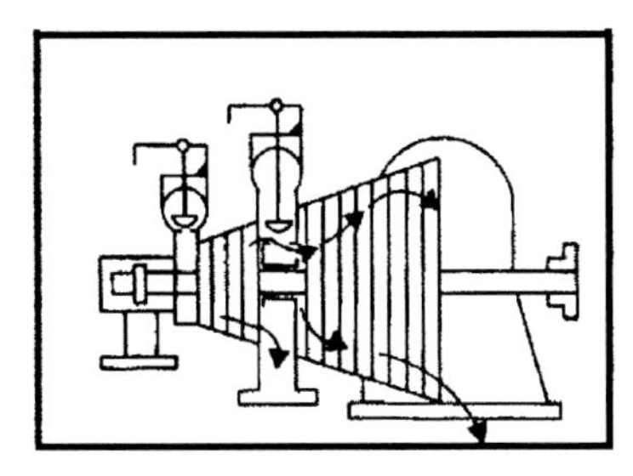

AUTOMATIC EXTRACTION and/or induction combines the best features of straight condensing and non-condensing turbines. Automatically supplies process steam or accepts excess steam at a given pressure.

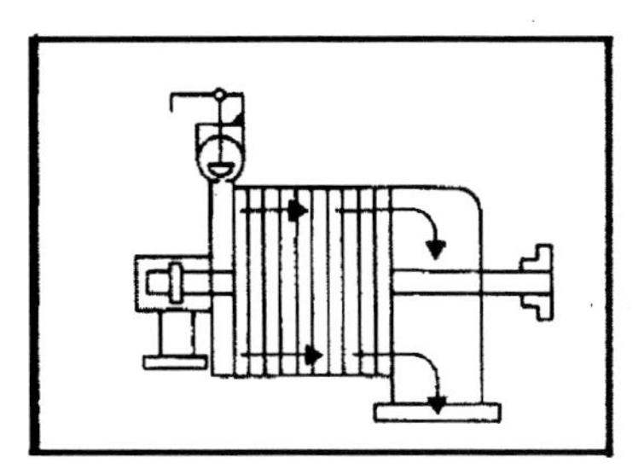

NON-CONDENSING or back-pressure is used to satisfy process steam requirements at selected pressure levels.

FIGURE 14

Basic Types of Turbines
(Courtesty of United Technologies – Elliott)

Many arrangements are possible when installing turbines in power plant applications. Fig. 15 illustrates some of the common applications.

Non-Condensing (Back Pressure) Turbine (Fig. 15A)

This type of turbine is used when all, or practically all the exhaust steam from the turbine, can be used for process or heating. This design is used primarily in process plants and acts as a reducing station between a boiler and a process steam header. A regulating station, maintaining the process steam header at the required pressure, controls the exhaust steam pressure. The process steam pressure is kept constant and the generator output depends upon the demand for process steam. The turbine may also have bleed points (points at which steam is drawn off before the turbine exhaust), and if so, it is called a backpressure bleeder turbine.

Condensing Turbine (Fig. 15B, I)

This type of steam turbine is used when exhaust steam from the turbine cannot be utilized and power must be generated on a minimum amount of steam. Condensing turbines are used primarily as a drive for an electric generator in a power plant. These units exhaust steam, at less than atmospheric pressure, to a condenser where the steam is condensed by cooling water. The condensate is returned to the boiler, as feed water.

Condensing Bleeder Turbine (Fig. 15C)

The condensing bleeder turbine reduces condenser losses by bleeding off steam at one or more points of the turbine. The bleed steam is used to heat the feed water. Up to 2% of the total steam may be bled off.

Mixed Pressure Condensing Turbine (Fig. 15D)

Mixed pressure turbines have excess process steam applied to the low-pressure part of the turbine. These turbines may have steam, at boiler pressure, added to the high-pressure part of the turbine, as required to handle the generator load.

Extraction Turbines (Fig. 15 E, F, G)

This design is used primarily in process plants where the exhaust steam from the turbine, can be used for process or heating. In extraction turbines, steam is extracted at one or more points, at constant pressure. Extraction turbines may be single or double extraction condensing turbines, or single or double extraction backpressure turbines. The turbines may also have bleed points for feed water heating.

Topping Turbines (Fig. 15 H)

Topping turbines have been used when old, low-pressure boilers are replaced with new high-pressure boilers. The turbine is a backpressure turbine for mechanical drive or electrical power generation and is usually custom built for specific customer requirements.

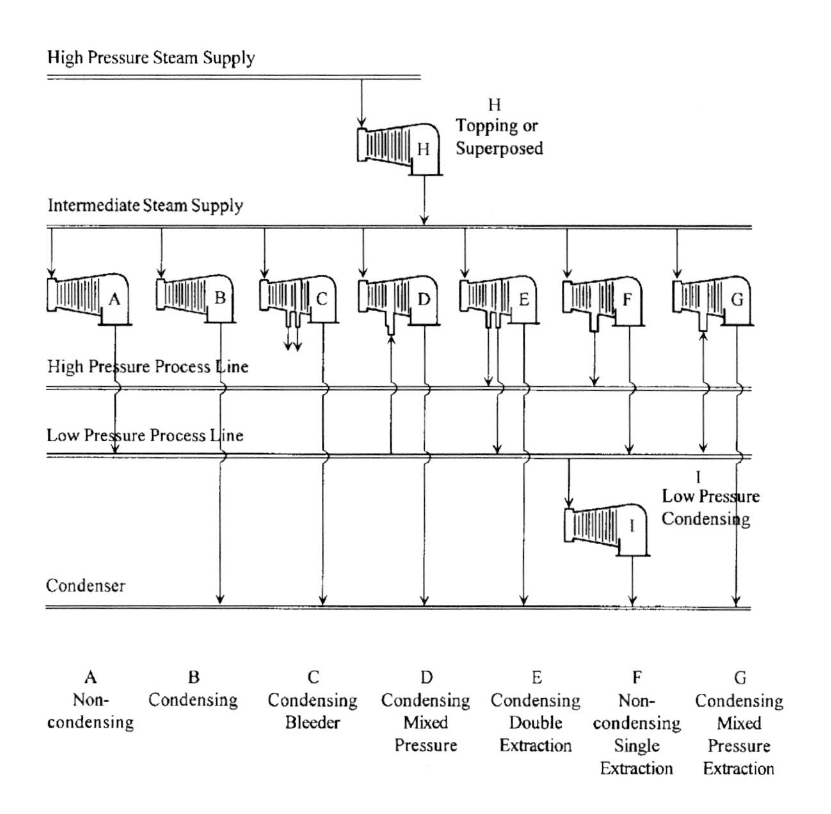

FIGURE 15

Turbine Types

Cross Compound Turbines

Cross compound turbines, are large turbines with a generator on each turbine shaft. The steam flows through the high-pressure turbine, as shown in Fig. 16 and then exhausts to the low-pressure turbine. Cross compounding for large units have the advantage of being easier to construct two half-sized generators than one large unit. Fig. 17 is also a cross-compound turbine, but with the steam entering the middle of the low-pressure turbine and flowing to each end.

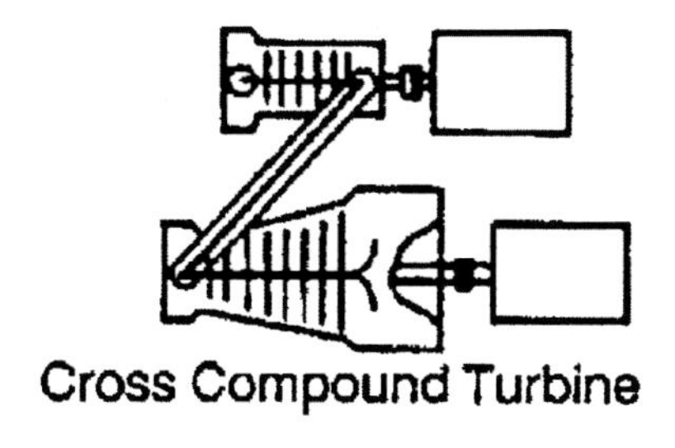

FIGURE 16

Cross-Compound Turbine

FIGURE 17

Cross-Compound Turbine With Double Flow Low Pressure Turbine

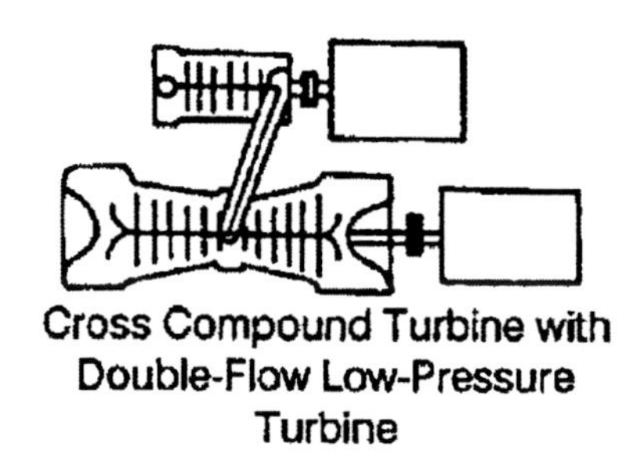

Tandem Compound Turbines

Tandem compound turbines, as shown in Fig. 18, are large turbines coupled together on a single shaft and applied to one generator. The steam flows through the turbines from high-pressure turbine to low-pressure turbine.

FIGURE 18

Tandem-Compound Turbine

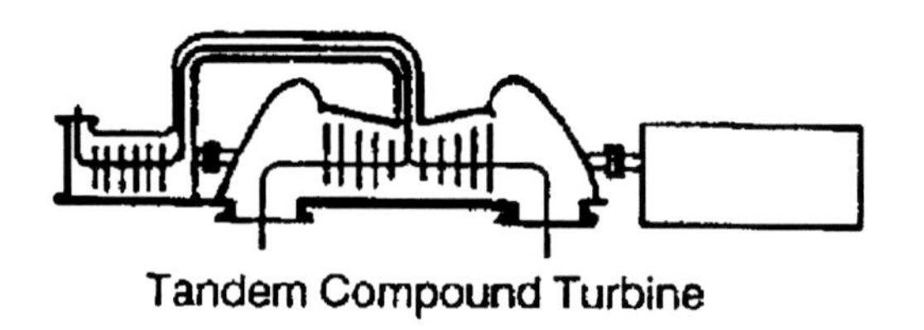

TURBINE CASINGS

Turbine casings must resist distortion under the operating conditions of high pressures and temperatures so that the small running clearances of the blading and labyrinth glands will remain constant, and that the alignment of the turbine rotor will not be adversely affected.

Split Casings

Horizontal split casings or cylinders are used to facilitate assembly and inspection. This is not ideal as the heavy flanges of the joints are slow to follow the temperature changes of the cylinder walls.

The casings are made of thick material in order to withstand the high pressures and temperatures to which they are exposed. It is general practice to let the thickness of walls and flanges decrease from inlet to the exhaust end.

Large casings, for low-pressure turbines, are welded plate construction. Smaller low-pressure casings are cast iron, which may be used for temperatures up to 450°F. Casings for intermediate pressures are made of cast carbon steel able to withstand temperatures up to 800°F. The high pressure, high temperature casings used with temperatures above 1020°F, are made of cast alloy steel with 3% chromium and 1% molybdenum.

The reason for using different casing materials is that materials, at the given maximum temperatures and under constant pressure, continue to deform with very slowly increasing strain of the material. This phenomenon is called "creep".

The casing joints are made steam tight without the use of gaskets by matching the machined flange faces very closely. The bolt holes in the flanges are drilled for smoothly fitting bolts, but dowel pins are often used to secure exact alignment of the flange joint. A boring mill then machines the assembled casing inside; grooves are made for the diaphragms (for impulse turbines) or for stationary blades (reaction turbines). The casing is also bored for shaft seals and in many cases for the bearings also.

For high-pressure casings, the flanges must be very thick. Consequently, they will heat up much more slowly than the casing walls. Flange heating is often used in order to assist the heating of these flanges. Steam flows through machined channels between the flanges or through holes drilled axially through the upper and lower flanges.

Fig. 19 shows the lower section of a horizontally split casing. The centerline support allows the casing to expand and contract evenly while maintaining alignment, at all times.

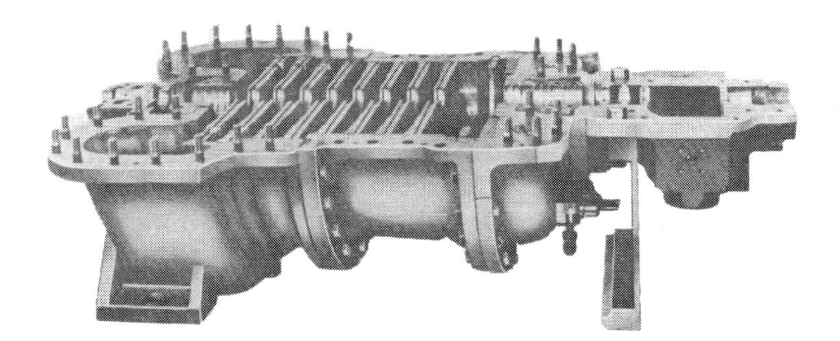

FIGURE 19

Turbine Lower Casing and Support

Double Casings

Double casings are used for very high steam pressure applications. The high pressure is applied to the inner casing, which is open at the exhaust end, letting the turbine exhaust to the outer casing. The pressure is divided between the casings, and more importantly, so is the temperature. Therefore, the thermal stresses on casings and flanges are greatly reduced. Fig. 20 shows a double shell HP turbine casing.

FIGURE 20

Double-Shell HP Casing

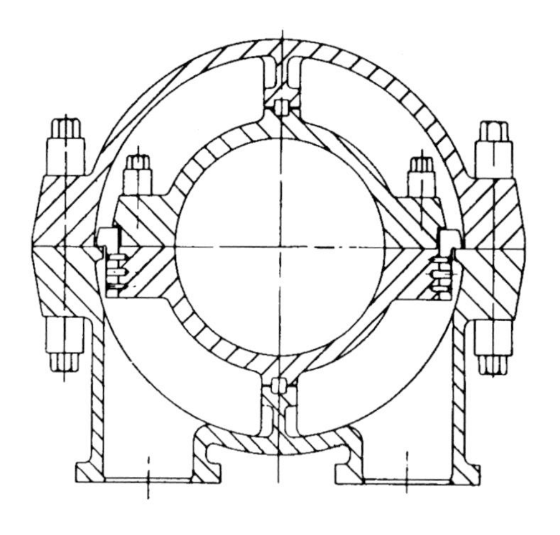

CYLINDER CASING DRAINS

Increased steam pressure and the higher temperatures of modern turbines have decreased the percentage of wetness of the steam at the exhaust end. 14% wetness is generally taken as the maximum allowable. The shape of the cylinder casing allows this water to drain to the condenser but special draining grooves are arranged in the cylinder casing to help remove this water more effectively. An example of this type of draining arrangement is illustrated in Fig. 21.

FIGURE 21

Cylinder Casing Drainage

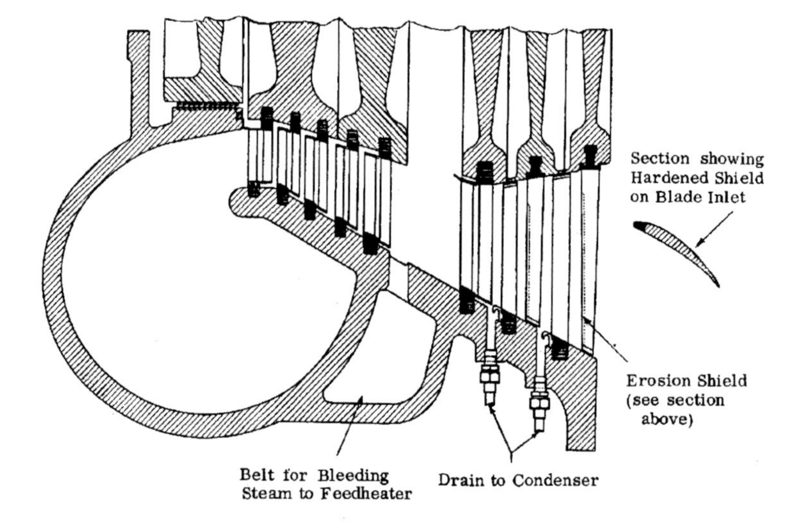

SENTINEL VALVES

Fig. 22 illustrates a non-condensing steam turbine, which has found wide application in the petroleum and pulp and paper industry as a prime mover. A sentinel valve, located on top of the casing, will discharge steam to the atmosphere when excessive backpressure exists within the casing. This will prevent the possibility of a failure due to the exhaust valve being closed, during startup.

Drains are provided on the steam chest and casing for removal of condensate, during startup.

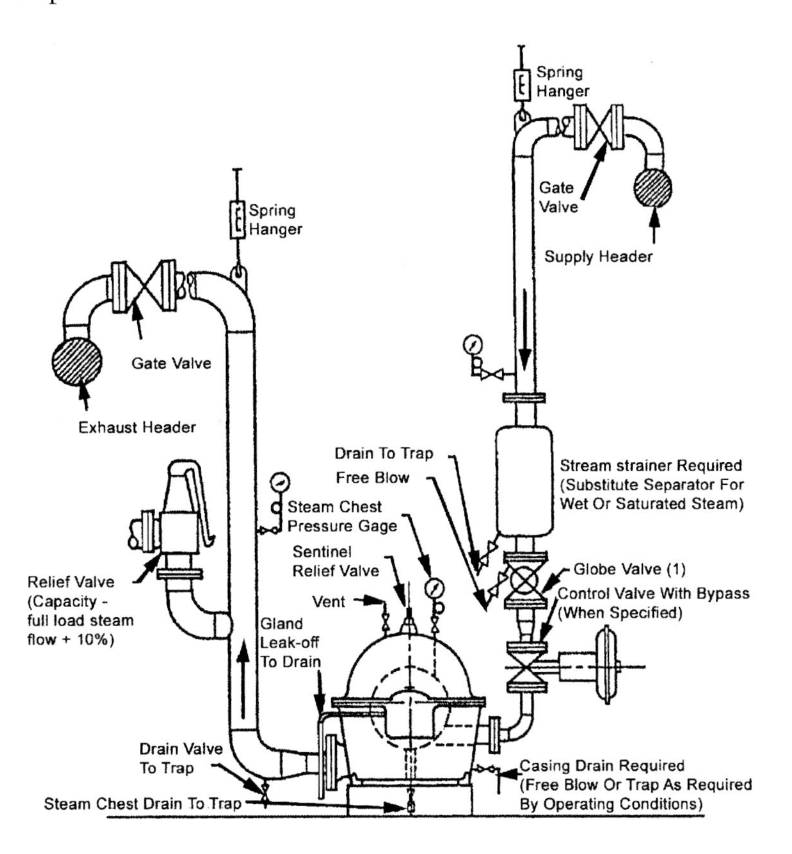

FIGURE 22

Industrial Steam Turbine

SHAFT SEALS

Shaft seals must be provided in order to prevent, or at least, reduce steam leakage where the shafts extend through the casings. Also, when low-pressure turbines are under vacuum, the seals must prevent air from leaking into the casing.

Carbon Ring Seal

On small turbines, ordinary soft packing or carbon rings may be used. The carbon ring, shown in Fig. 23, is made up of three segments, butting together tightly, under the pressure of a garter spring. The spring encircles the ring, allowing some radical adjustment, but preventing axial movement.

FIGURE 23

Carbon Ring Seal

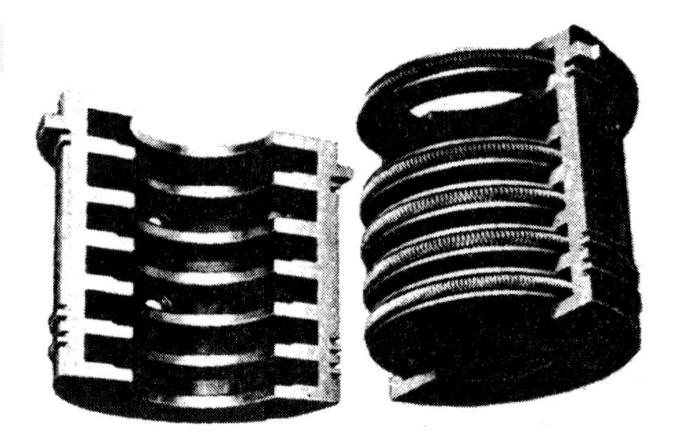

Labyrinth Seals

The rings may also create heat, when riding on the shaft. Because of this, carbon rings are limited to shafts less than 6 in. (150 mm) in diameter. For large turbines, labyrinth seals are used. The labyrinth seal has a number of rings, 1 to 2 mm thick, stationary only to the shaft and tapered at the outer periphery to a sharp edge with a minute clearance to the casing. The rings are made of either brass or stainless steel. The sharp edge gives better sealing and rubs off easily without excessive heating, in case of a slightly eccentric shaft. Fig. 24 illustrates different types of labyrinth seals.

FIGURE 24

Different Types of Labyrinth Seals

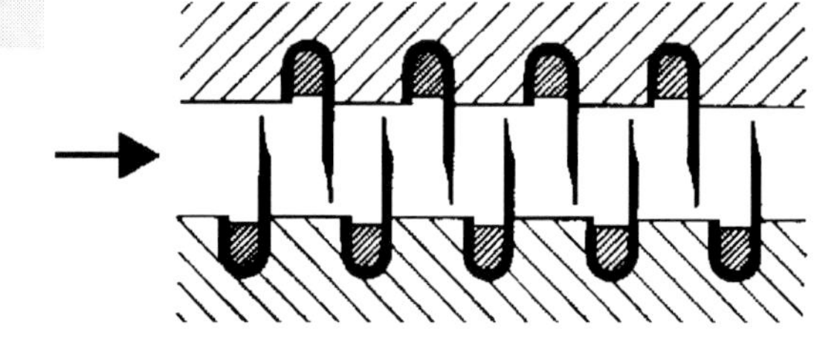

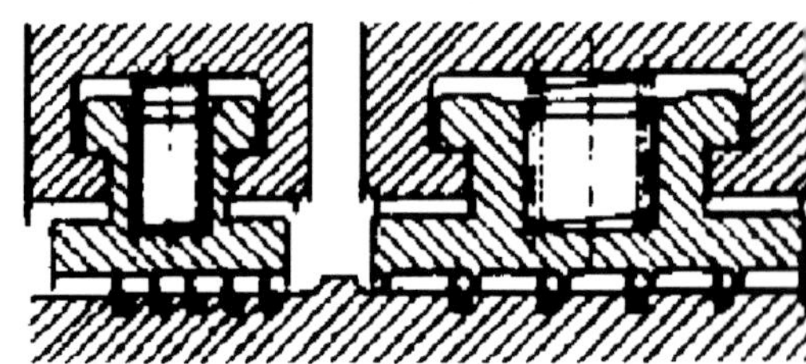

Water Seals

High pressure turbines, which operate at pressures above 1,450 psi, have a sealing problem since a straight labyrinth seal for this pressure would be extremely long or have excessive steam leaking through. This problem can be solved by using a series of steam pockets between sets of labyrinth seals. The steam pockets are exhausted to several different locations, such as feed water heater steam extraction lines and the turbine exhaust.

Neither the carbon rings nor labyrinth shaft seals prevent all leakage. If a positive or leak proof seal is needed, a water seal, as shown in Fig. 25, may be installed. The water seal consists of an impeller on the turbine shaft, which rotates in a casing, which is filled with water. The water is thrown out from the impeller and forms a leak proof water barrier. Water seals are mainly applied to low-pressure glands to guard against air infiltration, but they may also be applied as the final seal for high pressure and intermediate pressure glands.

The water seal cannot operate properly at low speed. Therefore, gland steam must be applied for sealing during start up until the turbine speed is high enough for the water impeller to produce sufficient pressure for sealing. Water seals are supplied with clean, cool condensate from the condensate extraction pump discharge. The water may be supplied directly or via a head tank with an automatic level control. Labyrinth packing is attached to the casing to reduce water leakage and also to reduce steam turbine leakage, in case of seal failure.

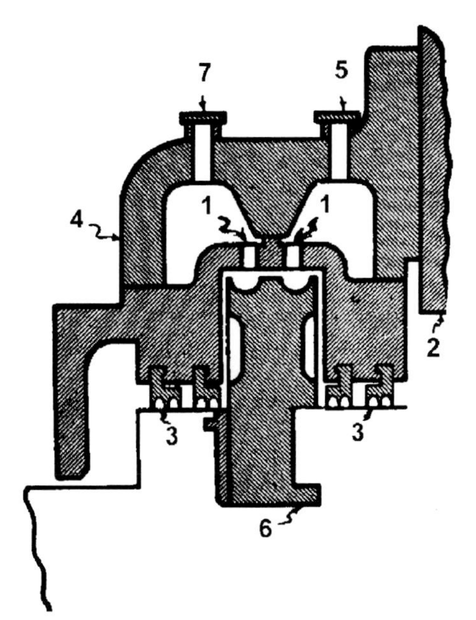

1. Hole for water to get to gland runner chamber
2. Turbine exhaust casing
3. Labyrinth packing
4. Gland casing
5. Circulating water inlet
6. Gland runner
7. Circulating water outlet

FIGURE 25

Water Sealed Gland

DISC ROTORS

The impulse turbine, which operates with a pressure drop across the stationary blades, must have seals between stationary blades and the rotor. The smaller the sealing areas the smaller the leakage, therefore, the stationary blades are mounted in diaphragms with labyrinth seals around the shaft. This type of construction requires a disc rotor design.

The disc rotor is made up of a number of separately-forged discs or wheels and the hubs of these wheels are shrunk or keyed onto the central shaft. The outer rims of the wheels have suitable grooves machined to allow for attaching the blades. The shaft is sometimes stepped so that the wheel hubs can be threaded along to their correct positions. Suitable clearances are left between the hubs to allow for expansion axially along the line of the shaft.

Under operating conditions, the temperature of the wheels may rise quicker than that of the shaft and this might tend to make the wheel hubs become loose. To avoid any such danger, considerable care is taken during construction of the rotor to ensure that the wheels are shrunk on tight and correctly stressed. Fig. 26 illustrates a disc type of rotor which is the type used in the LP (Low Pressure) cylinder of most designs of large turbines.

FIGURE 26

Disc Type Rotor

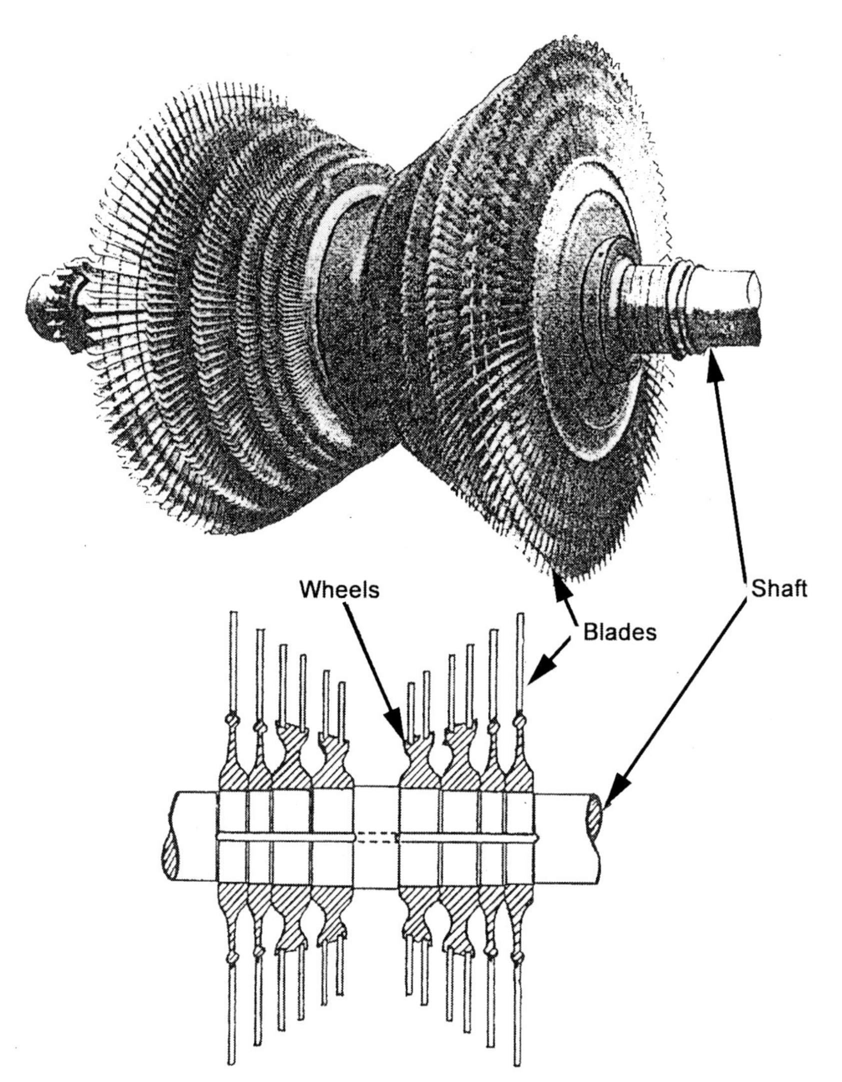

Section Through Disc Type Rotor

All large disc rotors are machined from a solid forging of nickel steel, as shown in Fig. 27. This produces a strong, fully balanced rotor. But, this type of construction is expensive, as the weight of the final rotor is approximately 50% of the initial forging. Small disc rotors have shaft and discs made in separate pieces with the discs shrunk onto the shaft. The bore of the disc is made 0.1% smaller in diameter than the shaft. The discs are then heated until they easily slide along the shaft and are located in their final position on the shaft and shaft key. A small clearance between the discs prevents thermal stress in the shaft.

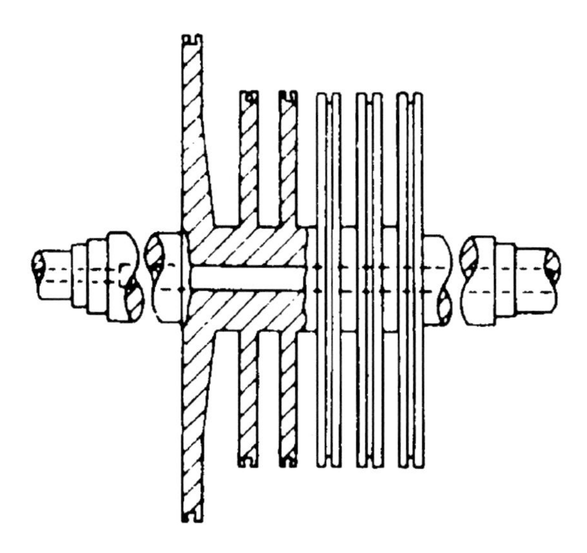

FIGURE 27
Solid Forged Disc Rotor

DRUM ROTORS

The reaction turbine has a pressure drop across both the moving blades and the stationary blades. The use of a disc rotor would create a large axial thrust across each disc. The application of a drum rotor, as shown in Fig. 28, eliminates the axial thrust caused by the discs, but not the axial thrust caused by the differential pressure across the moving blades.

The hollow drum rotor, as shown in Fig. 28, is made of two or more pieces. For good balance, the drum must be machined both outside and inside and the drum must be opened at one end. The second part of the rotor is the drum end cover with shaft. The end cover is made with a shrink fit and welded.

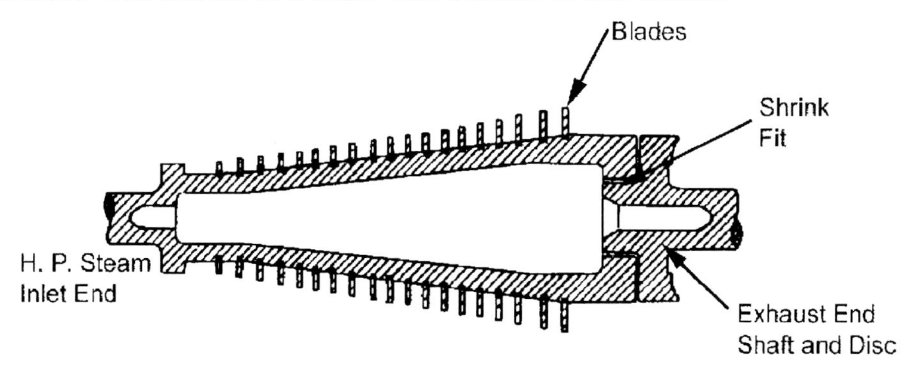

FIGURE 28
Hollow Drum Rotor

A fairly light and rigid drum rotor may be manufactured from discs welded together to form a drum, as shown in Fig. 29. Before welding, the rotor is heated by induction heating. Then the welding is performed with automatic welding machines using the "Argon Arc" process, where the arc burns in an argon atmosphere.

FIGURE 29

Welded Drum Turbine Rotor

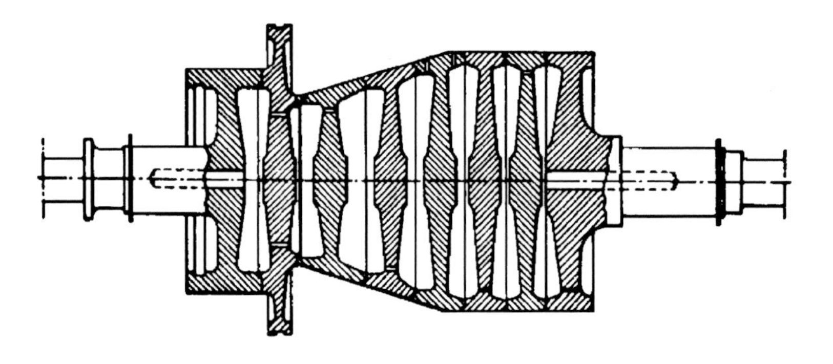

BLADE ATTACHMENT

The stationary blades or nozzles, in an impulse turbine, are mounted in diaphragms, as shown in Fig. 30. The diaphragm is made in two halves, one half being stationary to the upper half of the cylinder casing and the other half diaphragm to the lower half cylinder casing. The diaphragms are secured in the cylinder casing by means of keys.

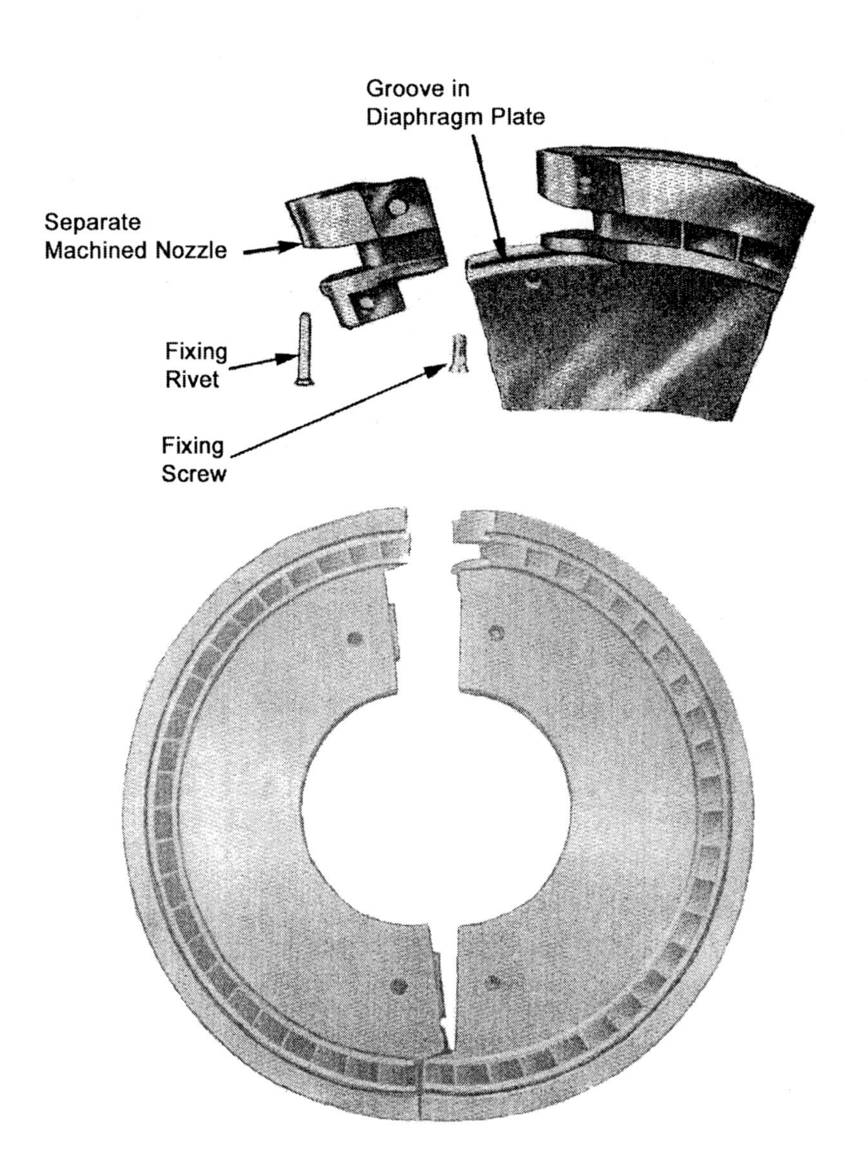

FIGURE 30

Built-Up Diaphragm

The HP (High Pressure) moving blades, for impulse type turbines are machined from a solid bar and the roots and spacers formed with the blade. This is illustrated in Fig. 31. This type of construction avoids the use of distance pieces or packers when assembling the blades to the wheels. Tangs are left at the tips of the blades so that when fitted in position in the wheel the shrouding can be attached. The shrouding is made from sections of metal strip punched with holes to correspond with the tangs. The strip is passed over the tangs, which are then splayed out to secure the strip in position. The shrouding is fitted in separate sections to allow for expansion.

There is not any pressure drop across the moving blades of an impulse type turbine. Therefore, the sealing arrangements are not of such great importance as in the reaction type. The shrouding on the impulse blading helps to guide the steam through the moving blades, allowing larger radial clearance, as well as strengthening the assembly.

FIGURE 31

Stages In The Manufacture Of HP Impulse Type Moving Blades

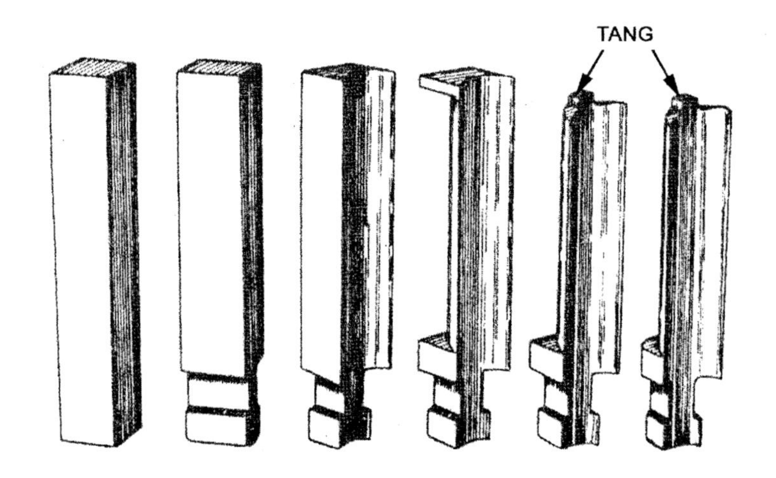

BLADE SEALING

The stationary blades in reaction turbines are fitted into grooves in the casing halves with the use of keys, as shown in Fig. 32 and Fig. 33, which lock the blades in place. In some cases, the blades have keys or serrations on one side of the root. A calking strip, on the other side of the root, is used to tighten the blades solidly in the grooves. The blades are often supplied with a shroud band with radial and/or axial sealing strips, to minimize leakage losses.

FIGURE 32

Drum Type Rotor With Shrouded Blades

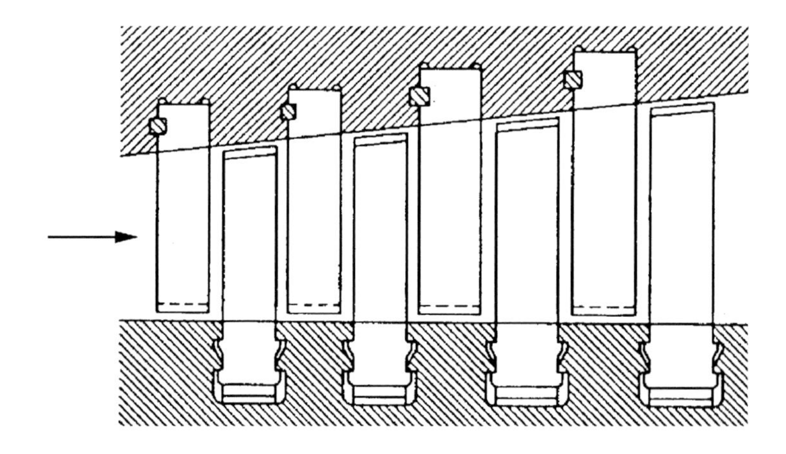

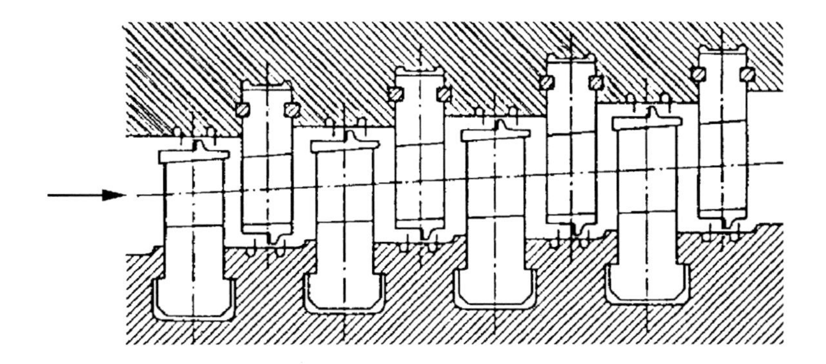

FIGURE 33

Drum-Type Rotor With Tip-Sealed Blades

Blade seals may be used on impulse turbines to help direct steam flow in high-pressure stages and prevent leakage across the stages. Blade sealing is used principally in reaction turbines to retard leakage across the blade tips, as there is a pressure difference across this type of blade. The thin edges and sealing strips permit close running clearances with little hazard from accidental contact. In effect, the seals allow close running clearances with relatively large clearances between heavy parts. Seal strips are often of chrome-iron alloy; the strips are rolled to shape and held in grooves by soft steel caulking strips.

TURBINE THRUST

In an impulse turbine, the pressure of the steam drops in the stationary nozzles and therefore, theoretically, the steam pressures on both sides of the moving blades are equal. For this reason, there is little tendency for the steam to exert an axial thrust on the shaft. However, there is always a small thrust in an impulse turbine, which tends to displace the shaft in an axial direction. This thrust must of course be counteracted since failure to do so would result in contact between the moving and stationary parts of the turbine with disastrous results.

The reaction turbine presents an entirely different picture. In this instance, there is a considerable pressure drop across each row of moving blades. As a result, an end thrust is imparted to the turbine shaft by each row of blades. This thrust is in addition to the thrust that is developed by the rotation of the shaft. One method of reducing the end thrust to zero is the double-flow principle of turbine design in which steam is admitted to a point midway along the turbine casing, after which it divides and flows axially in both directions. Opposing rows of blading are mounted on either side of the steam inlet and hence the equal end thrusts developed in these blades counteract each other since they are in opposing directions.

There are various methods that are employed to offset this thrust. They include the use of:

- Thrust bearings
- Dummy pistons
- Thrust adjusting gear

Thrust Bearings

The main purposes of the thrust bearing are:

- To keep the rotor in an exact position in the casing
- To absorb any axial thrust on the rotor

From the thrust bearing the shaft must be free to expand in either direction, thus, the shaft can have only one thrust bearing. The thrust bearing should be located at the steam inlet where the blade clearances are most critical. When shafts of a tandem compound turbine are joined together by a solid coupling, only one thrust bearing can be used. If flexible couplings take up axial expansion, then each shaft must have a thrust bearing.

The axial thrust is very small for impulse turbines as the pressure is equal across the rotor discs. Therefore, a simple thrust bearing such as a ball bearing or sleeve bearing with a radial Babbitt facing, is commonly used. In small turbines, the thrust and radial bearings are often combined in one single design, as shown in Fig. 34. The bearing metal is extended radially over the ends of the bearing shell to form thrust bearing surfaces which are sometimes provided with oil grooves to permit a more efficient distribution of the lubricating oil.

FIGURE 34

Ring Oiled Radial Bearings

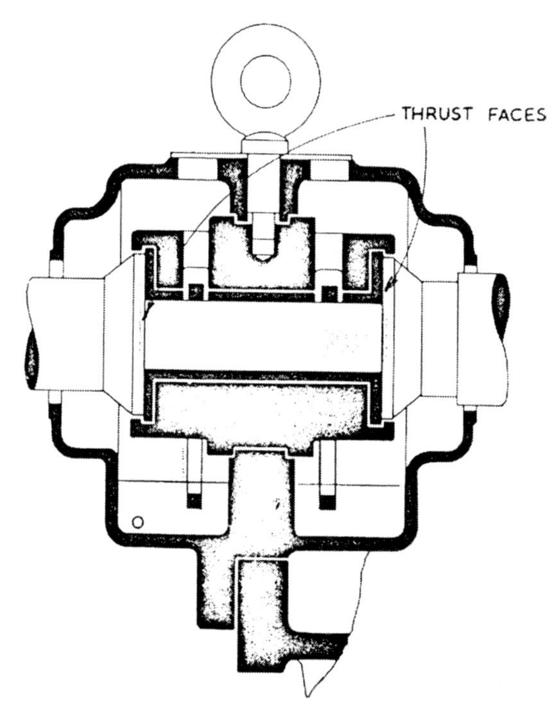

The pressure drop across the moving blades of reaction turbines creates a large axial thrust on the rotor in the direction of steam flow through the turbine. Therefore, a thrust bearing suitable for the large axial thrust loading is required. The tilting pad Kingsbury or Michel thrust bearings, as shown in Fig. 35, are used. The bearing is assembled around a collar on the shaft, which faces a number of thrust shoes or pads. These shoes are supported on pivots, which allow the shoes to tilt and form an oil wedge between the collar and the tilting shoes. The thrust load is carried on the oil wedges.

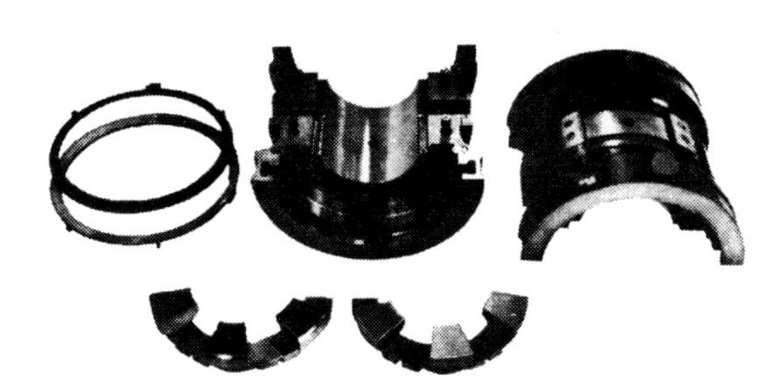

FIGURE 35

Journal Bearing With Kingsbury Thrust Bearing

Dummy Pistons

There is a pressure drop across each row of blades in a reaction type turbine and a considerable force is set up, which acts on the rotor in the direction of the steam flow. In order to counteract this force and reduce the load on the thrust bearings, dummy pistons, as shown in Fig. 36, are machined out of the rotor forging at the steam inlet end.

The dummy piston diameter is calculated so that the steam pressure acting upon it in the opposite direction to the steam flow, balances out the force on the rotor blades in the direction of the steam flow. It is preferable that the size of the dummy piston be arranged so as to keep a small but definite thrust towards the exhaust end of the turbine. To help maintain this condition at all loads, a balance pipe is usually connected from the casing, on the outer side of the balance piston, to some tap-off point down the cylinder.

FIGURE 36

Balancing Axial Thrust With A Dummy Piston

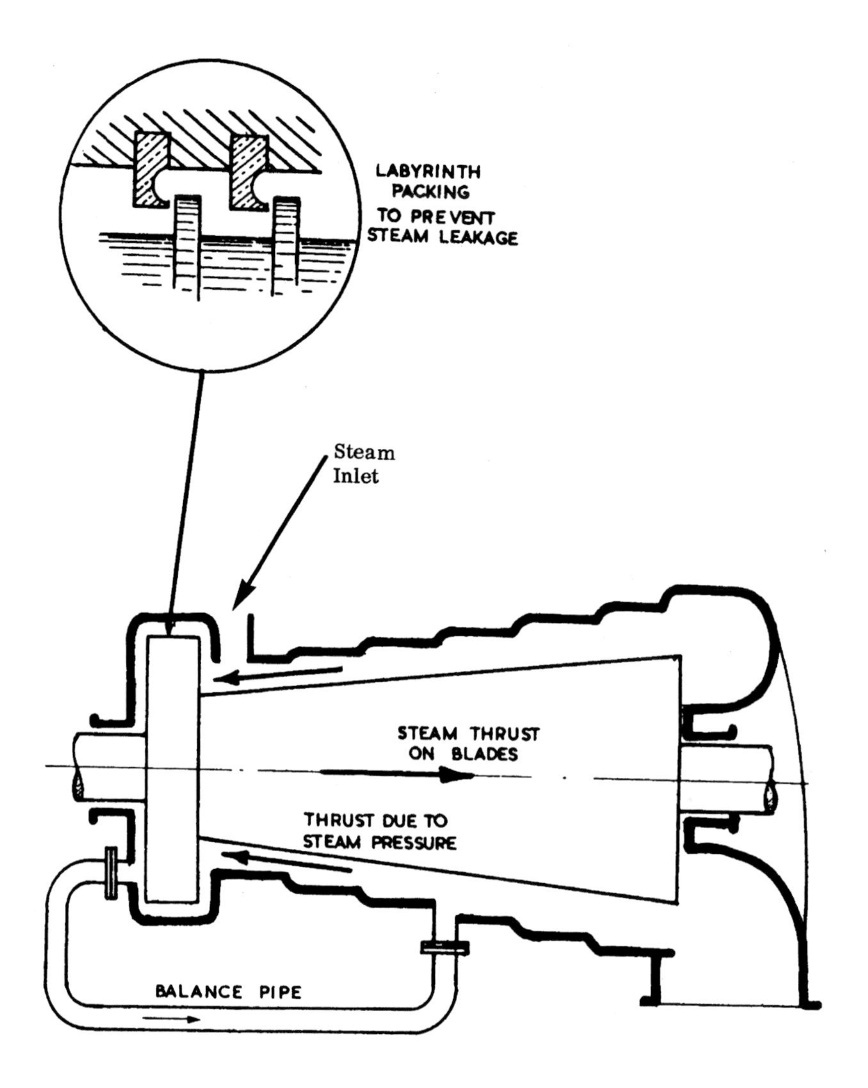

Thrust Adjusting Gear

The efficiency of reaction turbines depends upon the very close clearances between the stationary and moving blades. As protection for the axial seals, an adjustable thrust bearing, as shown in Fig. 37, is fitted. The whole thrust block is cylindrical and fits like a piston in the cylinder with the thrust block able to be axially located. This enables the axial position of the rotor to be controlled within strictly defined limits. During startup, the thrust block is pushed against a stop in the direction of exhaust for maximum clearance between the stationary and moving blades to avoid any danger of rubbing, due to uneven temperatures. When the turbine is heated up and has been on load, the clearances can be reduced by adjusting the thrust block for minimum clearance and, therefore, maximum blade efficiency.

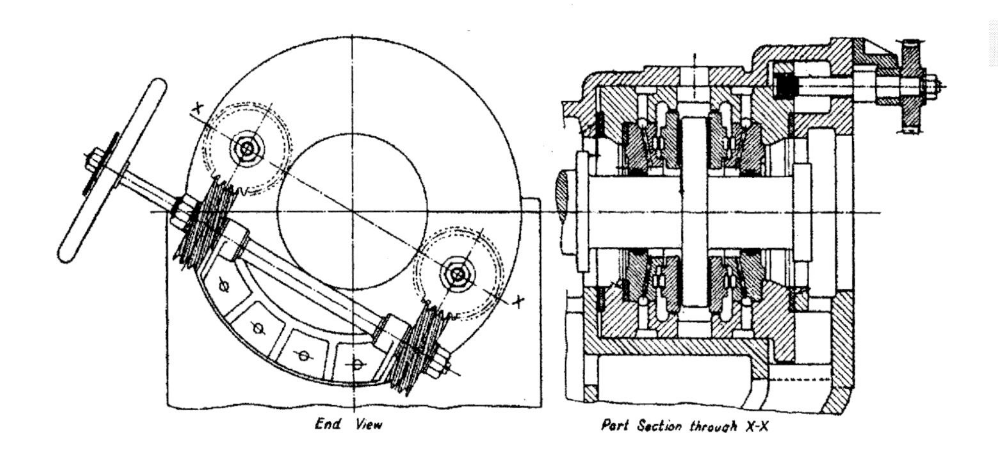

FIGURE 37

Turbine Thrust Adjusting Gear

TYPICAL TURBINE DESIGNS

Fig. 38 is an illustration of a General Electric Company mechanical drive turbine. These turbines are built in ratings from 10 hp to 1,200 hp, running at speeds from 1000 to 6500 r/min. They are used to drive pumps, compressors, fans, blowers, and similar equipment.

The turbine illustrated is a single stage, velocity compounded impulse type. Two rows of blades are arranged in the one stage with a row of stationary blades between them.

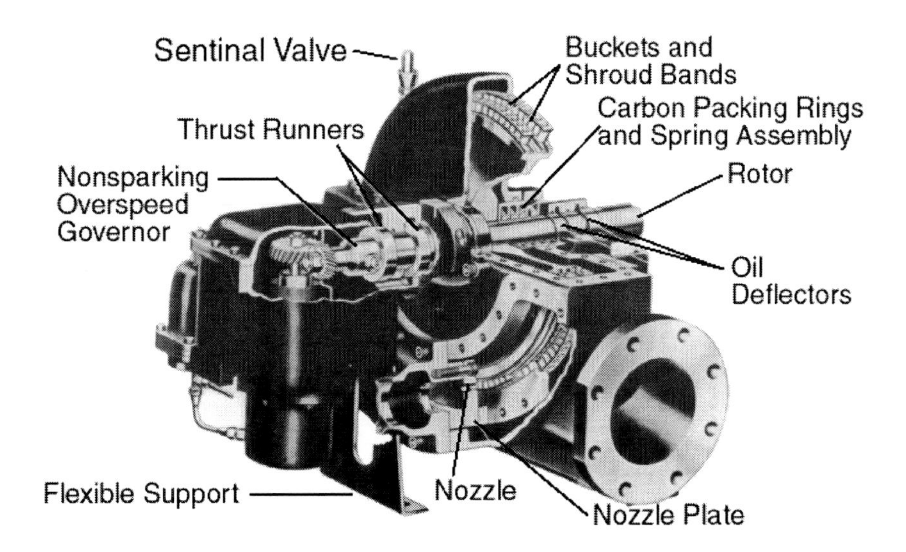

FIGURE 38

Single Stage Mechanical Drive Turbine *(Courtesy of General Electric)*

Fig. 39 shows an "opened up" view of a small industrial, mechanical drive turbine, manufactured by Skinner Engine Co. Dean Hill Turbine Division. These turbines are built in ratings from 120 to 1,200 hp, consuming steam at 600 psi and 750°F. This 120 hp turbine has a blade wheel diameter of 11 in., running at 1000 to 4000 r/min.

FIGURE 39

Mechanical Drive Turbine

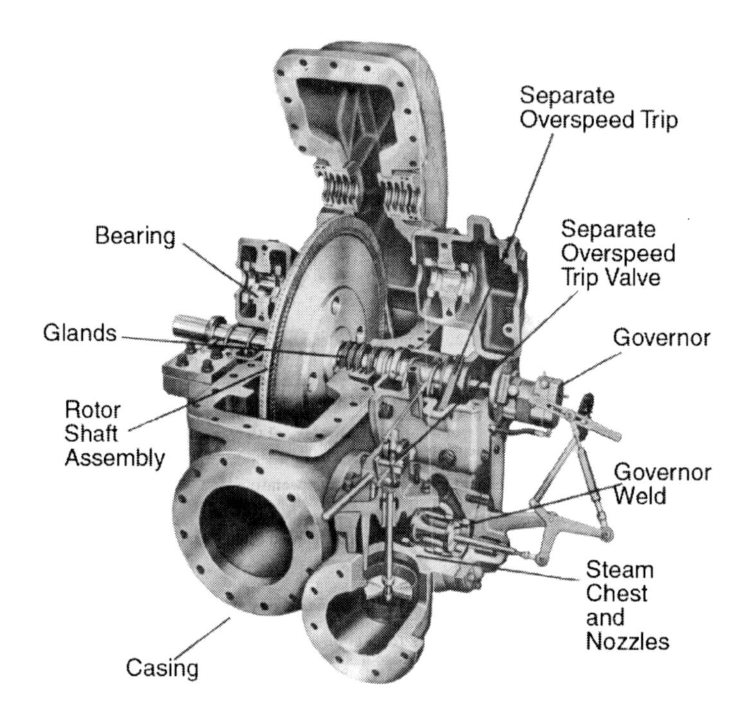

Fig. 40 illustrates a mechanical drive turbine, widely used in industry. It is a single stage, impulse type turbine with a two-row velocity stage wheel and a row of stationary reversing blades between the rows of rotating blades.

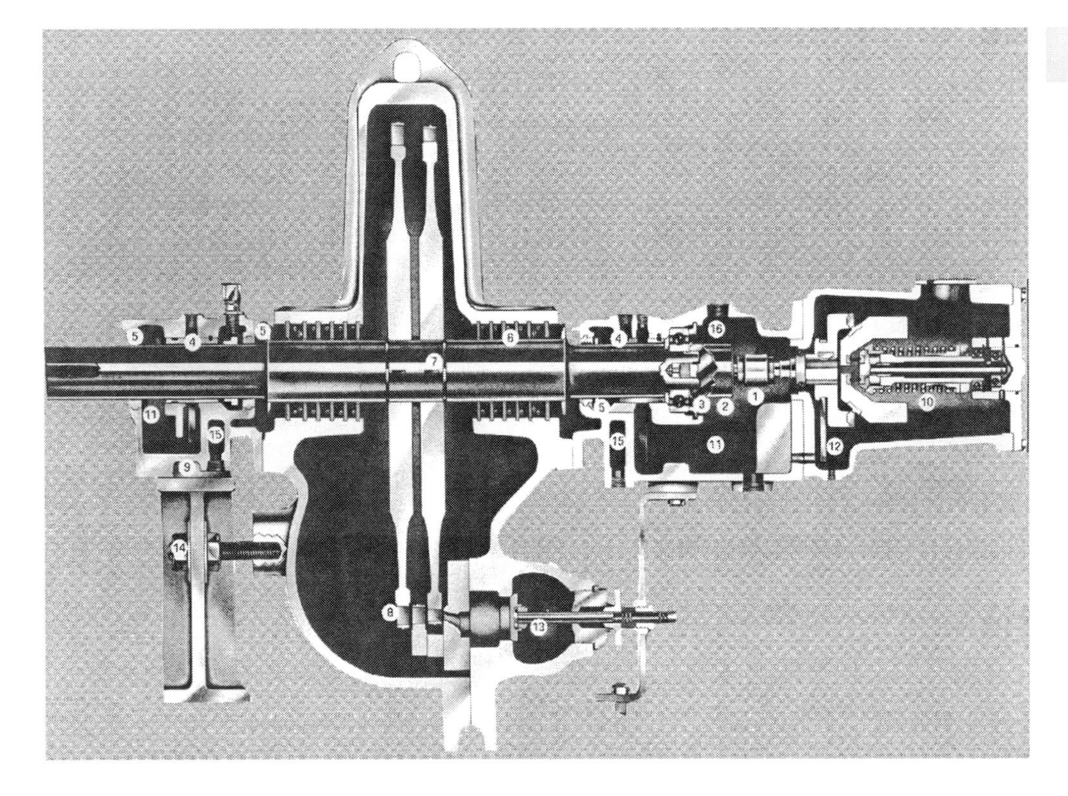

FIGURE 40

Mechanical Drive Turbine

1. Governor coupling
   support
2. Non-sparking, bolt type overspeed trip
   shaft governor
3. High capacity, anti-friction thrust bearing
   for positive rotor location
   (no oil cup)
4. Steel backed-babbitt lined journal bearings
   control
5. Stationary, labyrinth bearing case seals
   throughout
6. Angle type carbon ring packing
7. Built-up rotor construction
   adjusting port
8. High efficiency blading
9. True centerline
10 Standard mechanical
11. Internal oil reservoirs
12. Governor lubrication
13. Hand operated nozzle
14. Metric fasteners used
15. Water cooling jackets
16. Overspeed trip

The turbine, shown in Fig. 41, is an Allis-Chalmers with two extraction points. Two impulse wheels are used, one before the HP (High Pressure) reaction staging and one before the LP (Low Pressure) staging. Typical of the extraction type of turbine, it is rated at 5,300 hp at 3600 r/min.

FIGURE 41

Automatic Extraction or Mixed Pressure Type Turbine

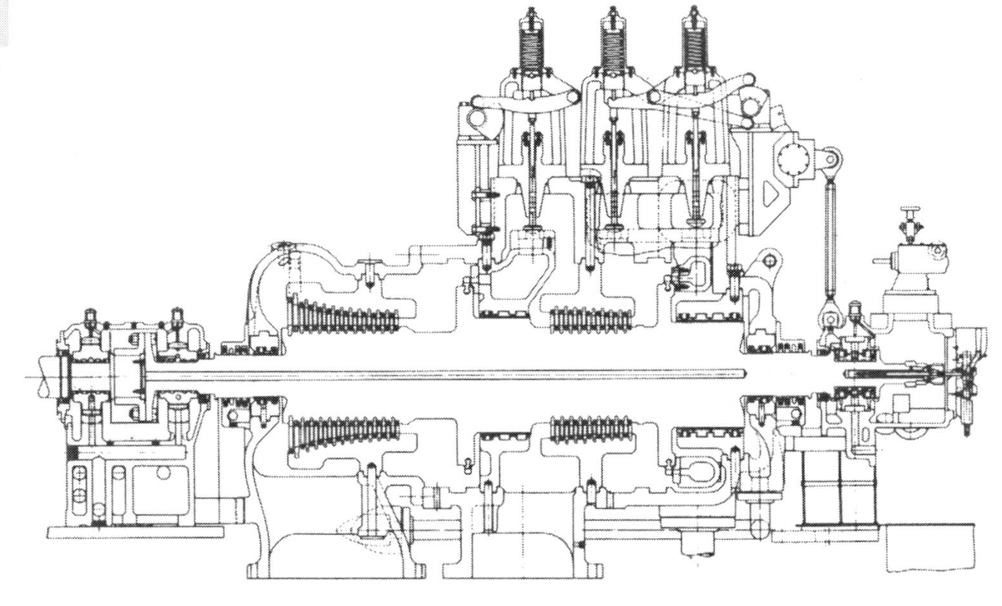

Fig. 42 illustrates a straight non-condensing turbine of 1,475 hp. This is an impulse type turbine. The first wheel is velocity compounded with the remaining eight stages of the pressure compounded impulse type. This is a very common type of turbine and is used where there is a large demand for lower pressure steam. The unit can be paralleled so that its output can vary directly with changes in the process steam requirements. Its governing system is sensitive only to low process steam pressure so that if steam requirements fall below the electrical load, the extra electrical load must be made up from another source.

FIGURE 42

Nine Stage Type GZF Turbine

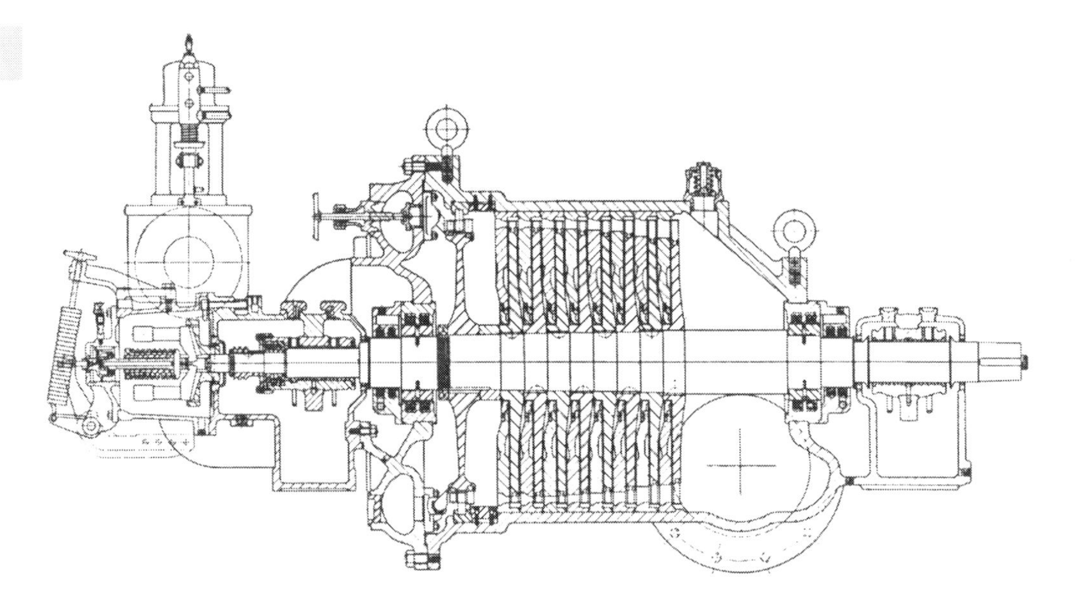

UNIT 4

Steam Turbine Auxiliaries and Control

Learning Objectives

Here is what you will be able to do when you complete each objective:

1. Describe the purpose, design and components of a turning gear.
2. Describe the purpose, design and components of an adjusting gear.
3. Explain critical speed.
4. Describe the design and components of lubricating oil and jacking oil systems.
5. Describe the design of speed reducing gears.
6. Describe the design and components of flexible couplings.
7. Describe the purpose and design of steam turbine governors and governor systems.
8. Describe the purpose and design of steam turbine stop valves and control valves.
9. Describe the purpose and design of steam turbine grid type extraction valves.
10. Describe the purpose and design of steam turbine casing pressure relief systems including rupture diaphragms.
11. Describe the purpose and design of steam turbine overspeed trips.
12. Describe the purpose and design of steam turbine supervisory equipment.

TURNING GEARS

When a turbine is left cold and at a standstill, the mass of the rotor tends to cause the rotor to sag slightly. This is called **bowing**. If left at a standstill while the turbine is still hot, the lower half of the rotor cools faster than the upper half. The rotor bends upwards. This is called **hogging**. In both cases, the turbine is difficult, if not impossible, to start up due to rubbing within the bearings, glands and diaphragms. To overcome this problem, the manufacturer supplies large turbines with a turning or barring gear. It consists of an electric motor and sets of reducing gears that turn the turbine shaft at low speed. The normal speed of a turbine rotor on barring gear is between 20 and 40 rpm, although some designs turn as slowly as 3 rpm.

The distance between bearings of large turbines is considerable (9.8 to 32.8 feet). Rotors operating at temperatures above 752°F need turning after shutdown to ensure uniform cooling takes place. The fan action in the casing caused by the slow turning turbine blades prevents temperature variations.

Before a cold turbine is started up, the barring gear turns it for approximately three hours. When a turbine is shut down, the barring gear turns it for the next 24 hours. The exact time required depends on the difference in temperature between the stationary and rotating parts. If a hydrogen-cooled generator is involved, the turbine is kept on barring gear to prevent loss of hydrogen through the shaft seals. The turning gear, illustrated in Fig. 1, uses a belt drive with a worm and wheel to reduce the motor speed. A yoke supports the disengaging gear wheel. An oil-operated piston rotates the yoke about the worm shaft to engage or disengage the turning gear from the turbine shaft.

The location of an under-slung barring or turning gear is shown in Fig. 2. This view shows a tandem double-flow turbine being assembled for testing. Positioning of the barring gear at the side of the bearing enables the pinion to engage the shaft below the turbine centre line. The top portion of the diagram illustrates a side-mounted barring gear with a vertical driving motor and their location in relation to the turbine shaft.

With the turbine revolving at slow speeds (on barring gear), the main lubricating oil pump does not provide sufficient oil to lubricate the bearings. An auxiliary oil pump is used when the turning gear is in operation. A separate motor driven oil pump is provided to supply oil to the bearings instead of using the turbine-driven oil pump.

FIGURE 1

Turning Gear

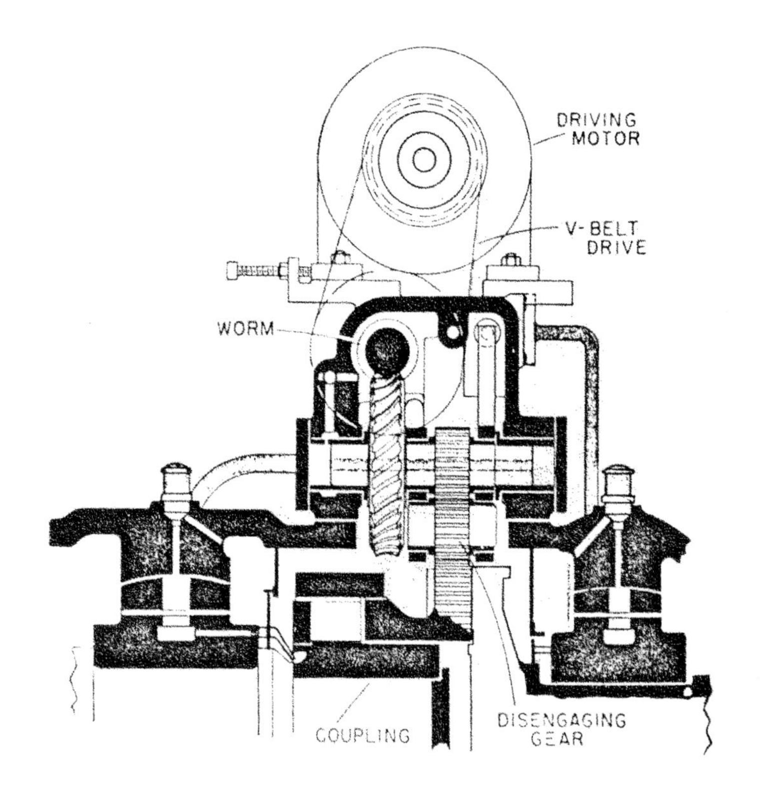

FIGURE 2

Illustrations of Barring (Turning) Gear

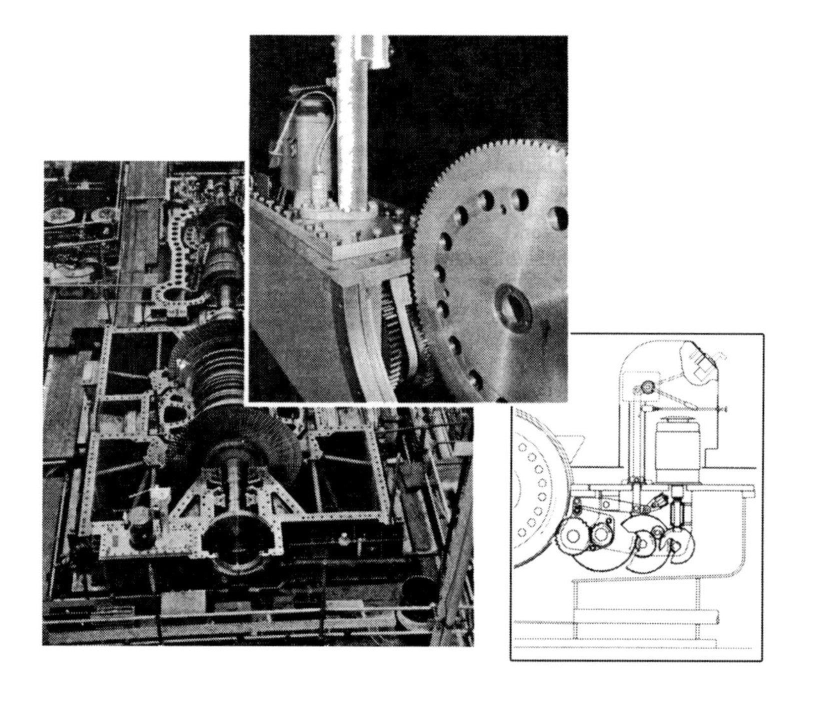

TURBINE BLADE CLEARANCES

Efficient operation of a turbine depends to a large extent on the maintenance of the correct clearances between fixed and moving elements. Excessive clearances cause increased steam consumption and reduced clearances may cause blade rubbing.

When a turbine is constructed, the clearances are carefully set and a record is kept at the plant. When the top halves of the casing are removed, the clearances are checked against the record. Care is taken to ensure that the rotors are in the running position when taking measurements. Provision is made to move the rotor axially to a position for lifting it from the casing. Particular care is necessary with clearances of velocity stages fitted to the high-pressure end of impulse machines, as in Fig. 3. A thorough check of clearances is essential if replacement blades, nozzles or packing rings have been installed.

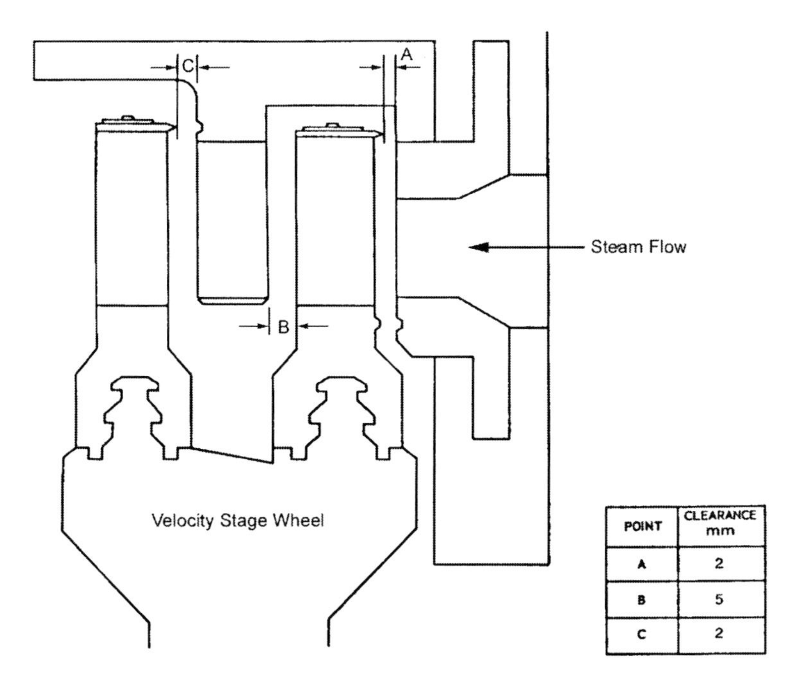

POINT	CLEARANCE mm
A	2
B	5
C	2

FIGURE 3

Velocity Stage Clearances

THRUST ADJUSTING GEAR

The efficiency of reaction turbines depends upon the close clearances between the stationary and moving blades. To protect the axial seals, an adjustable thrust bearing is used as shown in Fig. 4. The thrust block is cylindrical and fits like a piston in the cylinder. The thrust block can be adjusted axially. The axial position of the rotor is controlled within strictly defined limits. During startup, the thrust block is moved against a stop in the direction of the turbine exhaust.

This setting is for maximum clearance between the stationary and moving blades so that uneven temperatures during startup do not cause rubbing. When the turbine is heated up and loaded, the thrust block is adjusted to reducing the clearances to minimum, thus producing maximum efficiency.

FIGURE 4

Turbine Thrust Adjusting Gear

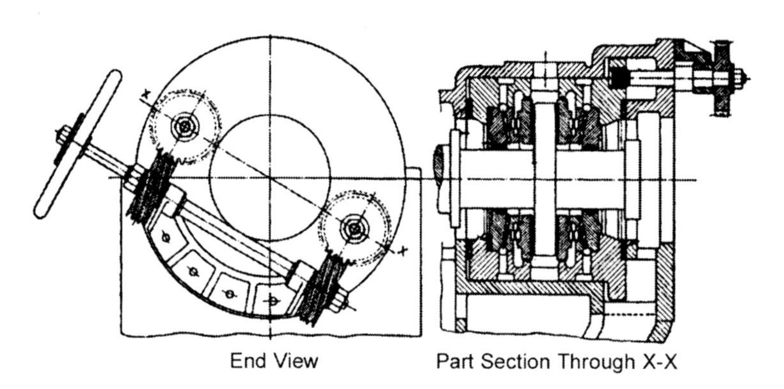

CRITICAL SPEED

If a turbine rotor were constructed so that it was an absolutely symmetrical body, its balance would be perfect. When rotating, the symmetrical rotor would have no vibration caused by out-of-balance mass. Errors of balance do take place in actual rotors. They are caused by:

- Differences in the density of the material
- Errors due to machining
- Differences in blade masses

These are kept to a minimum by careful workmanship. The completed rotor is balanced both statically (balanced at rest) and dynamically (balanced in motion) before being put into service.

Static balancing involves supporting the shaft journals on transverse "knife edges. The tendency of the rotor to roll is measured. Then mass is added or removed to delete the tendency to roll.

Dynamic balancing is done after the static process in a machine with flexible bearing supports. The rotor is run up to speed by an electric motor, and vibrations are measured. Mass is added or removed to the rotor before it is retested. The process is repeated until the vibration readings are in an acceptable range. The balanced rotor must have very low vibrations when running at designed speed. New rotors are balanced at the factory. Overhauled or refurbished rotors must also be dynamically balanced.

Note: At speed, a balanced rotor shows no more than 0.0009 or 0.002 in eccentricity.

A turbine shaft, supported between its two bearings can be likened to a piano wire. If the wire is "plucked," it vibrates with a natural frequency. Similarly, shaft rotation has a natural frequency depending upon its stiffness, as illustrated in Fig. 5. If the shaft is rotated, any out-of-balance force rotates with it and tends to deflect the shaft. As the speed increases, the deflection also increases. When a particular speed is approached (corresponding to the natural frequency of the shaft) the deflection increases very rapidly and may be sufficient to permanently bend the shaft.

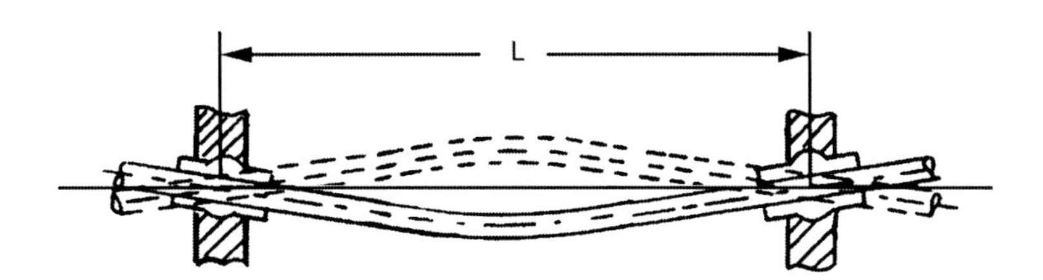

FIGURE 5

Exaggerated Bow of a Shaft

This speed is called the **critical speed** and is determined in the design stages of the machine. It depends upon the length of shaft between supports, the shaft diameter and the shaft stiffness. If the critical speed is approached rapidly, there is little time for the deflection to grow. Once above this speed, the deflection begins to decrease until smooth running is again achieved. Turbine manufacturers recommend passing through the critical speeds quickly. A turbine shaft, running in the critical speed zone, can be identified by very high vibrations throughout most of the turbine bearings.

A turbine rotor may have more than one critical speed. The others occur as the shaft takes up the forms shown exaggerated in Fig. 6.

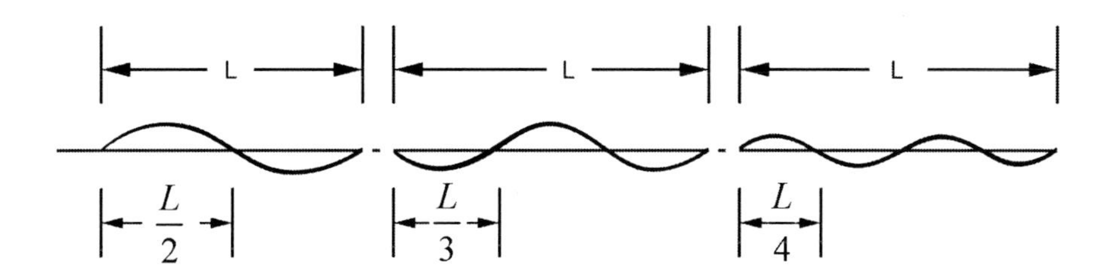

FIGURE 6

Forms of Whirling Shaft at Critical Speeds

These are the second, third and fourth critical speeds. After passing through the first critical speed the shaft settles down until the second critical speed is approached when it commences to bend in the curve shown with a **nodal point** at the centre of its length shown in Fig. 6 as $\frac{L}{2}$. Generally, the operating speed is arranged to be between the first and second critical speeds, though some short rotors may be so "stiff" that the operating speed is below the first critical speed.

Some turbine rotors tend to lose their straightness when heated. Many manufacturers guard against "thermal instability" by heating the rotor while it is slowly revolved. The eccentricity is measured during the process.

Most rotors tend to "bow" on heating. The deflection increases with temperature up to a point and then decreases again until the shaft is nearly straight. It remains in this condition when cooling down and shows no tendency to bend when the heating process is repeated. This process of heating and cooling of the rotor is carried out before blading is installed. This is a precaution to prevent rotor vibrations when the turbine is put into service.

LUBRICATING OIL SYSTEMS

Turbines are the prime movers that many plants depend upon. They must be provided with a reliable supply of lubrication oil. The size of the turbine determines whether to use a simple or complex lubricating system. Turbines of less than 150 kW, used to drive auxiliary equipment, are often provided with ring-oiled bearings.

Moderate-sized turbines, particularly if driving through a reduction gear, may have both ring-oiled bearings and a circulating system. These pressurized oil systems not only supply oil in the form of a spray to the gears but also supply oil to the bearings of the gearbox and the turbine.

Large turbines have circulating systems supplying oil to the:

- Turbine bearings
- Governor mechanisms
- Hydraulically operated steam throttle valves
- Bearings of the driven generators

A typical circulating oil system for a turbine and generator set is shown in Fig. 7. The oil pumps take suction from the oil tank through strainers and discharge the oil at high pressure, 80 to 120 psi. From the strainers, the oil flows in two different directions:

- To the power oil and governor relay oil systems
- To the oil coolers and then to the turbine generator bearings

Power oil, acting in servomotors, uses hydraulic pressure to open stop valves and governing valves. Governor relay oil acts as a sensitive regulating medium. It transmits oil pressure signals to various parts of the governor oil system. The power oil and the governor relay oil have to be at high pressure.

Lubrication oil is at a lower pressure, typically in the 10 to 20 psi range. Before the oil passes to the coolers, it flows through a pressure-reducing valve. If the turbine has been operating for a length of time, and the oil is at operating temperature, the oil from the oil tank will be quite warm. Therefore, the oil will need cooling in the oil coolers, before it flows through the bearings. Typical outlet temperatures, from the coolers, are in the 109 to 120 °F range.

Inside the bearings the oil acts as a lubricant between moving surfaces and as a coolant for the bearings. From the bearings, the oil drains into a return header leading back to the oil tank. A thermometer is placed in each return line from the bearings and indicates bearing temperature.

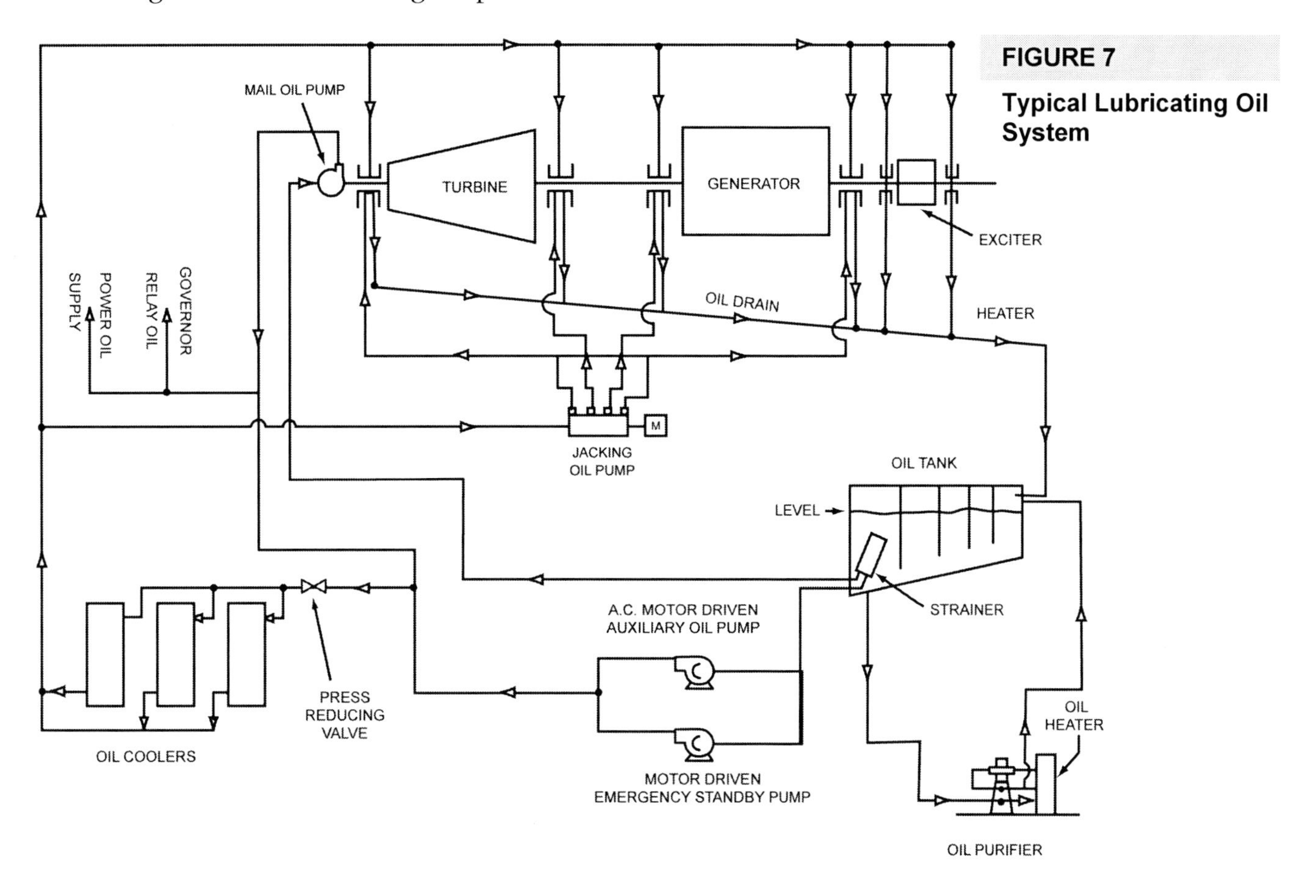

FIGURE 7

Typical Lubricating Oil System

JACKING OIL SYSTEMS

Large turbines, with heavy rotors, are generally equipped with a jacking oil pump. It supplies the lower part of the bearings with oil, at approximately 290 to 1,450 psi, lifting the shaft and supplying lubricating oil. Oil pressure lifts or jacks the shaft a few millimeters, so there is no metal-to-metal contact during the initial movement of the rotor. Jacking of the shaft reduces the load on the barring gear motor. Jacking oil is applied before starting the barring gear and while operating the turbine at slow speed. The jacking oil pump is shut down at turbine speeds of 50 to 60 rpm.

The turbine/generator lube oil system, shown in Fig. 8, incorporates a jacking oil pump. The jacking oil pump, # 4 on the drawing, takes suction from the lube oil header. The jacking oil pump boosts the pressure and feeds oil to the bottom of the bearings. After the jacking oil leaves the bearings, it then flows into the main return header along with the lube oil being drained from the bearings. These combined oil flows drain by gravity back to the lube oil tank.

FIGURE 8

Lube Oil with Jacking Oil System

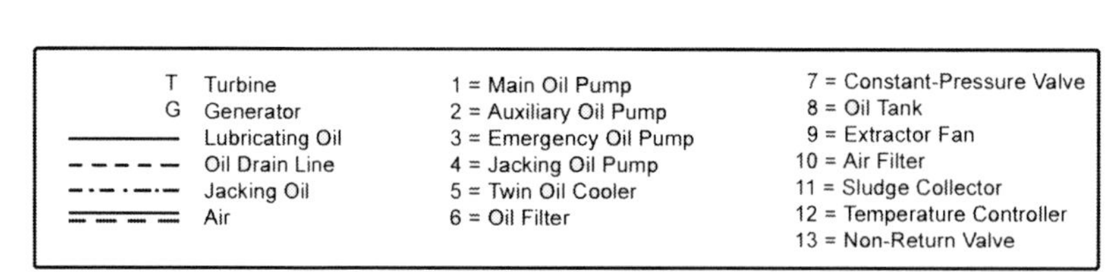

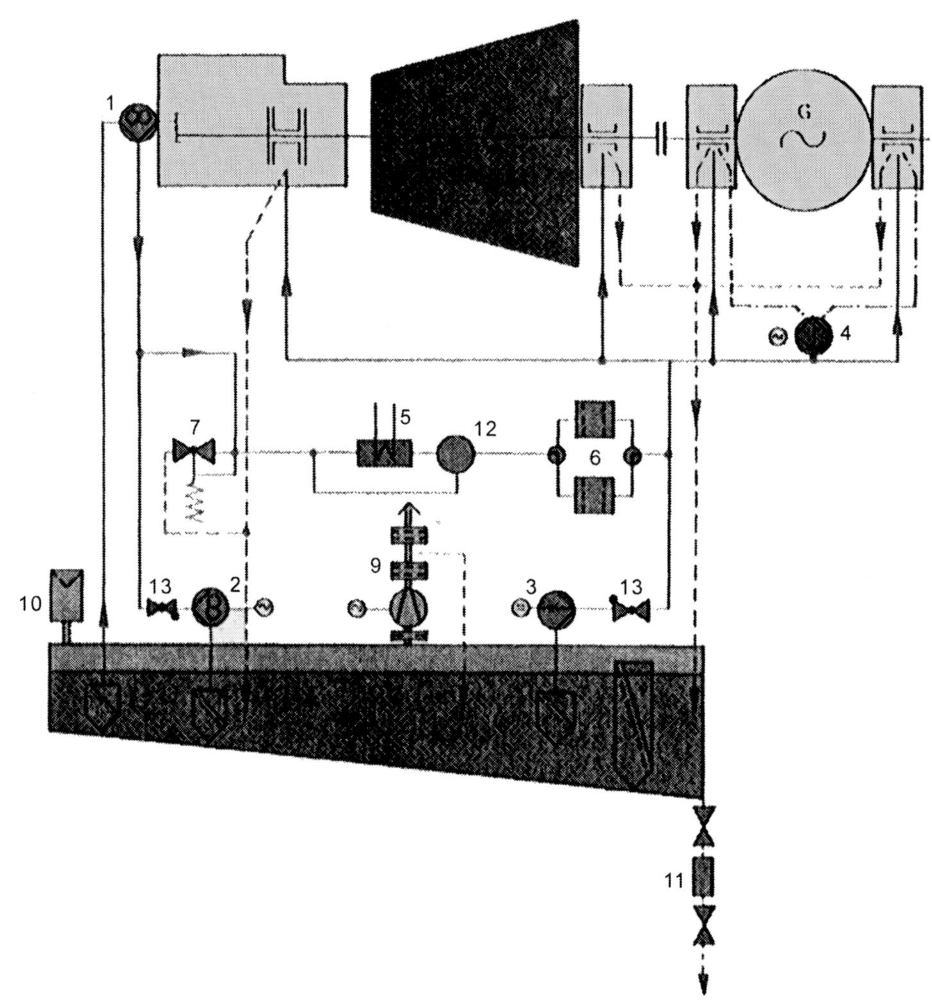

SPEED REDUCTION GEAR SETS

Steam turbines operate at speeds higher than the required operating speed of the driven machine. Examples of this include turbine-driven:

- Direct-current generators
- Paper making machines
- Centrifugal pumps
- Blowers and fans

In these instances reduction gear sets are used to reduce the shaft speed of the turbine to suit that of the machine being driven. Reduction gear sets used on medium and large-sized steam turbines are housed in an oil-tight casing. They are connected to the turbine and driven unit by flexible type couplings. Small turbines may be designed so that the gear housing is integral with the turbine casing. The pinion may even be connected directly to the rotor shaft. This type of arrangement is shown in Fig. 9.

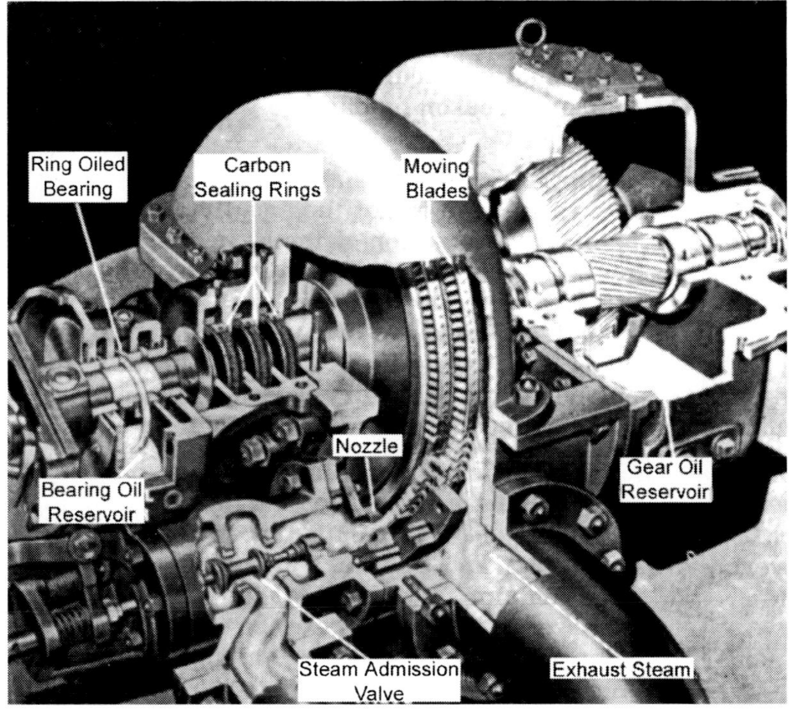

FIGURE 9

Turbine Driver with Gear Reducer

Fig. 10 shows a speed reduction gearbox with the top portion of the cover removed. The driver is connected to the coupling of the small gear shaft. The driven machine is connected to the opposite end of the large gear shaft. A pipe from the oil pump supplies oil mist to the gears at their mesh point. Note that the gears are set at an angle to reduce gear noise and vibration.

FIGURE 10

Gears in a Speed Reduction Gear Drive

FLEXIBLE COUPLINGS

Couplings are used to connect shafts of rotating equipment. Flexible couplings permit an axial movement of the driven shaft, and they can also be designed to transmit or eliminate end thrust from the driven unit to the turbine. Flexible couplings can accommodate minor misalignments or bearing wear. They are not intended to overcome shaft misalignment due to careless or faulty assembly.

Flexible couplings used on large direct-connected units are often enclosed in the same housing as the turbine and driven unit bearings. They are lubricated in an oil-tight case. Oil is supplied by the main lubricating oil system. Flexible couplings are often used to connect the turbine rotor to its driven machine shaft or to connect the rotors of tandem compounded turbines to each other. They are designed to absorb the differential expansion of the shafts due to temperature changes and, to a certain extent, any misalignment that occurs due to settlement of foundations or temperature changes.

Excessive wear on flexible couplings is often the result of faulty shaft alignment. A flexible coupling is not designed to act as a universal joint. It can take care of very small amounts of shaft misalignment, but its primary purpose is to allow for relative axial movement between the shafts it connects.

Coupling components must be kept in good condition. They are taken apart, inspected and cleaned when maintenance is performed on the driver. Couplings can lock up (fail to move) transferring axial movement through the shaft. This can cause overloading of thrust bearings and vibration problems.

Types of Flexible Couplings

There are many types of flexible couplings. They are selected based on the application and the type of machines they connect. Normally, the couplings are lubricated, but more types of dry couplings are being introduced. They are often made of hard rubber compounds and require no maintenance and do not lock up.

The coupling in Fig. 11, for turbines of small and medium output, has flanges keyed to the shafts. The coupling bolts are screwed into one flange and rubber bushes with metal cores are fitted over the plain ends of the bolts. The rubber bushes have a small clearance in the holes of the other coupling flange. This type is called a "pin and grommet coupling"

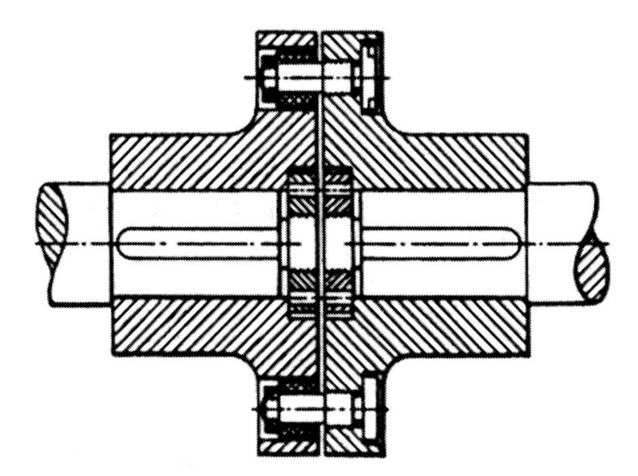

FIGURE 11
Turbine Coupling

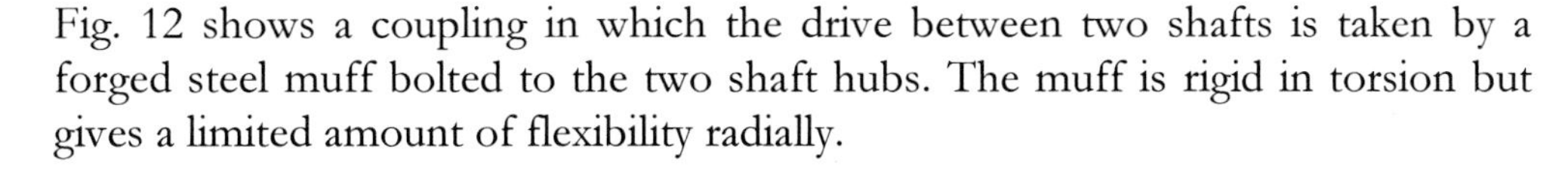

Fig. 12 shows a coupling in which the drive between two shafts is taken by a forged steel muff bolted to the two shaft hubs. The muff is rigid in torsion but gives a limited amount of flexibility radially.

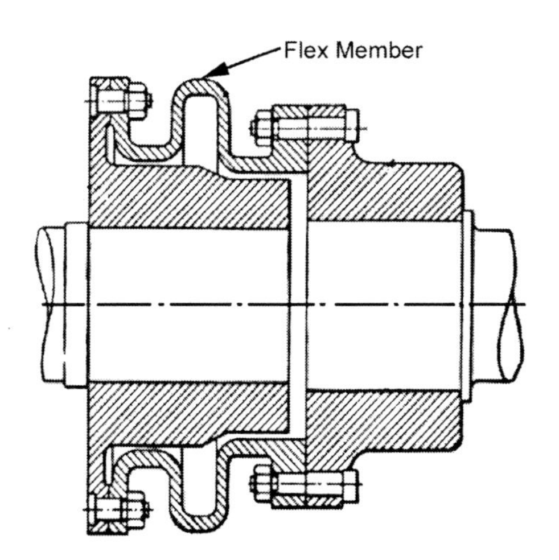

FIGURE 12
Semi-Flexible Coupling

Gear or tooth type couplings are shown in Figs. 13 and 14. The shaft hubs have a number of teeth around the periphery. The sleeve has a matching set of teeth to transfer torque to the drive while allowing small axial movements between the shafts.

FIGURE 13

Gear Type Flexible Coupling

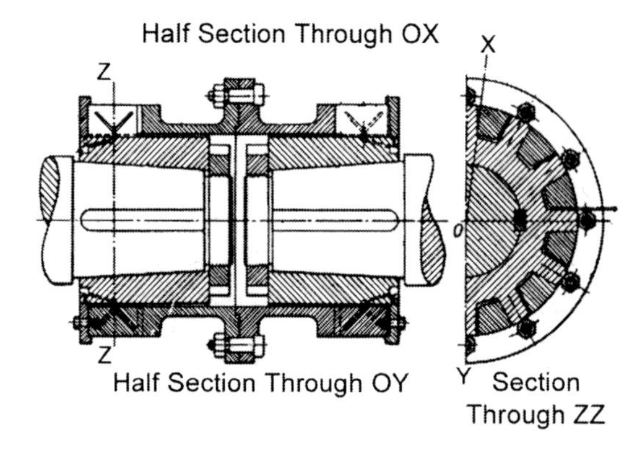

FIGURE 14

Gear Type Flexible Coupling

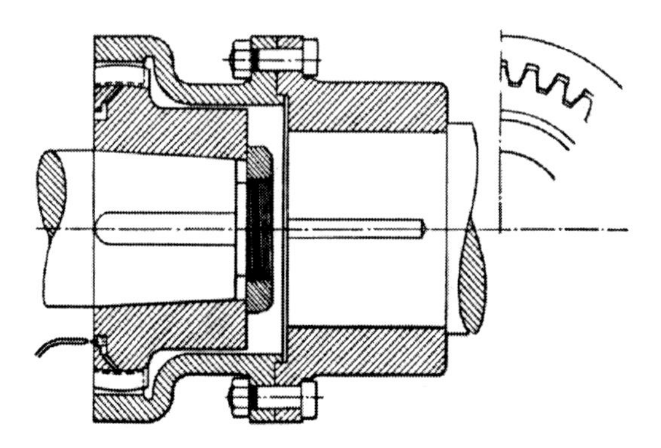

Fig. 15 shows a resilient grid (often called a Bibby or Flexsteel coupling). It has a tempered steel spring as the driving medium between the two hubs. The hubs are keyed to the shafts.

FIGURE 15

Resilient Grid (Flexsteel) Coupling

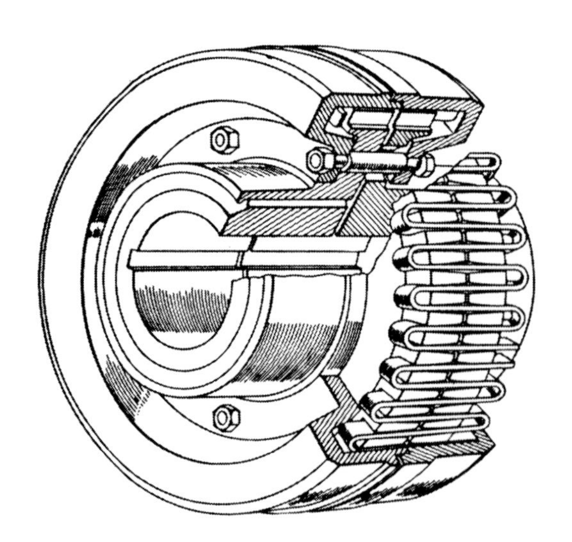

STEAM TURBINE GOVERNORS

Turbine governing systems vary the steam flow to keep the speed of the turbine constant with varying loads or to hold the pressure constant with varying demands for process steam. The governor on a turbine driving an alternator controls the turbine inlet steam flow to maintain constant speed with varying alternator load. In a backpressure turbine supplying exhaust steam for process work, the steam supply to the turbine is controlled to maintain a constant backpressure.

In an extraction turbine, the governor controls the steam flow so that both the turbine speed and the pressure of steam, at the point of extraction, are maintained reasonably constant. This involves regulation of the total amount of steam admitted to the inlet stages of the turbine and of the steam supplied to the turbine stages following the extraction point.

Governor Terminology

Speed Droop

Speed droop is the change in speed caused by an increase in load. An ideal governor can maintain a constant speed at any load. But, mechanical losses within most governors mean that they cannot achieve this speed control. If the load on a turbine changes from zero (no-load) to maximum (full-load), the turbine slows down and the governor may not be capable of restoring the turbine to set speed.

The difference between the no-load and full-load speed, expressed as a percentage of the set speed, is called the "droop" of the governor. As the load increases, the speed will "droop" below the set speed. For example, if the set speed of a turbine is 5000 rpm, where it operates with no load, and the governor system can only achieve 4500 rpm, when the turbine becomes fully loaded, the droop of the governor is (500/5000) x 100 = 10%. Governors with low droop are more sensitive to load changes and generally have more accurate control than governors with high droop.

Isochronous Governing

Isochronous governing gives perfect speed regulation with zero speed droop. An isochronous governor regulates the turbine at constant speed at all loads, so the speed regulation or droop is zero percent. Isochronous governing is used when prime movers are operating alone.

If turbines are sharing load in a parallel operation, an action called ***hunting*** can occur. Each turbine attempts to pick up the change in load and they begin "fighting" each other for control. This creates an uncontrollable cycling of the load and turbine speeds. The result may be that one machine ends up fully loaded while another machine may have no load.

Governors fall into two main classes:

- Speed sensitive
- Pressure sensitive

Speed-Sensitive Governors

The speed-sensitive governor is a proportional-action controller because each change in power causes a change in the turbine speed. The governor controls the opening of the control valves as a function of this speed change. Due to the governor speed droop, the frequency is not constant over the full range of load without an external adjustment.
The speed-sensitive governor may consist of the following types:

- Nozzle
- Throttle
- Bypass or overload
- Mechanical
- Mechanical – hydraulic
- Electronic – hydraulic

Nozzle Governing

Nozzle governing is only used in impulse turbines. Regulating the flow of steam to inlet nozzles and the turbine blades maintains a set turbine speed. Common nozzle arrangements are the bar-lift and the cam-lift systems.

Fig. 16 shows the bar-lift design with a row of inlet nozzles above the first stage turbine blading and a set of nozzle valves, or plugs, held by a horizontal bar. Notice that the lengths of the stems on these plugs vary. The flyweight action moves the bar up and down to open and close the nozzles as required. The different lengths of the plug stems determine the sequence in which they open and close.

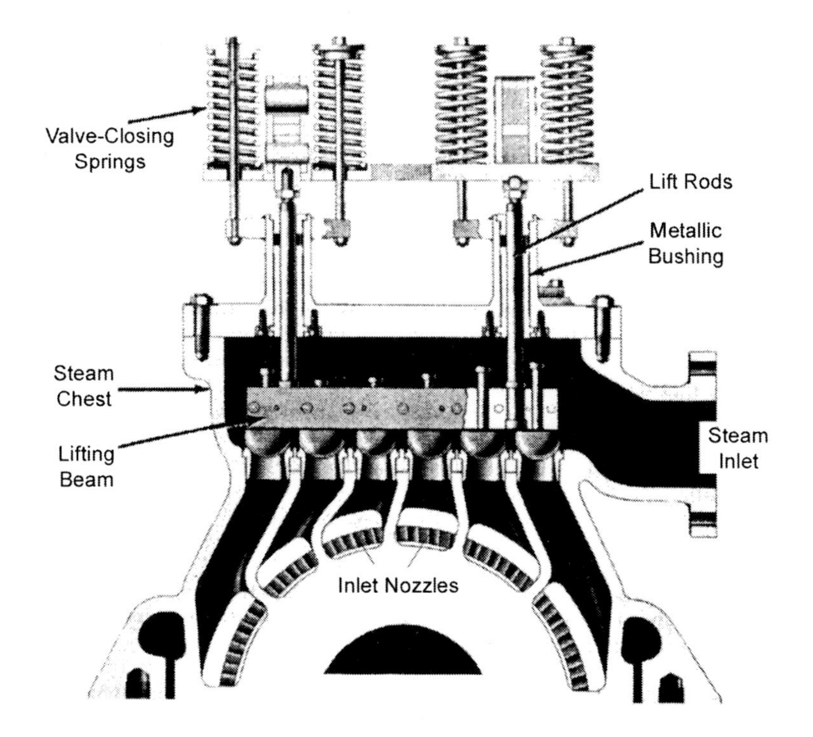

FIGURE 16

Bar-lift Nozzle Control Gear

Other designs use a cam-like device to control the sequence and opening of each nozzle. Fig. 17 illustrates how oil under governor control acts on the underside of the spring-loaded operating piston. As the piston rises, a rack on the piston rod causes a layshaft to rotate. On this layshaft are a number of cams, one for each admission poppet valve. Each cam operating through a follower and a rocker arm actuates a steam valve which supplies a group of nozzles. The cams on the layshaft are indexed so that the valves are opened in a predetermined sequence and closed in the reverse order.

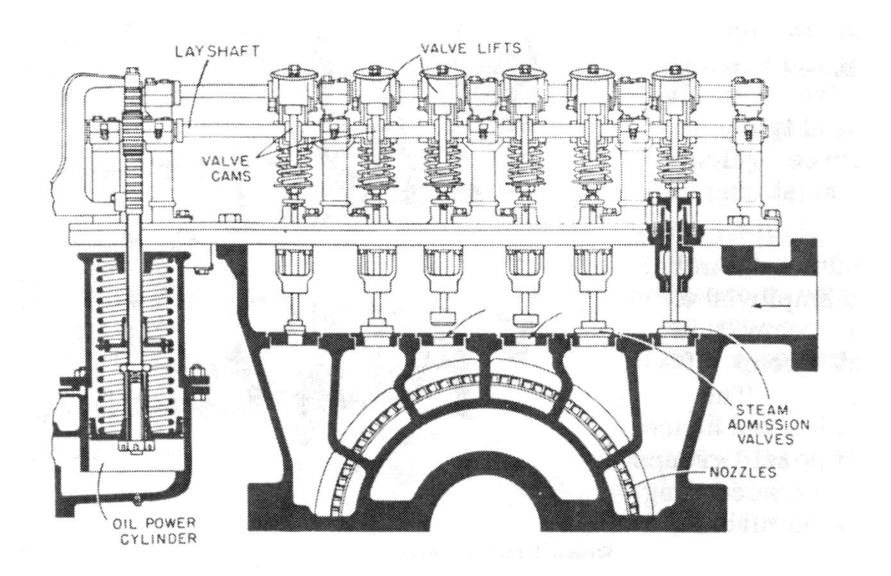

FIGURE 17

Cam-lift Steam Admission Valves

Throttle Governing

An example of throttle governing is shown in Fig. 18. A single valve at the inlet to the turbine adjusts the steam flow equally into the turbine casing and to the nozzles. The inlet, or throttle valve, responds to the governor to increase or decrease the steam flow for more or less speed. A hydraulic servomotor is often used to help move the throttle valve. In larger turbines, there may be more throttle valves arranged in parallel in the steam line.

Throttle governing is used with reaction turbines because the pressure drop in the moving blading requires steam admission to the full circumference. The multi-valve arrangement supplying steam to nozzle groups cannot be used. With throttle governing, one or two control valves control the load from 0% to 100%.

FIGURE 18

Mechanical-Hydraulic Governor with Servo

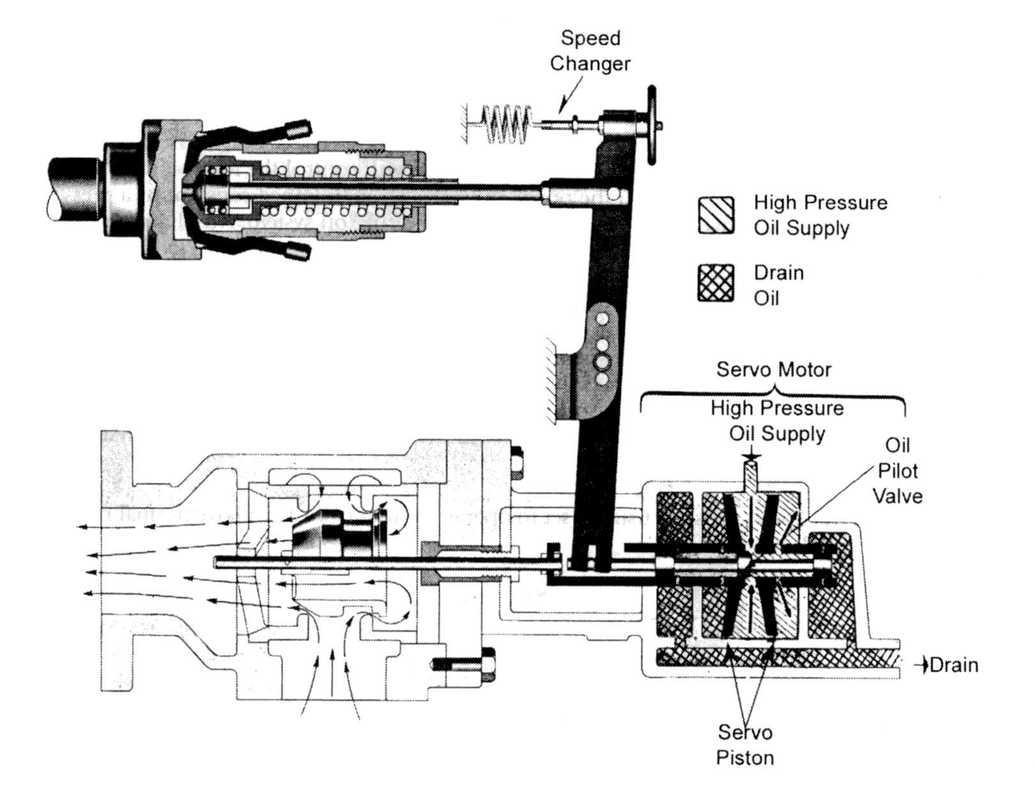

Bypass or Overload Governing

Bypass or overload governing is used on both impulse and reaction turbines. It consists of two throttling valves: one at the inlet of the first stage of the turbine, and the other at an inlet downstream from the first few stages. The purpose of the second inlet point is to allow the turbine to maintain speed while producing extra power, during high load or overload conditions.

Fig. 19 shows a steam chest with a stop and trip valve (on the left), followed by the main steam throttle valve and the bypass throttle valve (on the right). This steam chest/valve arrangement is mounted on the turbine so as to direct steam to the appropriate nozzles, as shown in the turbine cross-section of Fig. 20.

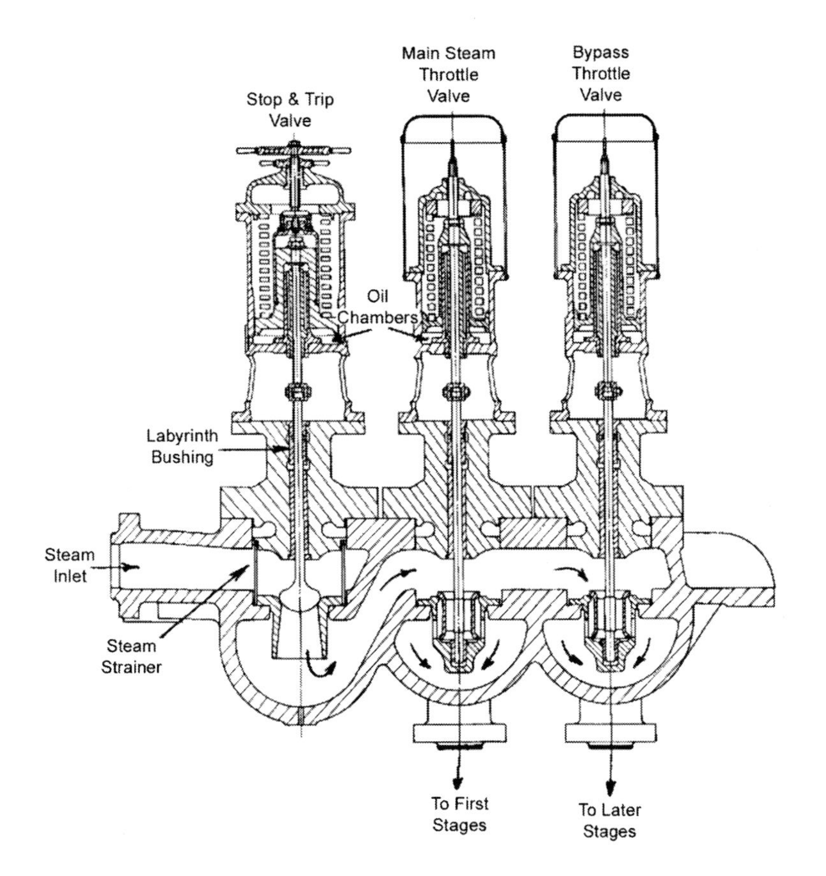

FIGURE 19

Steam Chest with Stop, Trip and Throttle Valves
(Courtesy of C.A. Parsons)

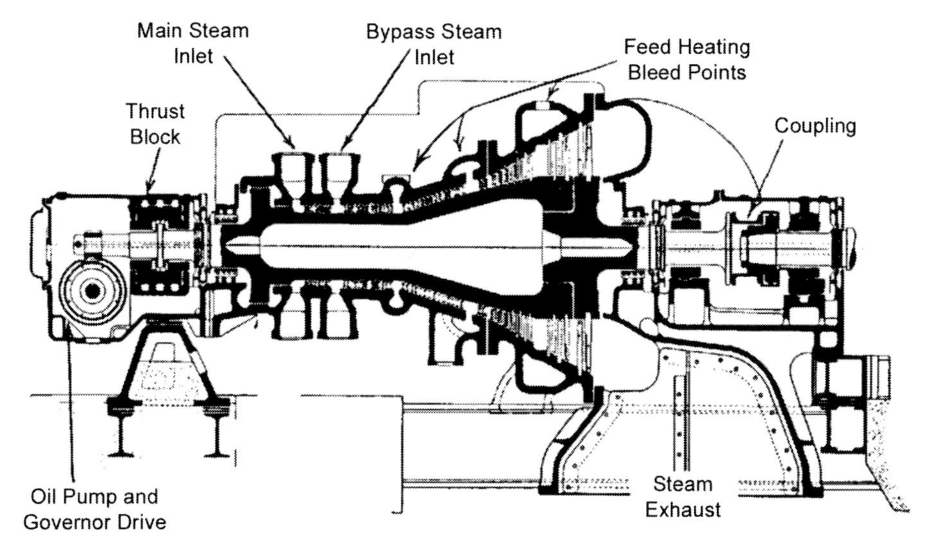

FIGURE 20

Bypass-Governed Turbine

Mechanical Governors

Fig. 21 shows the components and arrangements of a simple mechanical governor. A set of weights, called flyweights, that pivot and move in and out are attached to the end of the turbine shaft. The shaft ends of the flyweights contact the end of a governor, which is free to move to the left or right, but is also acted upon by a counterspring. A governor valve, or steam inlet valve, is mounted at the inlet of the turbine. It is connected to the external steam supply line. The valve disc is double seated and has a stem that extends out of the valve casing. A lever, connecting the valve stem to the governor rod, is pinned and is free to pivot on a fixed fulcrum. This allows movement in the governor rod to be transmitted to the valve stem.

Rotation of the turbine shaft causes the flyweights to pivot outwards due to centrifugal force. The greater the speed of rotation the greater the centrifugal force and the further outward the flyweights move. Movement of the flyweights causes movement of the governor rod which causes movement of the governor valve.

FIGURE 21
Mechanical Governor

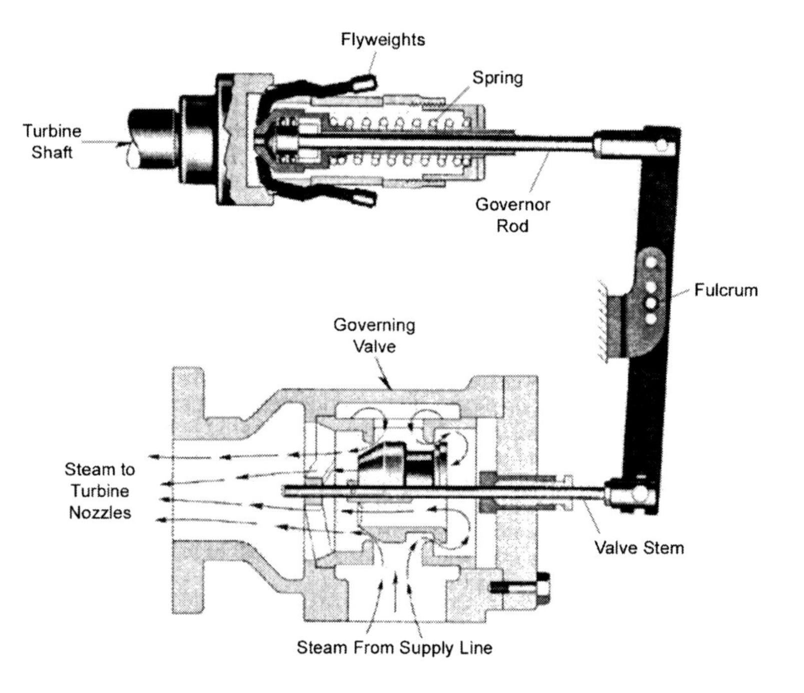

The operation of a simple centrifugal mechanical governor is shown in Fig. 22. If the load on the turbine increases, it slows down slightly. This causes the flyweights to move inwards (due to less centrifugal force) and the governor rod moves to the left due to the force of the counterspring. The lever pivots at the fulcrum and the lower end moves to the right, thus opening the governor valve further. As more steam enters the turbine, the speed begins to increase. The flyweights move outwards again until the system becomes balanced at the set speed under the new load.

The disadvantage of simple mechanical governors is they have a high-speed droop, usually around 10%. They are not suitable for large machines or where control must be extremely accurate. Within limits, changing the pivot point at the fulcrum can reduce the effects of droop, so the governor rod movement has more affect on the governor valve movement.

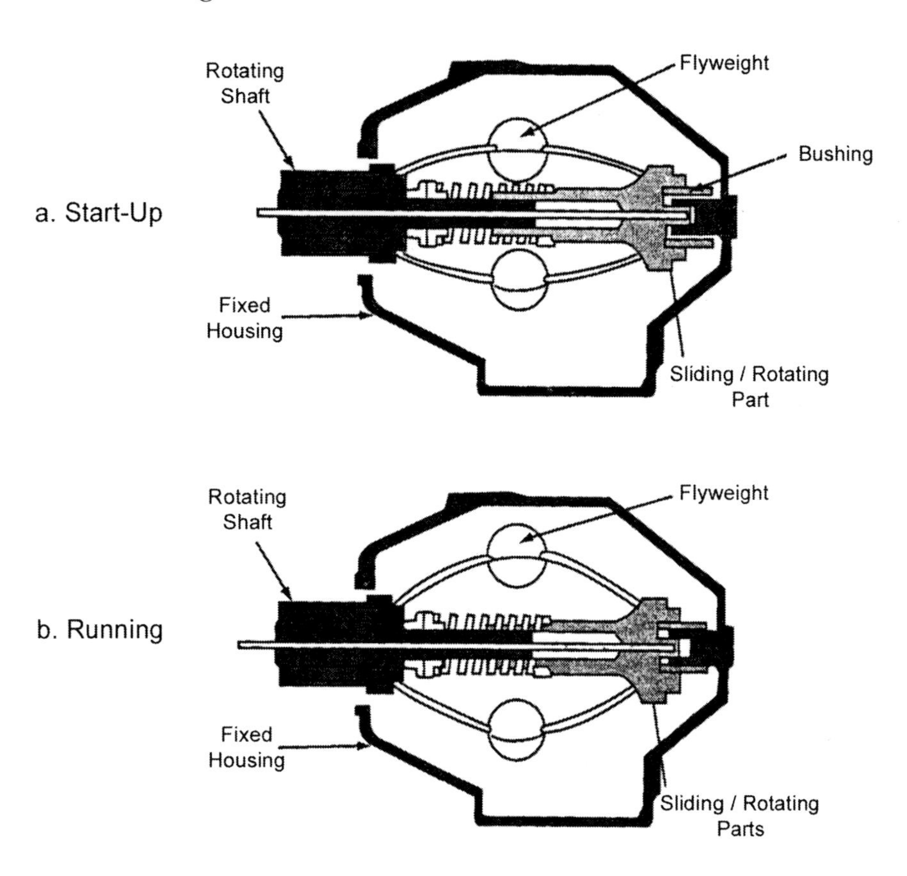

FIGURE 22 (a) (b)

Simple Centrifugal Mechanical Governor

Mechanical-Hydraulic Governors

The mechanical-hydraulic governor has a pilot valve and a hydraulic amplifier. This arrangement removes the direct linkage of the flyweights to the governor valve. The flyweights position an oil pilot valve that admits high-pressure oil to a piston that moves the governor valve. The advantage of the design is that the mechanical losses of the governor are greatly reduced. The flyweights require less force to position the pilot valve. The pilot provides the power to move the governor valve. The droop of this governor is reduced to almost zero.

Fig. 23 is a diagram of a mechanical-hydraulic governor. Oil, at approximately 70 psi, is continuously supplied to the centre of the pilot valve. At normal speed, the pilot valve covers the oil ports to the amplifier cylinder so that oil cannot enter or leave the cylinder. If the load drops and the turbine speed increases, the flyweights move outwards. This pulls the pilot valve upwards, admitting oil to the top of the cylinder while allowing oil to drain from the bottom of the cylinder. The piston moves downward forcing the steam valve to close.

As the steam valve closes, the turbine speed decreases and the flyweights move inwards. At normal speed, the pilot valve returns to the central, or neutral, position and the turbine continues to operate at the set speed under the new load. Conversely, if the turbine load increases and the turbine speed drops, the pilot valve admits more oil below the piston causing the governor valve to open.

FIGURE 23

Mechanical-Hydraulic Governor

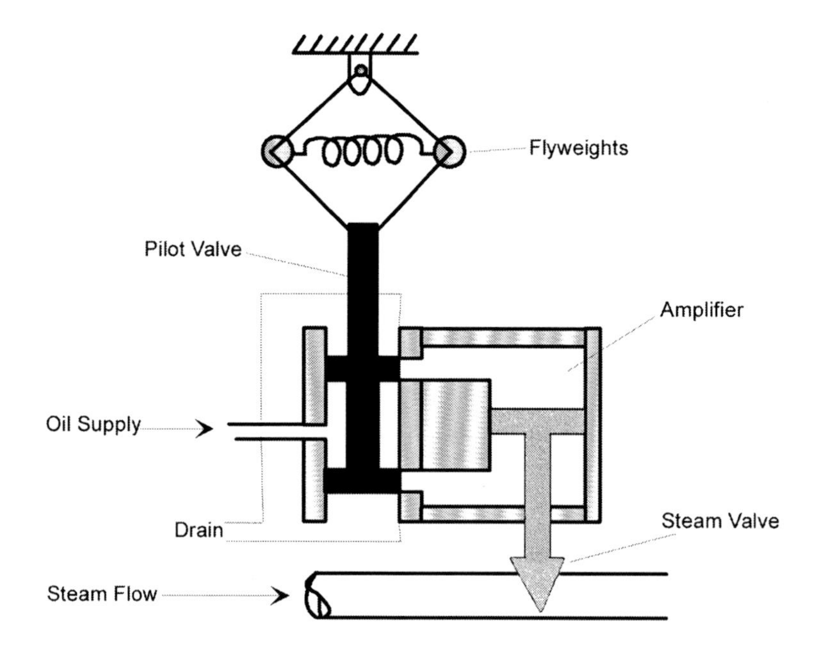

Mechanical-Hydraulic Governor Systems

A complete mechanical-hydraulic governor system is shown in Fig. 24. It demonstrates how components relate to each other to provide a complete governor system. Referring to the diagram, the turbine shaft drives a main, gear-type oil pump which supplies the hydraulic oil pressure to the various governor components. An electric motor drives an auxiliary oil pump which provides oil pressure during start-up of the turbine, until the main oil pump can provide sufficient operating oil pressure.

Before start-up, the overspeed trip assembly is manually re-latched so that the oil trip valve B is open, allowing oil pressure and flow to the other governor components. This includes the turbine stop valve which is held open by the pressure under the operating piston in cylinder C.

When the turbine is operating steadily, the spinning flyweights take a position balanced by their counterspring. Flyweight movement controls the position of a plunger sliding within sleeve G, which is part of the servo, or speed adjuster. The relative position of the plunger and the sleeve determines the opening of the oil ports in the sleeve.

High-pressure oil goes directly to the pilot valve K in the control oil cylinder. The pilot valve regulates the oil pressure below the throttle valve cylinder J increasing pressure when the speed is high. The position of the throttle valve responds accordingly.

The piston in the cylinder H determines the position of the moveable governor fulcrum which affects the droop, proportionally, and speed control of the governor. Oil to this cylinder is taken from the main oil supply, through valve F. The pressure in the line, and therefore the pressure below piston H are determined by the position of the oil ports at G in the servo. Adjusting the handwheel L changes the servo port openings causing more or less oil to be drained, affecting the pressure to cylinder H and causing the speed of the turbine to change. The movement of L may be done manually or it may be activated by a small electric motor with remote control.

In an overspeed situation, the overspeed trip closes the oil supply cylinder B. This causes all oil pressure to be lost beneath the trip valve and the throttle valve. The turbine comes to a quick stop due to immediate loss of the steam supply.

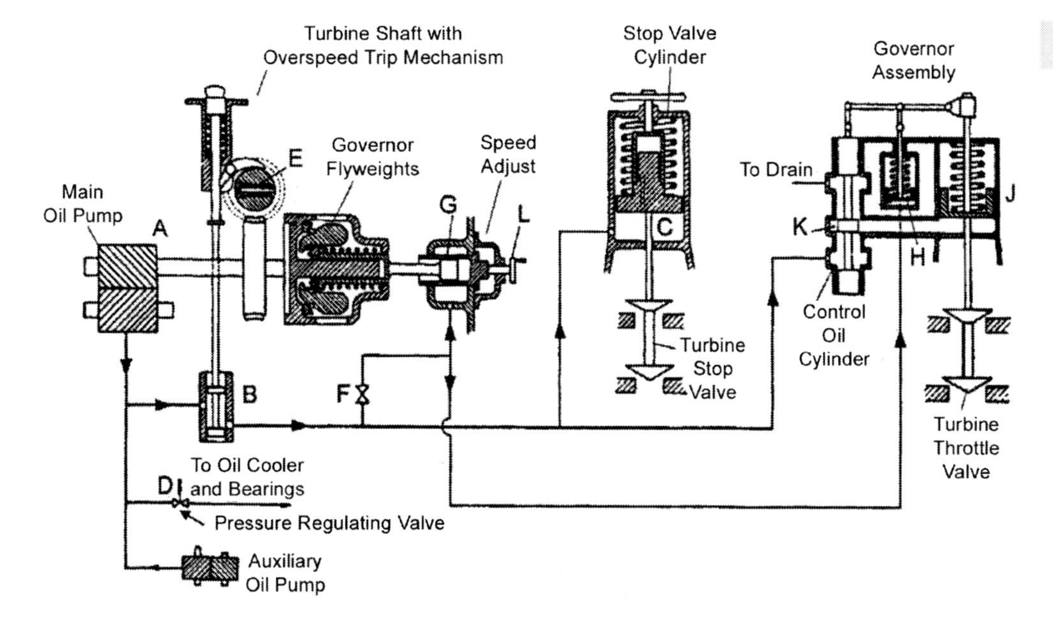

FIGURE 24

Mechanical-Hydraulic Governor System

Electronic-Hydraulic Governors

Electronic-hydraulic governors use a combination of electronic and hydraulic controls. The turbine control console contains all the controls necessary for starting, accelerating, and loading the turbine and for controlling the extraction steam flows and pressures if applicable.

Referring to Fig. 25, the speed measuring device is a permanent magnet generator. It produces an electrical output signal that is amplified and compared to a reference signal by the computer in the control console. The difference is then amplified and applied to a servo-valve, which hydraulically positions the servo-rams, moving the steam valves and controlling the steam flow. The valve position is measured and fed back to the control console, providing more exact control. Provisions are made for on-line servicing of the computer circuit cards while the turbine is carrying load.

Electro-hydraulic governor systems use a separate fluid power unit to provide high-pressure hydraulic oil to operate the servo-rams. The fluid power unit supplies hydraulic oil at pressures in the range of 1,200 to 1,600 psi.

FIGURE 25

Electro-Hydraulic Governor System

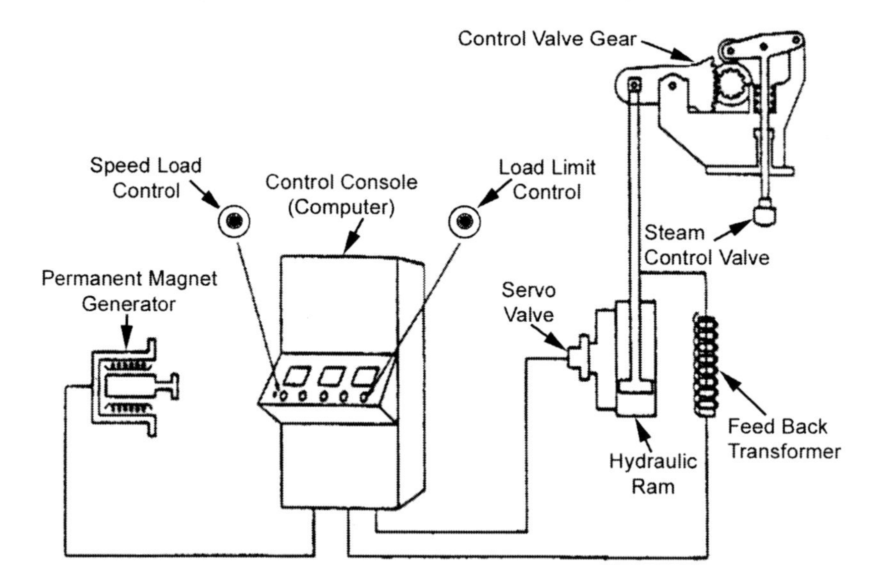

Fig. 26 shows an example of a basic electronic governor system for a turbine generator. The actuator controls the pilot valve to readjust the position of the steam control valve which maintains the desired speed as the generator load changes. The force to move the throttle valve is usually hydraulic power acting through the actuator.

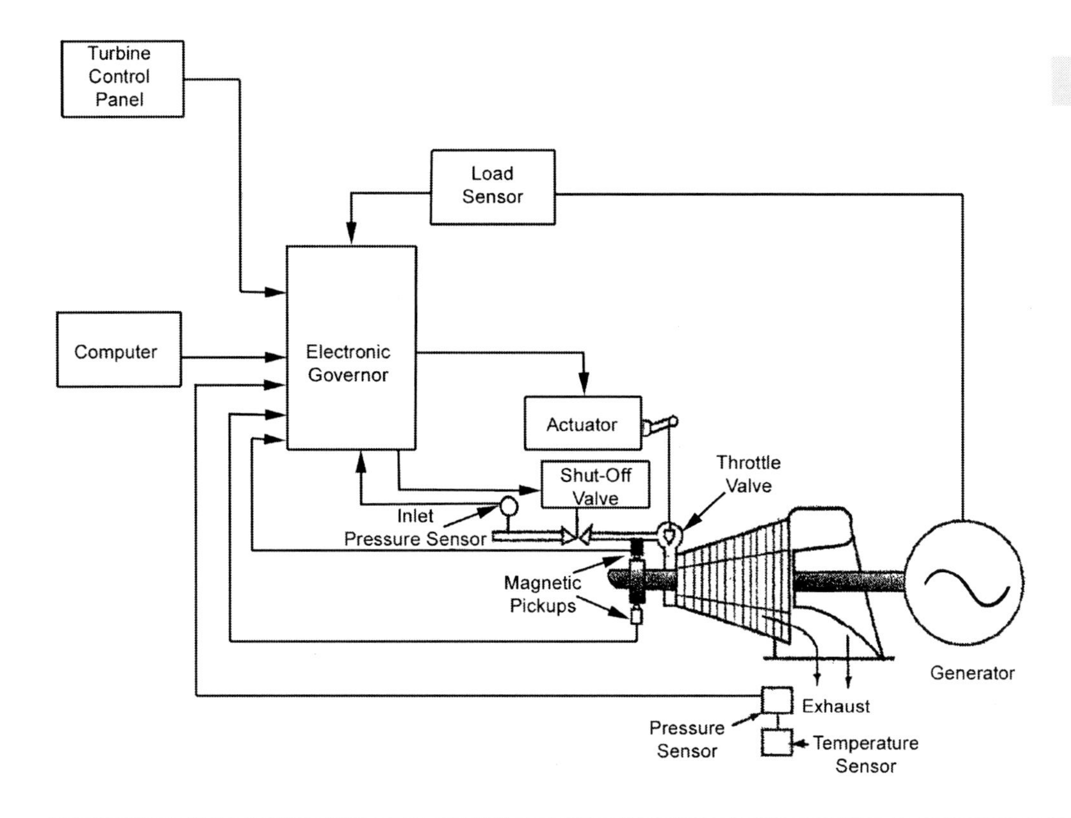

FIGURE 26

Electronic-Hydraulic Governor System

PRESSURE SENSITIVE GOVERNORS

Pressure sensitive governors control a steady backpressure at the steam exhaust (outlet) of the turbine. They may also control the extraction steam pressure part way through the turbine. The extracted steam is discharged at a controlled pressure from that point. There is a combination of speed and pressure control to assure relatively steady turbine operation.

Backpressure Governing

Backpressure governing uses a pressure sensing element on the line from the turbine. A set-point is entered into the controller which adjusts the position of the inlet steam throttle valve. If the pressure is low, the throttle valve opens to admit more steam and raise the exhaust pressure. If the pressure is high, the throttle valve closes to reduce the pressure. It is used in processes where the exhaust steam from the turbine is used for heating and where the pressure must be steady to ensure good heat control.

The efficiency of the backpressure turbine is very high because there are no exhaust steam losses. The disadvantage of this system is that the load output of the turbine is completely dependent on the demand for process steam.

Extraction Governing

Process steam is supplied by extracting steam, at a controlled pressure, from intermediate stages of a turbine. The control systems for extraction turbines are complex and allow changes in the turbine load without affecting the steam extraction. They also allow changes in the quantity of steam extracted without affecting the turbine output.

A schematic of such a system is shown in Fig. 27. When the extraction steam demand increases, the extraction pressure decreases forcing the pressure regulator piston downwards. This moves point G down. Since point D is kept stationary by the speed governor, the linkage makes point F move the extraction valve down. Point E moves the steam inlet valve up. Less steam then passes through the extraction valve, increasing the flow of extraction steam. The pressure remains constant.

As the load on the turbine increases, the speed decreases and the speed governor forces point A downwards. Since point B is fixed and point G is held stationary by the pressure regulator, points C and D move upwards. Points E and F move their respective valves upwards. More high-pressure steam is admitted. The extra steam flows via the more open extraction valve to the low-pressure stages of the turbine, resulting in increased load with no change in the extraction flow and pressure.

FIGURE 27

Combined Speed and Pressure Governor

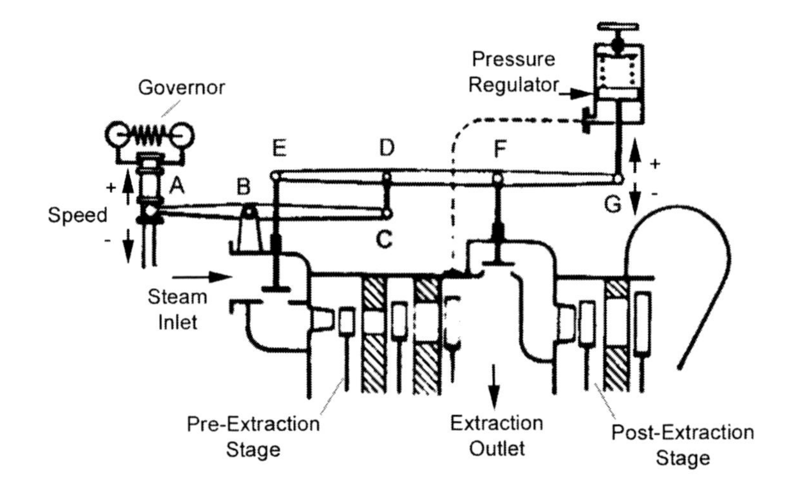

TRIP AND THROTTLE VALVES

Trip valves, used to provide a positive isolation of the turbine steam supply, are always either fully open or closed. Throttle valves are adjusted as needed to control the turbine speed or load. All turbines require trip and throttle valves to operate safely. They also may have a combined trip and throttle valve. Trip and throttle (T/T) valves find applications in the following types of turbine arrangements:

- Single-valve
- Multi-valve

Single-Valve Turbines

In a single-valve turbine, all the steam flows through a single governing or throttling valve to the turbine nozzles. Changing the position of the throttling valve varies the steam flow and the pressure of the steam flowing to the turbine nozzles.

Trip and throttle valves have two separate and distinct functions. When a safety device such as an overspeed governor manually or automatically trips the trip and throttle valve, it acts as a quick-closing valve. The emergency trip drains the oil causing the servomotor to shut the steam valve. A manual throttling or block valve is used to bring the machine up to minimum governor speed and to totally block the steam in after shutting down. The throttling valve is not a 100% tight shut-off valve. The valve in Fig. 28 acts as a throttling and a trip valve.

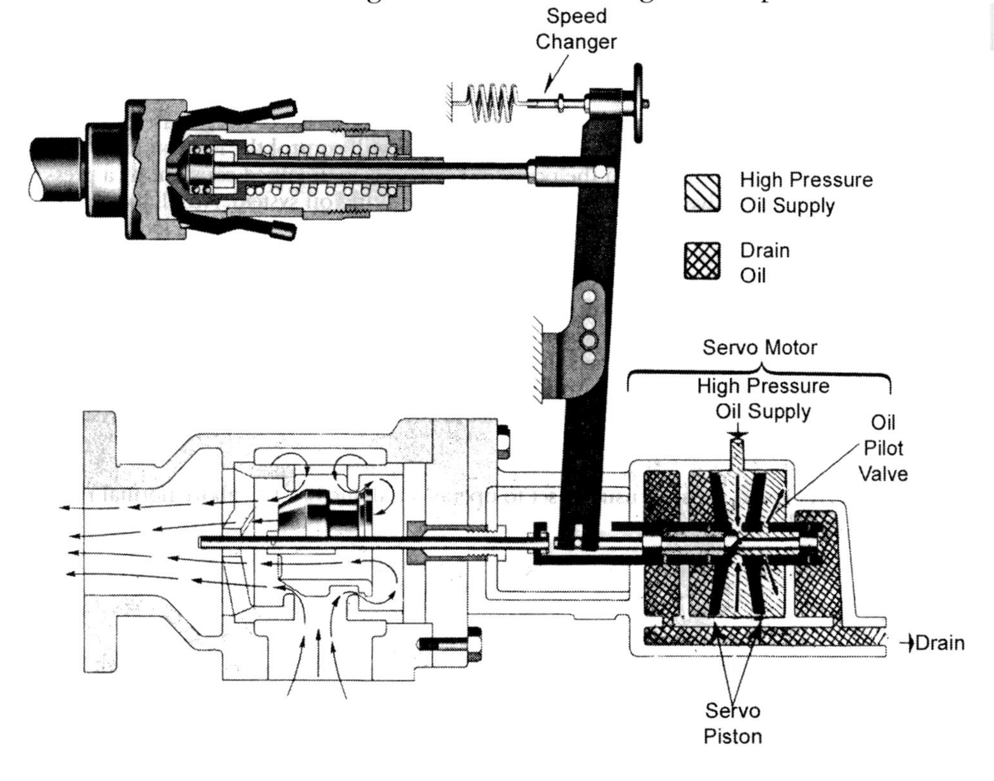

FIGURE 28

Double-Seated Steam Valve

The trip and throttling valve can also operate as a hand throttle valve for starting and bringing the turbine up to speed. An example is shown in Fig. 29. It may be operated by hand using the handwheel on top of the actuator or by a motor actuator which opens or closes the valve. The trip hook or latch is used to trip the valve shut. When it is tripped shut, the valve must then be completely closed to be able to re-latch the trip mechanism.

FIGURE 29
Trip/Throttle Valve

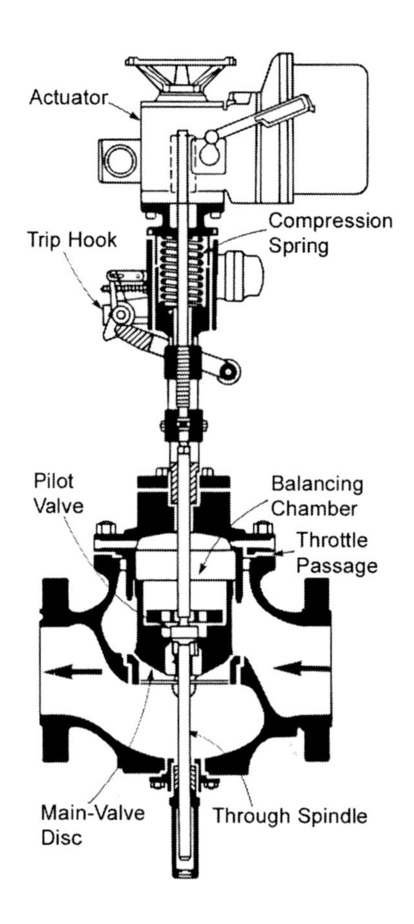

Multi-Valve Turbines

Fig. 30 shows a section through the steam chest of a large reaction turbine containing a shut-off or trip valve and two throttle valves. The first throttle valve controls the admission of steam to the turbine to about 80% of maximum load. The second controls the admission of steam through the bypass for the remaining 20%.

The trip valve is sometimes called the emergency stop valve. It is opened wide at startup and oil pressure keeps it in the open position. Spring pressure opposes the oil pressure and tries to shut the valve. In an emergency condition such as machine overspeed, the oil pressure is released and the spring closes the valve. The throttle valves are the balanced or "double seat" type. Steam flows past both the upper and lower seats eliminating forces tending to thrust the valve shut.

A steam strainer is fitted around the trip valve, and the valve spindles are sealed against leakage with metallic labyrinth bushings. The steam chest is separate from the turbine casing.

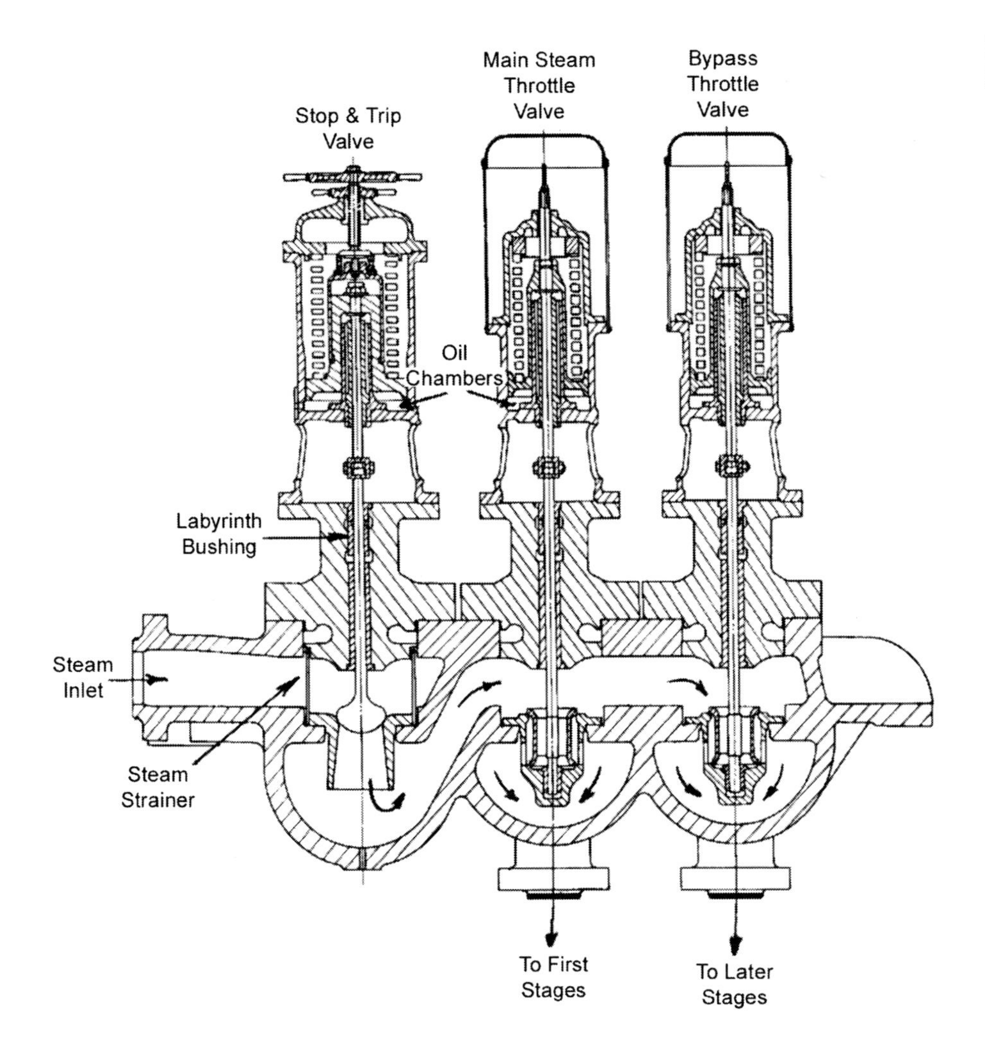

FIGURE 30

Steam Chest with Stop and Throttling Valves

When a turbine has separate trip and throttle valves, the steam always goes through the turbine stop valve before going through the throttling or governor valves. Fig. 31 illustrates the separate stop valve and control valve of a steam turbine in a fossil fired generating plant. The assembly is separate from the turbine casing and is welded to the steam piping on the inlet and the steam chest on the outlet. Both valves are operated hydraulically and fit into the governor oil system of the steam turbine. The stop valve must be open to allow oil pressure to the stop valve and control valve. The turbine control valve is used to bring the turbine up to operating speed. The governor valves then begin to close or take over speed control as the turbine speed increases. The speed at which the governor takes control is called **minimum governor** speed. The governor assembly controls the throttle valves and thus the steam flow to the turbine. The speed adjustment on the governor controls the turbine speed when the turbine is on governor control.

FIGURE 31

Turbine Trip and Governor System

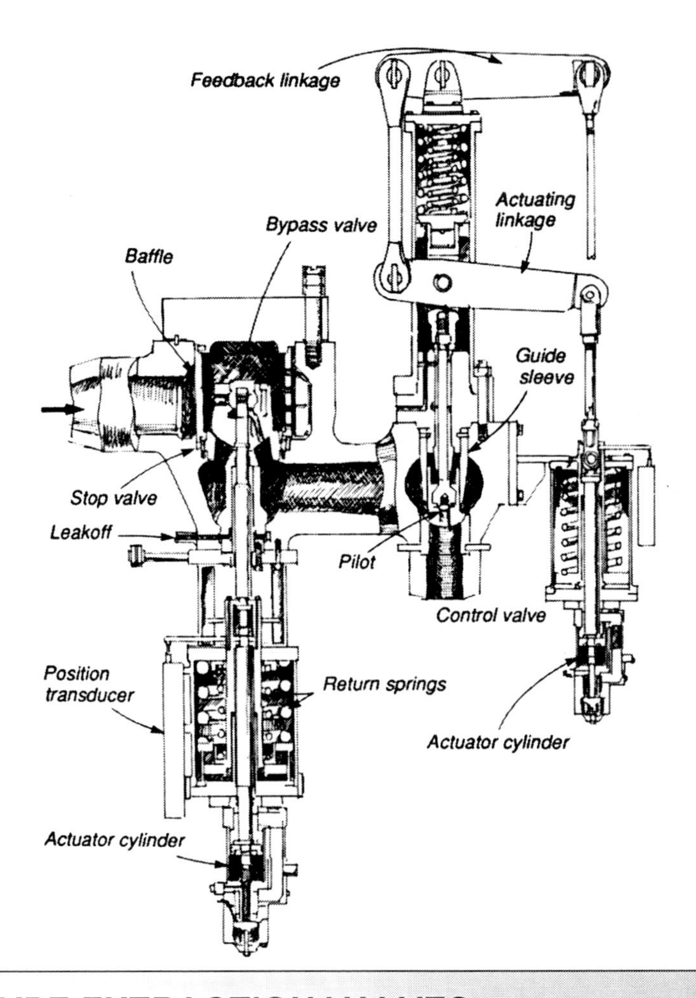

GRID TYPE EXTRACTION VALVES

Grid type extraction valves are placed inside the turbine casing after the stage that the steam is extracted from. It controls the flow of steam to the remainder of the turbine. An example of a grid extraction valve is shown in Fig. 32.

The valve consists of a ported stationary disc and a ported grid that rotates. When the openings in the disc and the grid coincide, the valve is open and a full flow of steam passes to the remainder of the turbine. When the grid is rotated from the fully open position, the ports in the disc are partially covered by the grid. The steam flow is restricted and the desired pressure maintained. A pilot valve, operated by a pressure governor, controls the oil or steam supply pressure to either side of the operating piston. The operating piston rotates the grid valve with a gear and teeth. The linkage from the pressure governor is interlocked with the speed governor. Changes in the rate of steam extraction do not interfere with the turbine speed.

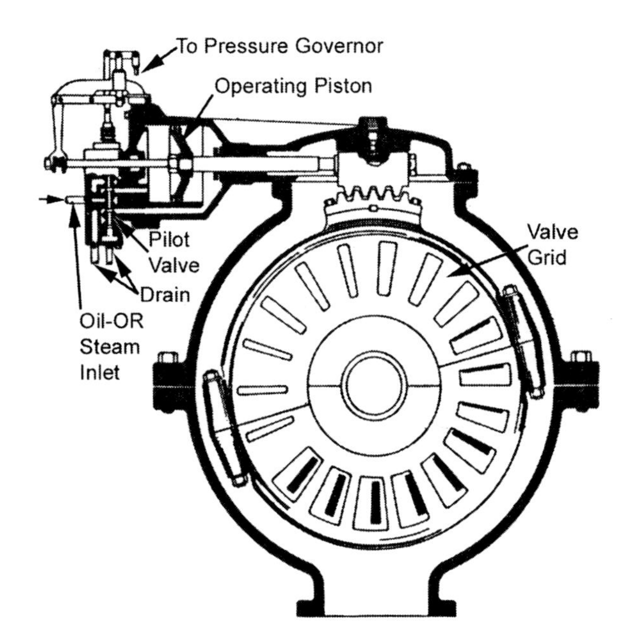

FIGURE 32

Grid Type Extraction Valve

A cutaway view of a grid type extraction valve is shown in Fig. 33.

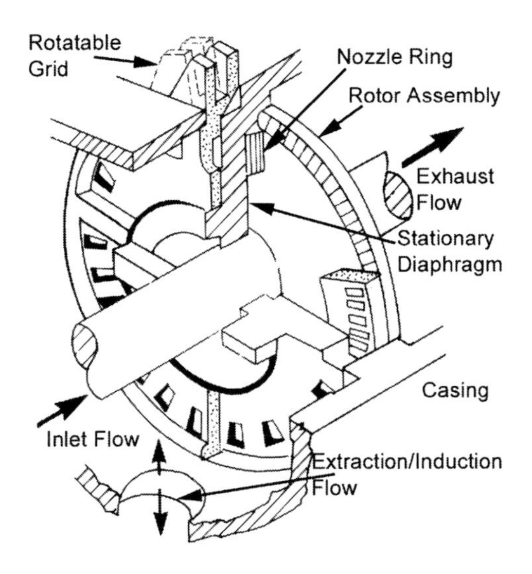

FIGURE 33

Grid Type Extraction Valve Construction

Plant process or heating needs may require that steam is extracted at more than one pressure. An example of a steam turbine with two extraction pressures is shown in Fig. 34. Steam passes through the admission valve and then through the first stages of the turbine. Steam is bled off upstream of the first extraction grid valve. The steam that passes through the first grid valve passes through more turbine blading. More steam is bled off upstream of the second extraction grid valve. The remaining steam passes through the second extraction grid valve and the remaining turbine blading. It exits the turbine blading and enters the surface condenser.

FIGURE 34

Turbine with Two Grid Type Expansion Valves

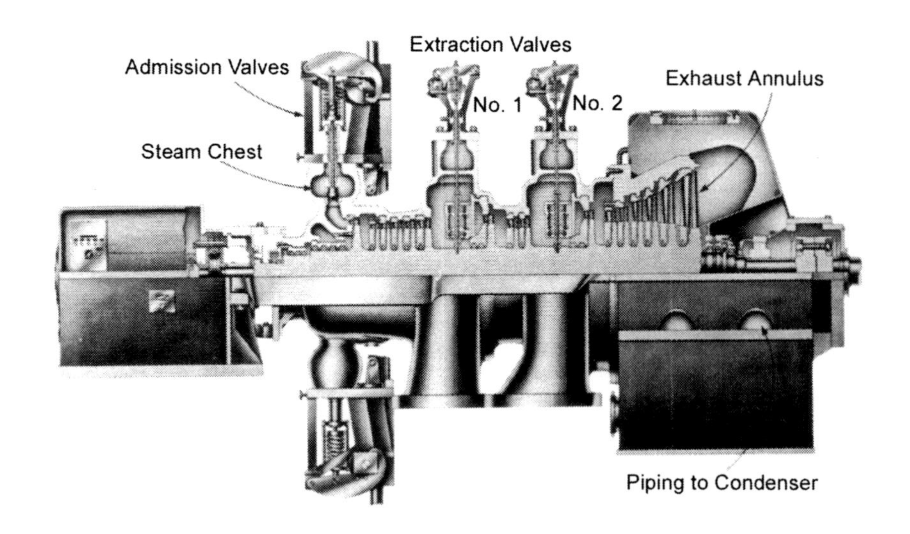

TURBINE CASING PRESSURE RELIEF SYSTEMS

Some manufacturers fit rupturing diaphragms to the turbine exhaust branches. They are designed to protect the condenser and LP turbine against overpressure. If over pressured they rupture or blow out. Fig. 35 shows a condensing turbine with a relief diaphragm at the top of the exhaust. Fig. 36 shows steam flowing out the rupture diaphragm on a low-pressure casing. The rupture diaphragms protect the casing as well as the condenser. The pressure can reach rupture pressure if the condenser is not functioning properly. Causes of condenser malfunction are air leaks or loss of cooling water.

FIGURE 35

Condensing Turbine with Relief Diaphragm

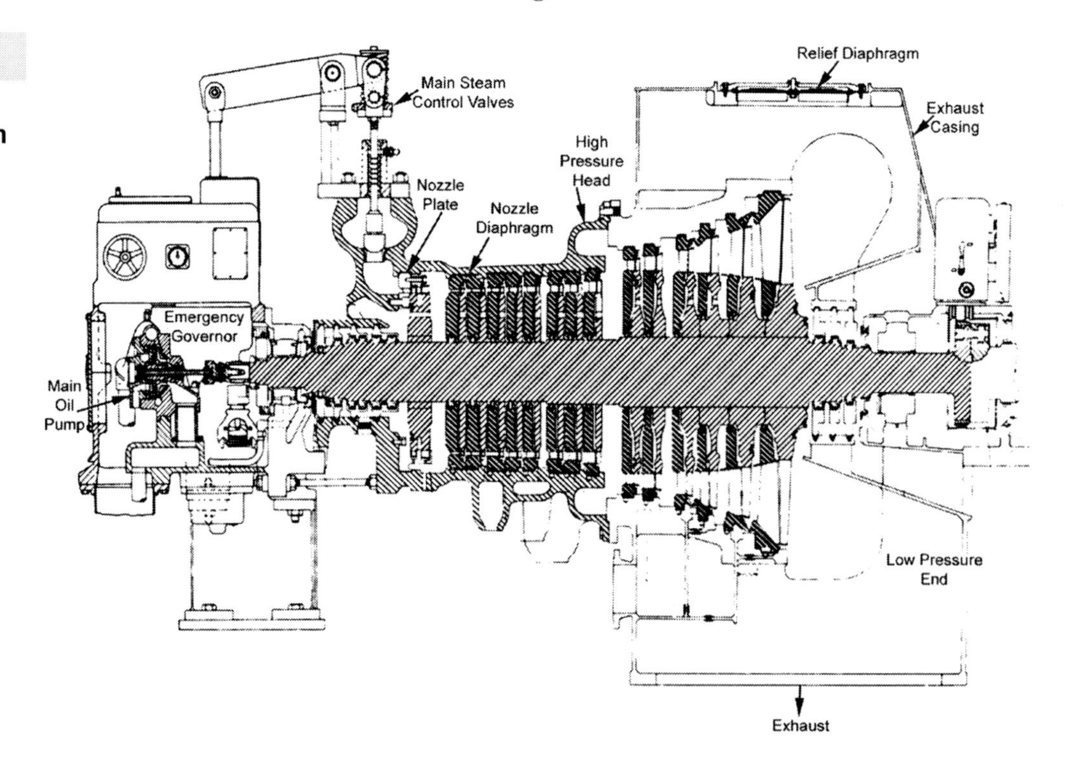

FIGURE 36

Rupture Disc Test on LP Casing

MECHANICAL OVERSPEED TRIP SYSTEMS

The mechanical overspeed trip on a steam turbine is an integral part of the governing system. It prevents steam from entering the turbine if the speed becomes dangerously high. The mechanical overspeed trip gear is generally located at the front end of the high-pressure turbine shaft and is designed to shut off the steam supply to the turbine. The trip speed is usually 10 to 12% above the standard operating speed.

A basic trip bolt in the normal operating position is shown in Fig. 37. It consists of a weighted bolt that is held inside a specially made hole in the shaft. A spring is held in compression to keep this trip bolt inside the shaft during standard operating conditions.

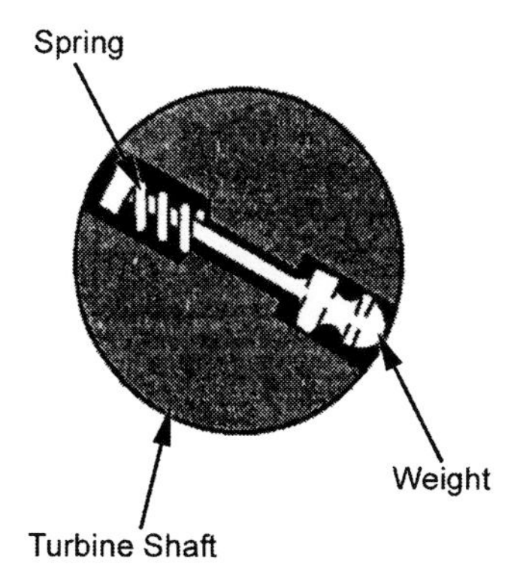

FIGURE 37

Trip Bolt

If the turbine shaft reaches the overspeed setting, the spring compression is overcome and the bolt will be thrown out by centrifugal force, as shown in Fig. 38.

FIGURE 38

Overspeed Trip Position

Fig. 39 shows a mechanical overspeed trip system using a mechanical linkage to control the flow of steam to the turbine, during standard operating conditions.

FIGURE 39

Mechanical Overspeed Trip System (Turbine Normal Operation)

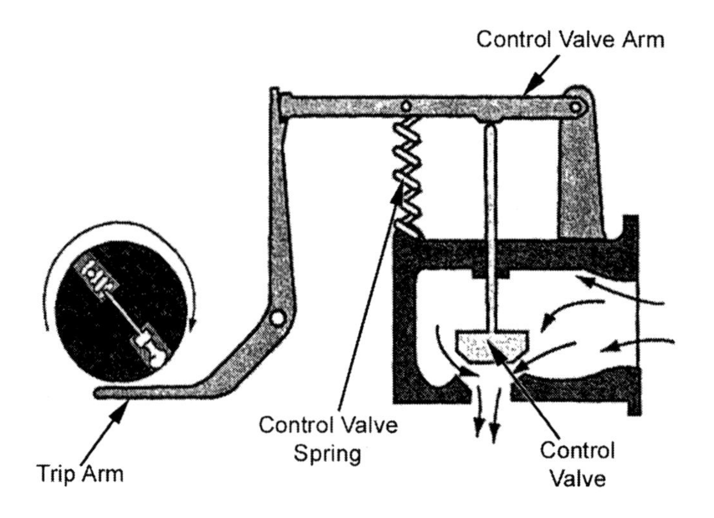

Fig. 40 illustrates an overspeed situation (movements are exaggerated for clarity). Using the trip lever, the overspeed trip can be manually operated at any time.

FIGURE 40

Mechanical Overspeed Trip System (Turbine Tripped)

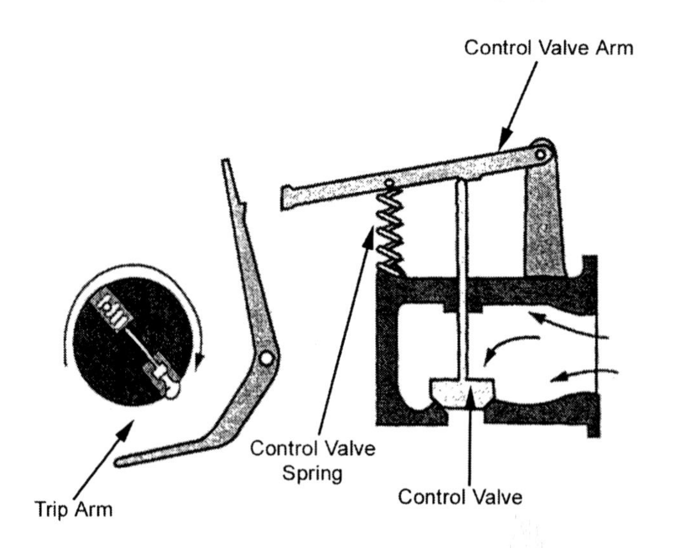

The overspeed trip, shown in Fig. 41, shows clearly the operating principle of all overspeed trips for turbines with hydraulic governor systems. The spring-loaded tripping bolt, located in the turbine shaft, has the centre of gravity slightly off the centre of the shaft in the direction of the bolt head. The nut, at the end of the bolt, provides a stop for the bolt in the tripped position and for the tripping speed adjustment. During standard operation, the main spring holds the trip rod against the tripping lever. Piston A closes the oil drain and the high-pressure oil passes between pistons A and B, to the stop valve. **Note**: The gear is shown in the set position.

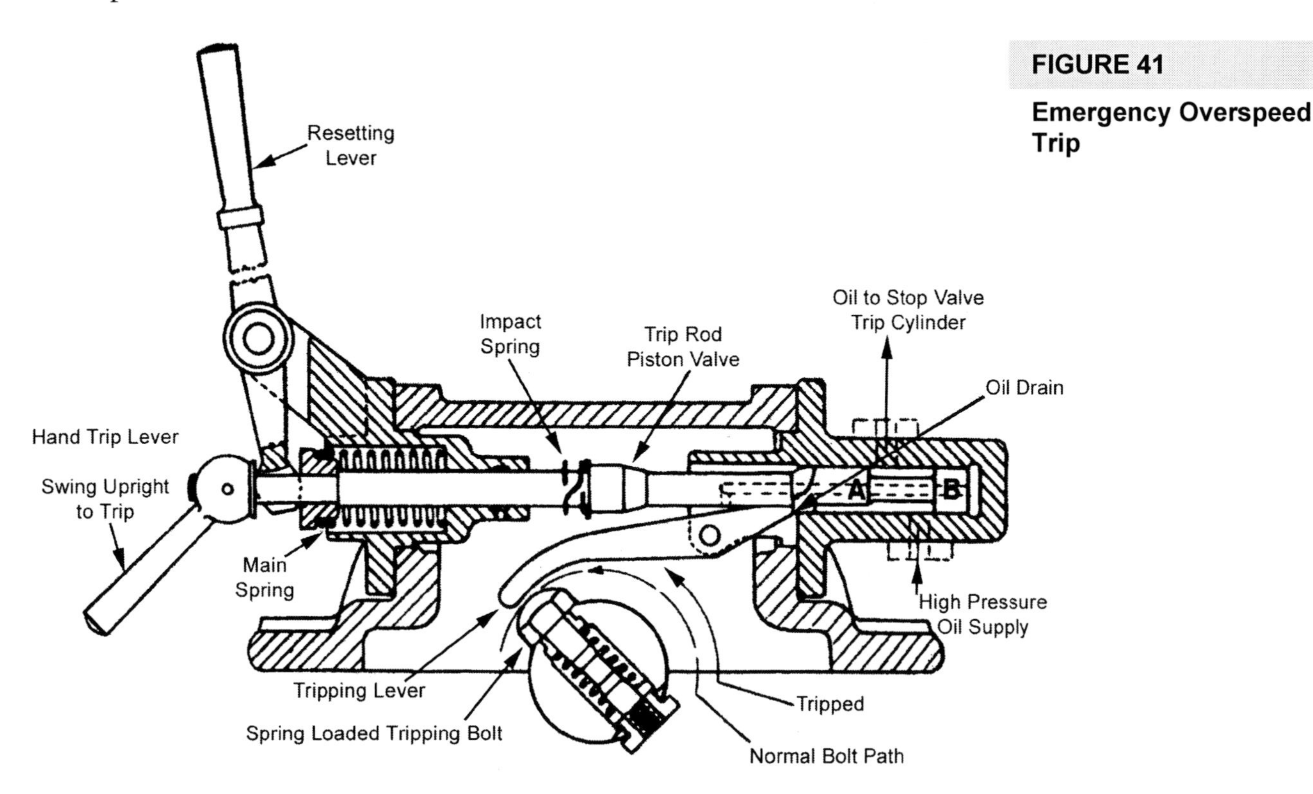

FIGURE 41

Emergency Overspeed Trip

When the turbine speed increases to the trip setting, usually 110% of operating speed, the following occurs:

1. Centrifugal force overcomes the bolt spring tension
2. The bolt moves to the trip position and strikes the tripping lever
3. The trip rod is unlatched
4. The main spring moves the rod to the tripped position
5. Piston A opens the stop valve oil port to drain
6. Piston B closes off the high-pressure oil inlet port

Fig. 42 shows a bolt type overspeed trip located in the high-pressure turbine shaft end. The bolt is eccentric in the shaft, but the spring holds it in position at normal speeds. The oil supply, maintaining the steam valves open, passes through ports P and U in the standard position. At an overspeed condition, the pin (bolt) trips the latch R. When R is tripped, the trip relay spring lifts the trip relay piston so that P is closed off and U is open to drain.

FIGURE 42

Overspeed Trip Gear

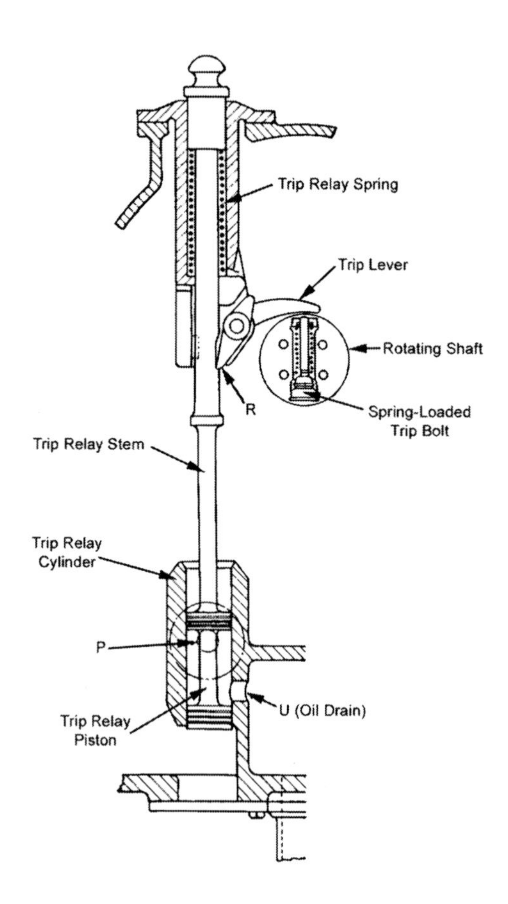

ELECTRONIC OVERSPEED TRIP SYSTEMS

In Fig. 43, the turbine shaft contains a notched gear wheel. Inductive sensors, also known as magnetic speed pickups, are mounted in or on the turbine casing. As the gear teeth pass the sensors, the principle of magnetic induction generates an AC voltage that can be read by the ECM (Electronic Control Module), which contains pulse-counting sensors.

These units then convert the electronic pulse signals to revolutions per minute for calculating the turbine shaft speed. Some steam turbines' overspeed trip systems, installed with three magnetic speed pickups, require that two out of the three sensors agree the unit has reached the overspeed condition before a trip is initiated.

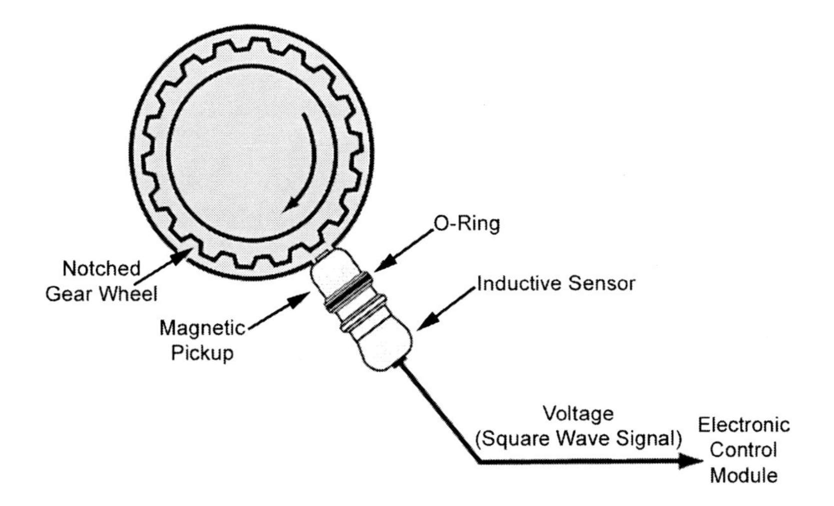

FIGURE 43

Magnetic Speed Pickup Sensor

When the measured speed reaches the setpoint, an action is initiated to shut the emergency stop valve. Referring to Fig. 44, electronic signals are sent from the electronic control module to the trip block. If the electronic control module receives input from 2 out of 3 speed pickups that there is an overspeed condition, it will then shut off the supply of hydraulic oil that maintains the stop valve in an open position. Another signal is sent from the electronic control system to close the control valve and stop the flow of steam to the turbine.

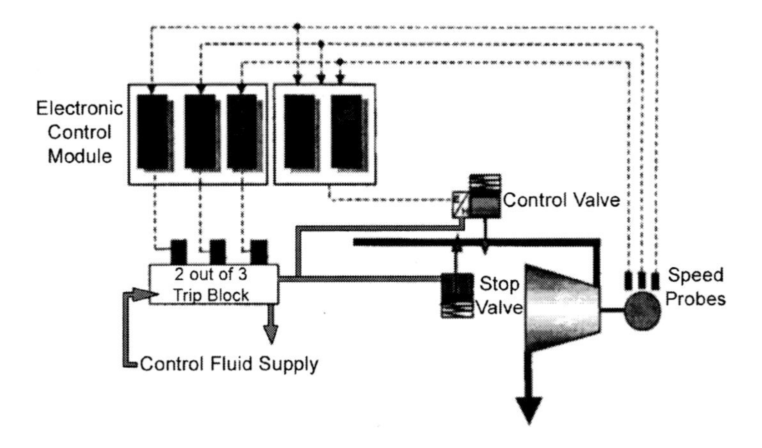

FIGURE 44

Electro-Hydraulic Control System

STEAM TURBINE SUPERVISORY EQUIPMENT

Steam turbines come in many sizes from drivers of small pumps and fans to multi-case power station generator drivers. They range in output from a few kW to over 1000 MW. The smallest turbines may have a little instrumentation such as a few temperature and pressure gauges. They may have vibration monitoring that is monitored in the control room. Some turbines are started and stopped from remote locations.

The larger a turbine, the more likely it is to have extensive supervisory equipment to monitor its operation. Fig. 45 illustrates the turbovisory equipment connected to a turbine and generator set. This schematic represents a layout with separate panels or cubicles, which can be located next to the machine in the field or in the control room. The recorders and indicators can also be field or control room mounted. All of the data from the machine may also be fed into a digital control system. Vibration monitoring input is often sent into a vibration monitoring system to analyze readings and to predict problems.

FIGURE 45

Turbovisory Equipment Schematic Diagram

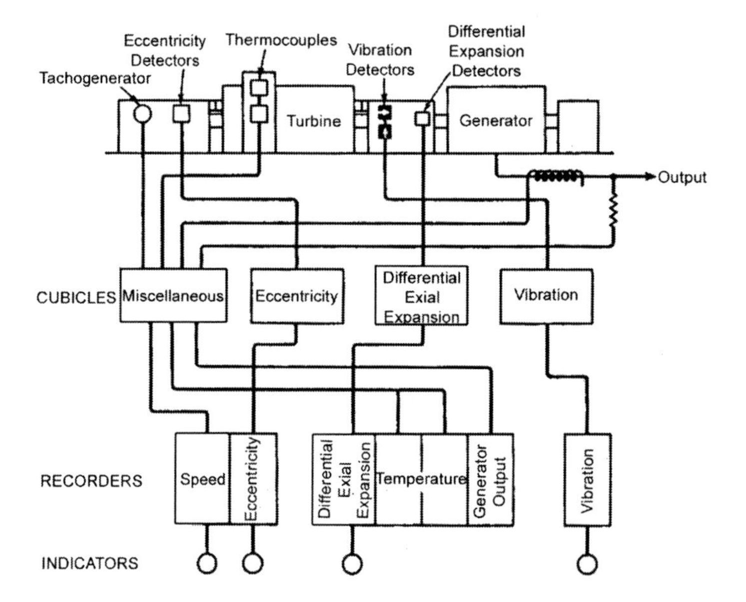

Fig. 46 illustrates the locations of instruments on the three cases of a large turbine. The bearings for each rotor normally have vibration and temperature probes. Thrust bearings have temperature (oil and/or pad) indications. High-thrust bearing temperatures indicate high-thrust loads. There are eccentricity coils for the HP (high pressure) and IP (intermediate pressure) rotors located next to the thrust bearings. The differential expansion indicators for the HP and IP cases are located at the opposite end of the shaft from the thrust bearings. Differential expansion refers to the relative difference in expansion between the rotor and the turbine case. If excessive, it will lead to the rotor blades rubbing the turbine diaphragm. The thrust bearing is a fixed location and the shaft movement is measured as far as possible from the thrust bearing.

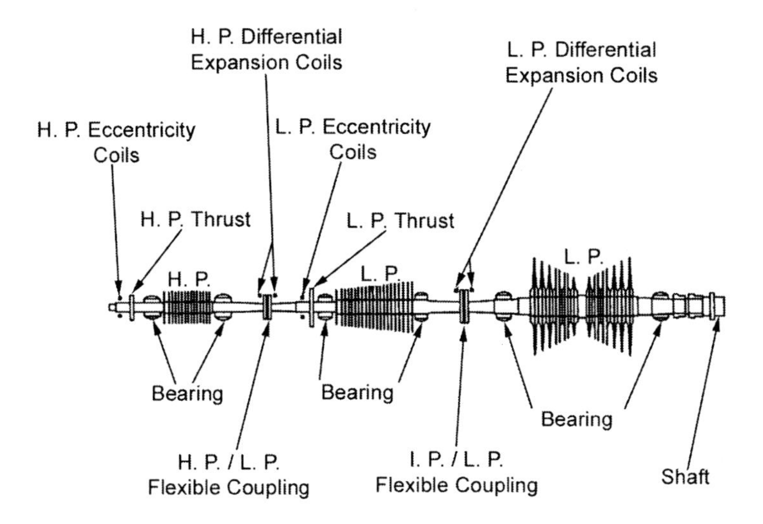

FIGURE 46

Layout of Supervisory Equipment

The expansion of the HP and IP rotors is shown in Fig. 47. The HP case has a thrust bearing and a thrust collar at the front of the machine. The bearing pedestals have sliding feet for expansion and indicators to monitor movement. The cylinders are anchored at the exhaust end and expand towards the inlet. The flexible coupling between the two rotors takes up the relative movement of the shafts. The arrows in Fig. 50 indicate expansion of the cylinders and rotors.

When starting up the machine, careful monitoring of expansion is essential. Operators soon know the positions of the machine when cold, when starting up, and when in standard operation.

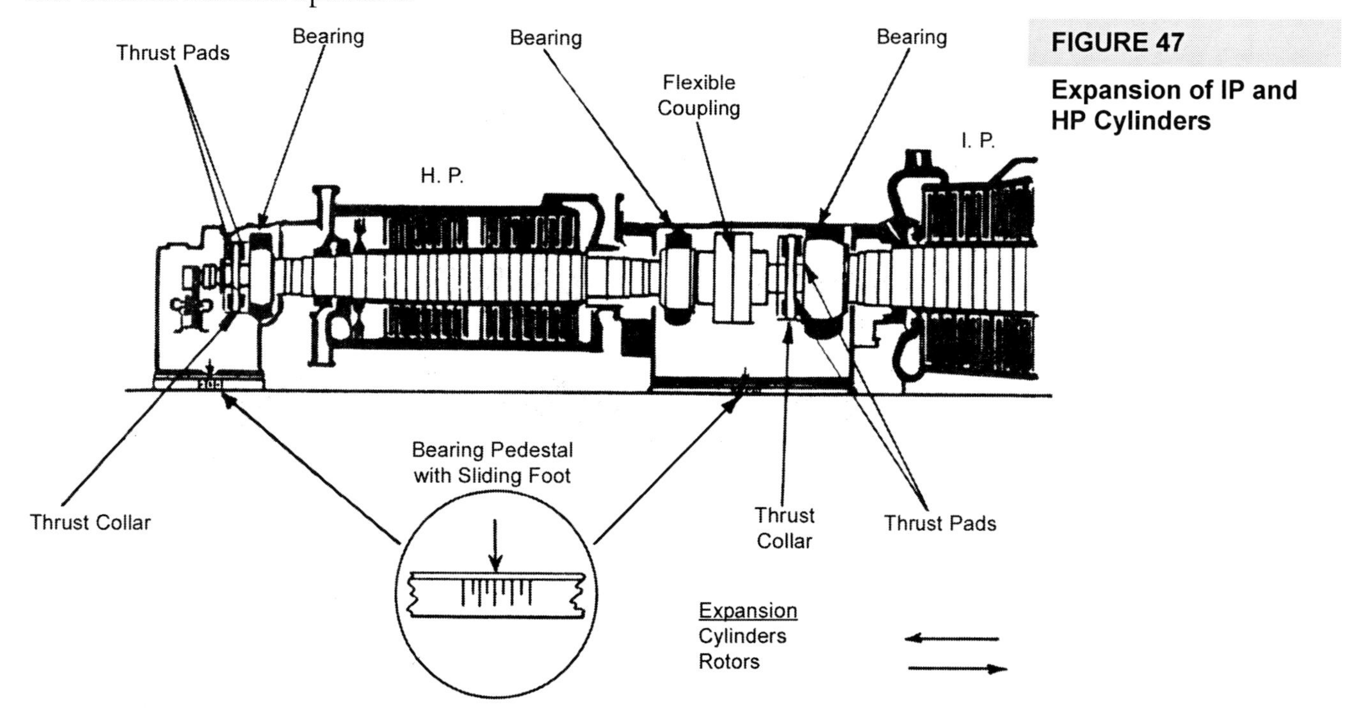

FIGURE 47

Expansion of IP and HP Cylinders

Vibration Monitoring

Vibration monitoring systems are often separate from the remainder of the monitoring equipment on large machines. The turbine in Fig. 48 has a computer based monitoring system. Vibration sensors on the machine send signals to the transducer panel. Signals from the transducer panel then go to the vibration monitoring input unit. Digital signals are fed to the vibration monitoring computer.

The computer system is used to analyze the vibration data and maintain a history on the equipment. The system in the graphic also has a remote service station which can be used by engineers and or managers to view and analyze the vibration data.

FIGURE 48

Vibration and Monitoring System

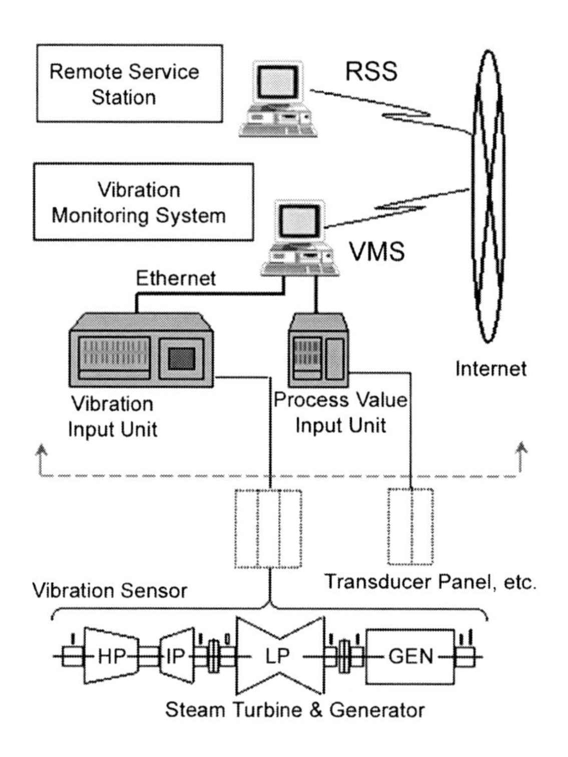

UNIT 5

Steam Turbine Auxiliaries & Operation

Learning Objectives

Here is what you will be able to do when you complete each objective:

1. Describe typical lube oil systems for small and large steam turbines.
2. Explain the purpose and describe the design and operation of barring gear and jacking oil systems on a large turbine.
3. Describe a condensing turbine circuit and explain typical operating parameters.
4. Explain and state the applications, where applicable, of the following governor types: speed-sensitive, pressure-sensitive, nozzle, throttle, and bypass. Explain governor droop and isochronous control.
5. Explain the operation and the major components of the three main speed-sensitive governor systems: mechanical, mechanical-hydraulic, and electronic-hydraulic.
6. Explain the operation and describe the components of typical mechanical and electronic overspeed trip systems.
7. Explain the sequence followed for the cold start-up and the shutdown of a non-condensing steam turbine.
8. Explain the sequence followed for the cold start-up and the shutdown of a condensing and extracting steam turbine.

LUBE OIL SYSTEMS

Turbines are the prime movers upon which the operation of a whole plant may depend and they must be provided with lubricating systems, which will ensure a reliable supply of lubrication oil to all parts in motion. The size of the turbine is the main criterion in deciding whether the lubricating system shall be of a simple or complex design. Small turbines of less than 200 hp (150 kW), used to drive auxiliary equipment, are normally provided with ring-oiled bearings. The other moving parts are usually lubricated by hand.

Moderate-sized turbines, particularly if driving through a reduction gear, may have both ring-oiled bearing and a circulating system. These oil systems not only supply oil in the form of a spray to the gears but also supply oil to the bearings of the gear set and the turbine.

Large turbines have oil-circulating systems, which supply oil not only to the turbine bearings but also to the governor mechanisms, the hydraulically operated steam throttle valves and the bearings of the driven generators.

The arrangement, shown in Fig. 1, represents a typical lube oil system. Oil is drawn from a reservoir and delivered at full pump discharge pressure, 50 psi to 70 psi, to a header, which supplies oil to the governing and control mechanisms. Oil from this header, after being reduced in pressure to between 8 to 15 psi, flows through the oil cooler to another header, which supplies oil to all the bearings and other parts requiring lubrication. The oil, returning from the bearing and governor mechanism, drains back into the reservoir.

Fig. 2 is a schematic diagram of a typical lubricating oil system for a turbine generator. The oil tank has a capacity of 1,200 to 2,400 gallons, or more, depending on the size of the unit. The oil pumps take suction from the oil tank through strainers and discharge the oil at high pressure, 80 to 120 psi. From here, the oil flows in two different directions:

- To the power oil and governor relay oil systems
- To the oil coolers and then to the turbine generator bearings

Power oil, acting in servomotors, opens the emergency stop valves and governing valves by hydraulic pressure. Governor relay oil acts as a sensitive regulating medium. The power oil and the governor relay oil have to be at high pressure.

Oil, used for lubrication, is at a lower pressure, typically in the 10 to 20 psi range. Therefore, before the oil passes to the coolers, it flows through a pressure-reducing valve. If the turbine has been operating for a length of time, the oil from the oil tank will be quite warm. Therefore, the oil will need cooling, in the oil coolers, before it flows through the bearings. Typical outlet temperatures, from the coolers, are in the 100° – 120°F range.

Inside the bearings, the oil acts as a lubricant between moving surfaces, and also acts as a coolant for the bearings. From the bearings, the oil drains into a return header, which leads back into the oil tank. A thermometer is placed in each return line from the bearings to indicate bearing temperature.

FIGURE 1

Turbine Lubricating Oil System

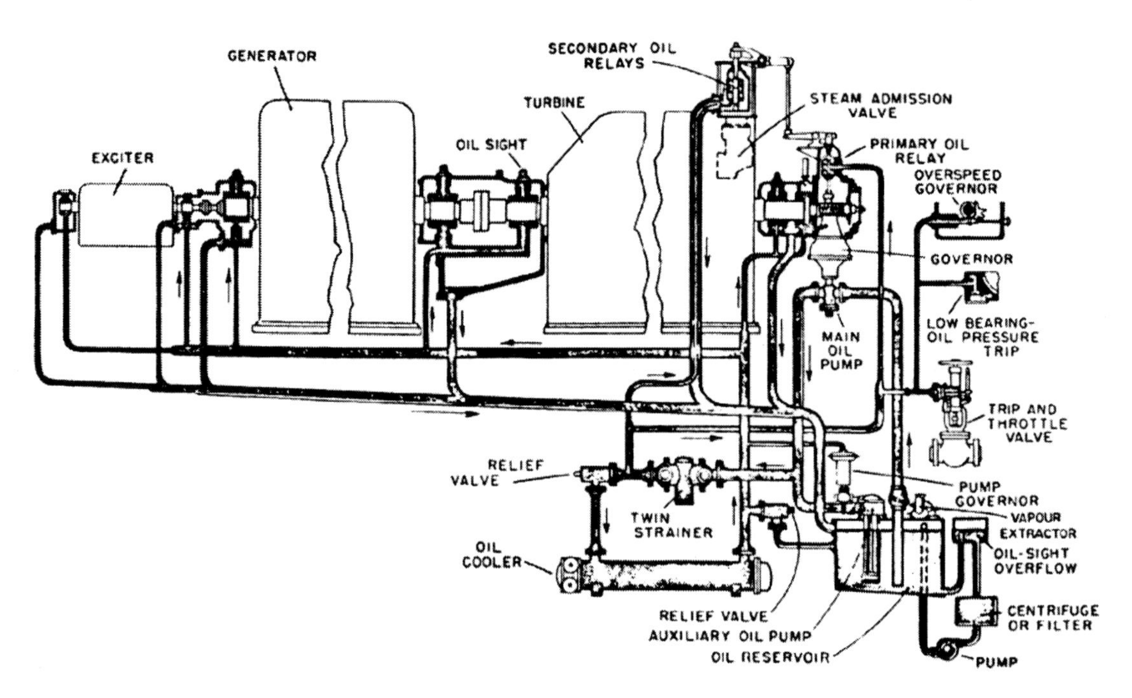

FIGURE 2

Typical Lubricating Oil System

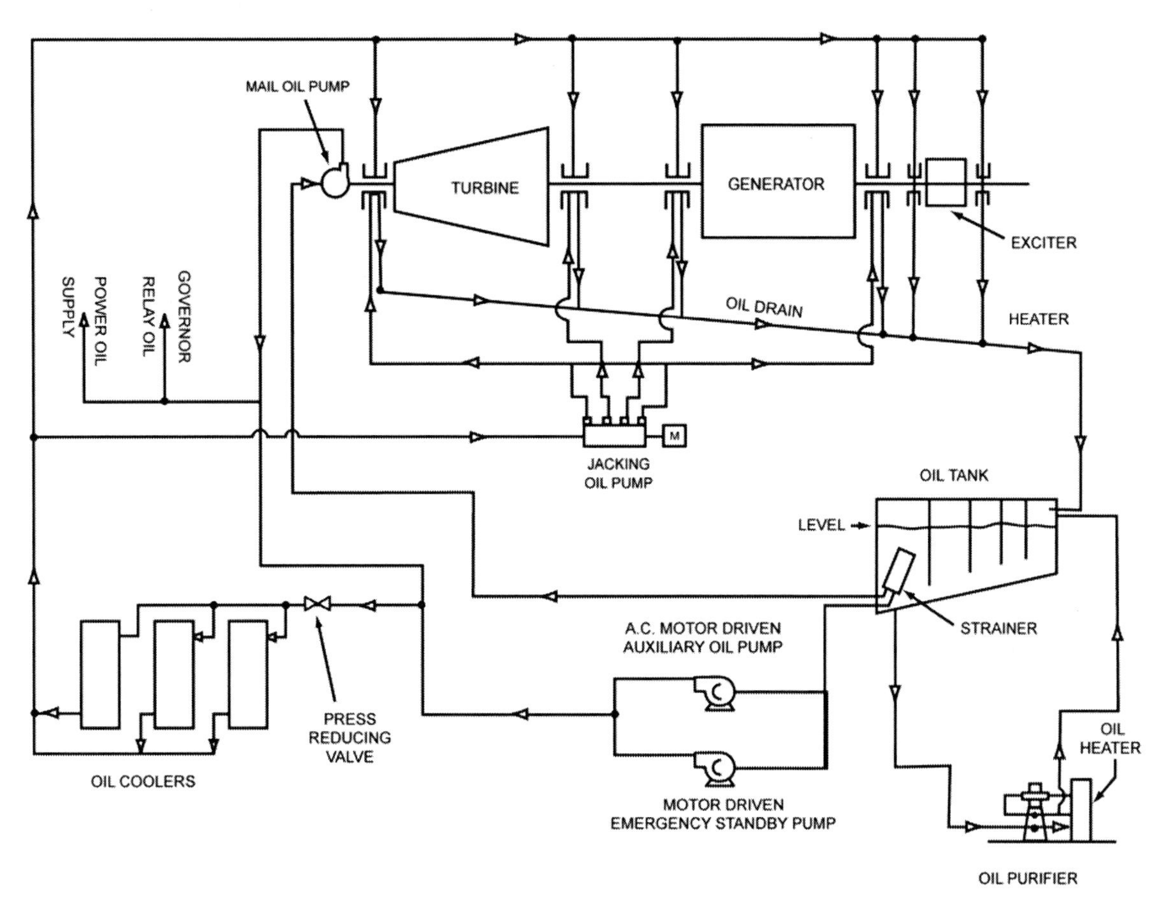

BARRING GEARS

When a turbine is left cold and at a standstill, the weight of the rotor will tend to cause the rotor to sag slightly. This is called bowing. If left at a standstill while the turbine is still hot, the lower half of the rotor will cool faster than the upper half and the rotor will bend upwards. This is called hogging. In both cases, the turbine would be difficult, if not impossible, to start up. To overcome this problem, the manufacturer supplies large turbines with a turning or barring gear consisting of an electric motor, which, through several sets of reducing gears, turns the turbine shaft at low speed. The normal speed of a turbine on barring gear is between 20 to 40 r/min.

Before a cold turbine is started up, it should be on the barring gear for approximately three hours. When a turbine is shut down, it should be barring for the next 24 hours. If a hydrogen cooled generator is involved, the turbine should be kept on barring gear to prevent excessive loss of hydrogen. In the turning gear illustrated in Fig. 3, a belt-drive and a worm and wheel reduce the motor speed. The disengaging gear wheel is carried on a yoke, which is slung from the worm shaft. An oil-operated piston is arranged to rotate the yoke about the worm shaft and so engage or disengage the turning gear from the turbine shaft.

FIGURE 3
Turning Gear

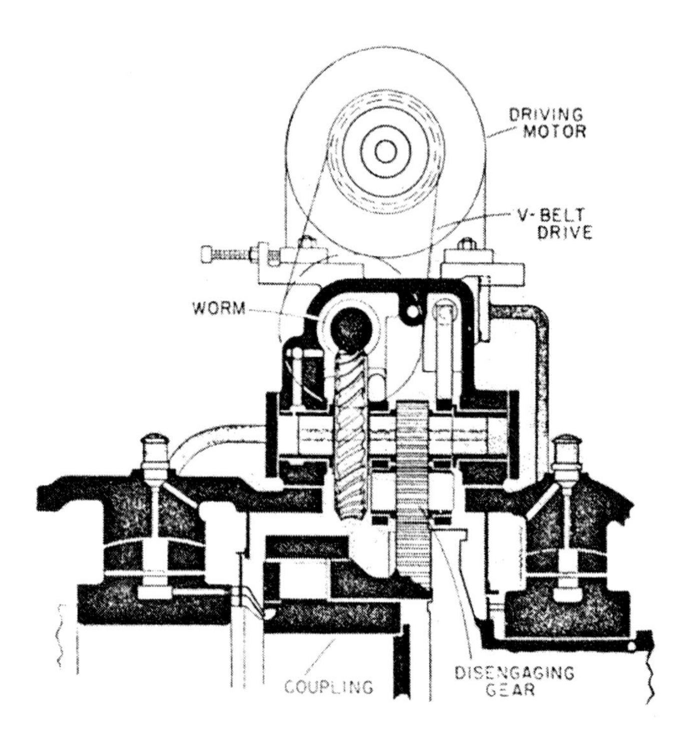

The distance between the bearings of large turbines is considerable and when operating at temperatures above 750°F, it becomes necessary to keep the shaft turning after shut down to make sure that uniform cooling takes place throughout the turbine. The location of the under slung barring or turning gear is shown in Fig. 4. This view of a tandem double-flow turbine is being assembled for factory testing. Positioning of the barring gear at the side of the bearing enables the pinion to engage the shaft, below the turbine centerline. This diagram also illustrates a side-mounted barring gear and vertical driving motor and their location in relation to the turbine shaft and control console.

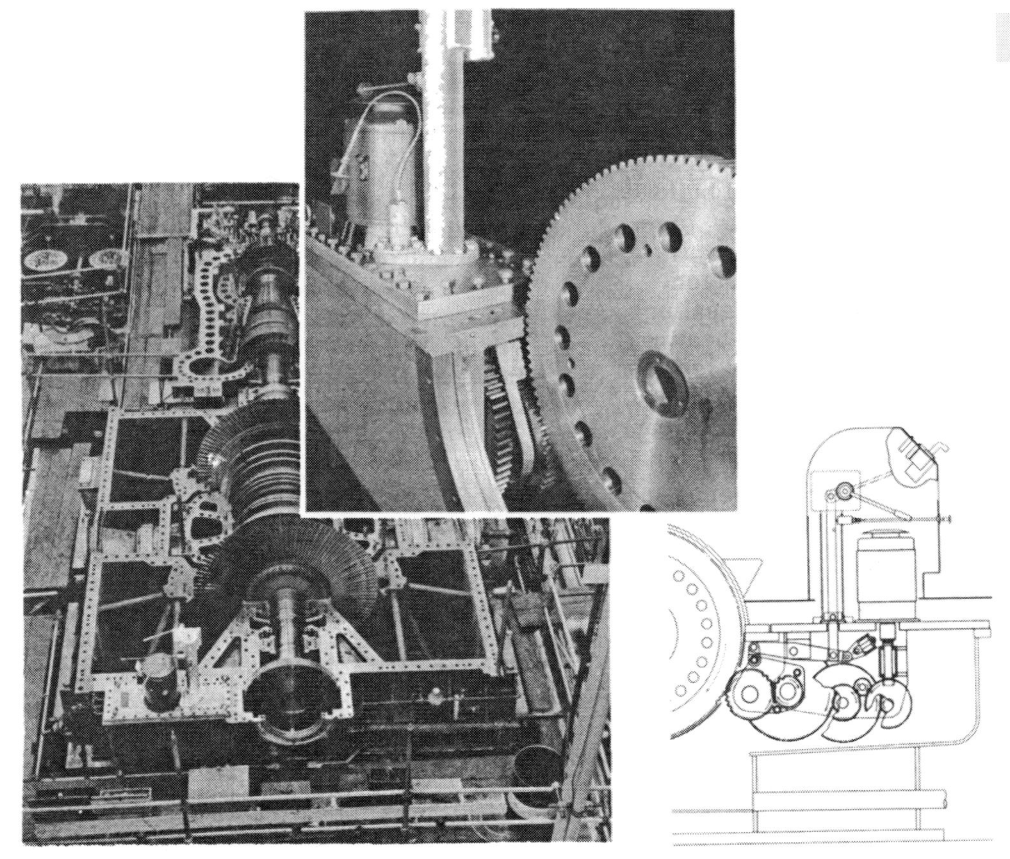

FIGURE 4

Illustrations of Barring (Turning) Gear

Fig. 5 shows the installation of the barring or turning gear in a LP (Low Pressure) end of a turbine.

FIGURE 5

Barring Gear

JACKING OIL SYSTEM

Large turbines with heavy rotors are generally equipped with a jacking oil pump supplying the lower part of the bearings with oil, at approximately 1,450 psi, thereby lifting the shaft and supplying lubricating oil. This oil pressure lifts or jacks the shaft a few millimeters, so that there will be no metal to metal contact during the initial start-up of the turning gear operation and also to reduce the starting load on the electric motor. The jacking oil is applied before start up of the barring gear and for operating the turbine at slow speed. The jacking oil pump is shut down at a turbine speed of 50 to 60 r/min.

CONDENSING TURBINE CIRCUITS

There are two general classes into which all turbines fall:

- Condensing units, which exhaust at pressures below atmosphere
- Non-condensing units, which exhaust at or above atmosphere

Fig. 6 shows a simple steam power plant in diagrammatic form. Heat, released in the boiler furnace, is transformed through the medium of steam produced in the boiler, into mechanical work, at the turbine shaft.

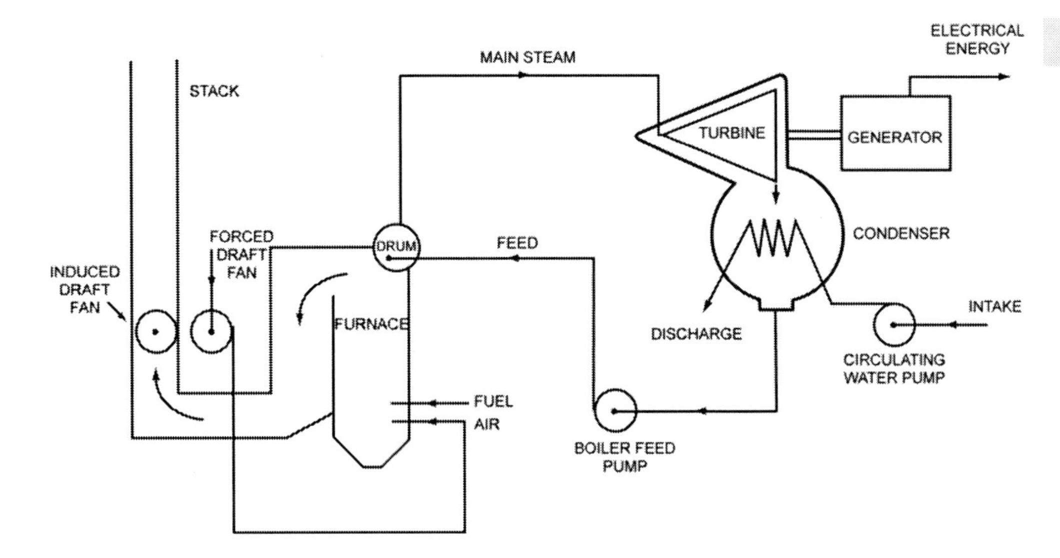

FIGURE 6

Simple Steam Power Plant

Fig. 7 shows a similar cycle, but using a nuclear reactor as the heat source. A nuclear plant uses heat in a similar manner to do work in a prime mover, but in this case, the heat is produced from the reaction of a nuclear fuel. The heat produced is transferred to the heat exchanger by a circulating coolant. The working fluid in the cycle is steam flowing through the turbine, in the same manner as in Fig. 6.

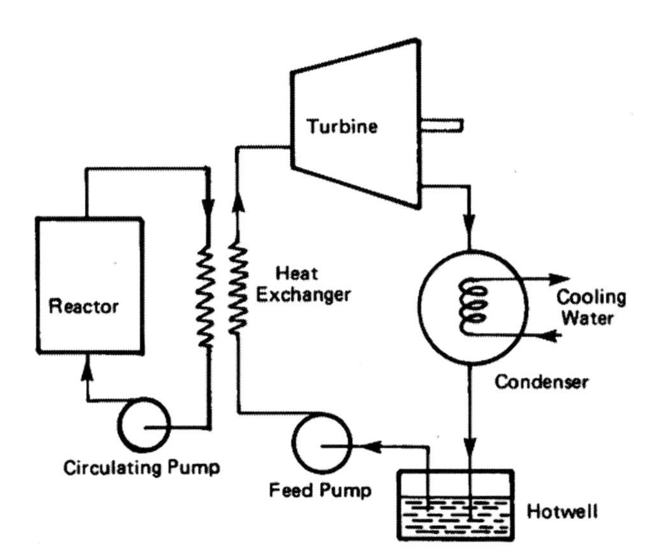

FIGURE 7

Simple Nuclear Steam Power Plant

Fig. 8 shows a condensing steam turbine circuit, in more detail. The prime purpose of the steam in any power plant is to supply the turbine with heat energy, which can be transformed into mechanical power. However, there are several auxiliary pieces of equipment, such as feedwater heaters, evaporators and deaerators that depend upon the steam supply, which are essential to efficient and economic turbine operation.

The main steam from the boiler expands in the HP (High Pressure) turbine, does work, and is then piped back to the reheater section, in the boiler. The steam from the reheater section then expands in the LP (Low Pressure) turbine, also doing work. The exhaust steam from the LP turbine passes to the surface condenser where the water from the circulating water pump removes the latent heat from the steam and condenses it into water.

The condensate, from the condenser hotwell, is pumped to the low pressure feed heaters where the exhaust or extraction steam from the LP turbine is used to preheat the feedwater going to the boiler, in the low pressure feed heaters. The boiler feed pump pumps this water to the high pressure feed heaters where the exhaust or extraction steam from the HP turbine is also used to preheat the feedwater going to the boiler in the HP feed heaters. After passing though the high pressure feed heaters, the water then enters the economizer in the boiler where it is further heated through the use of the hot combustion gases in the boiler.

FIGURE 8

Condensing Turbine Circuit

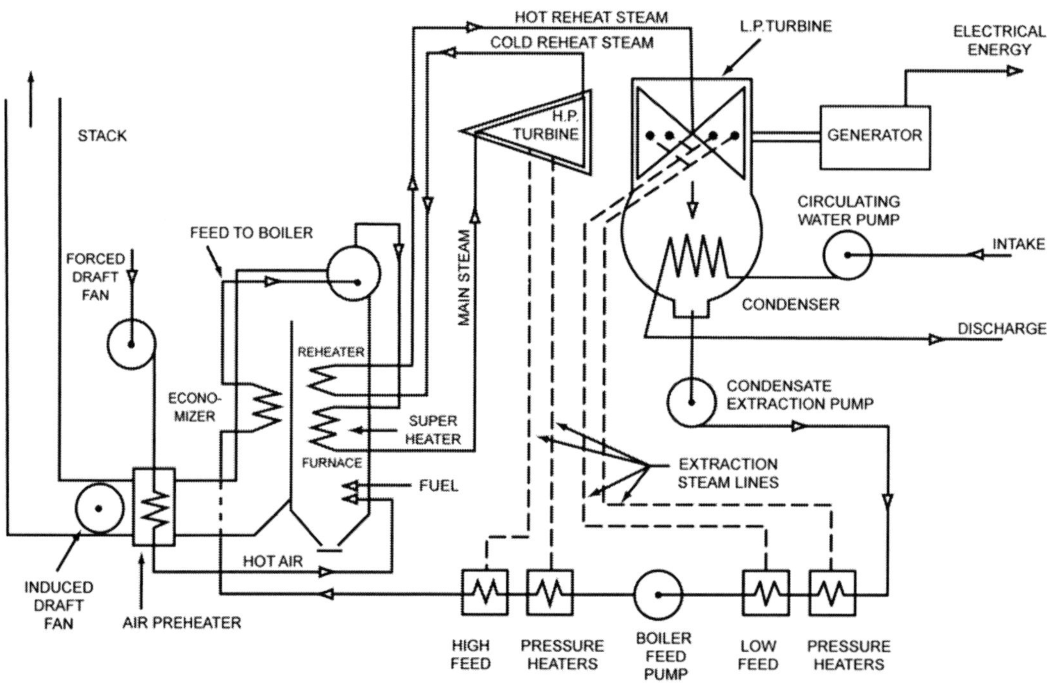

STEAM TURBINE GOVERNORS

Turbine governing systems control the steam flow to hold the speed of the turbine constant with varying loads, or to hold the pressure constant with varying demands for process steam.

The governor on a condensing turbine driving an alternator will be required to control the turbine inlet steam flow so as to maintain constant speed with varying alternator load. In a backpressure turbine, supplying exhaust steam for process work, the supply of steam to the turbine must be controlled in such a way as to maintain the backpressure constant.

In an extraction turbine, the governor must control the steam flow so that both the turbine speed and the pressure of steam, at the point of extraction, are maintained reasonably constant. This involves a regulation of the total amount of steam admitted to the inlet stages of the turbine and of the steam supplied to the turbine stages, following the extraction point.

Governors fall into two classes:

- Those responsive to speed changes
- Those responsive to pressure changes

SPEED SENSITIVE GOVERNORS

Three methods of speed-sensitive governing are used in steam turbines:

- Nozzle governing
- Throttle governing
- Bypass or overload governing

Nozzle Governing

Nozzle governing is only used in impulse turbines. It maintains a set turbine speed by regulating the flow of steam to inlet nozzles, which then direct the steam to the turbine blades. Two common arrangements are the bar-lift and the cam-lift systems, shown respectively in Figs. 9 and 10, respectively.

In Fig. 9, the bar-lift design has a row of inlet nozzles above the first stage turbine blading and a set of nozzle valves, or plugs, that are held in a horizontal bar. Notice that the lengths of the stems on these plugs vary. The flyweight action moves the bar up and down to open and close the nozzles as required. The different lengths of the plug stems determine the sequence by which they open and close.

FIGURE 9

Bar Lift Nozzle Control Gear

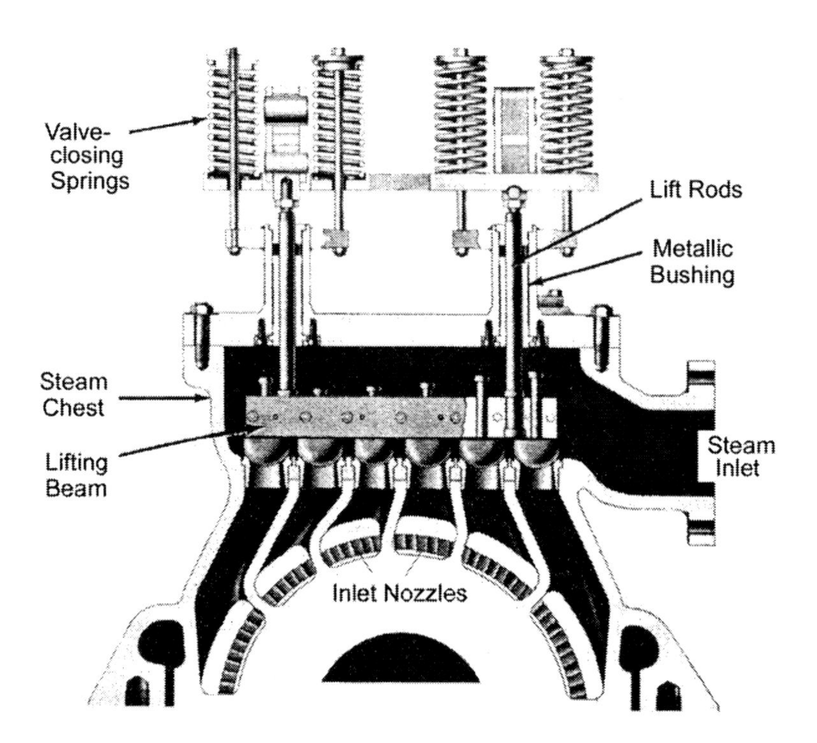

In Fig. 10, the same principle is applied, but a cam-like device, which controls the sequence and opening of each nozzle, individually operates the nozzle valves.

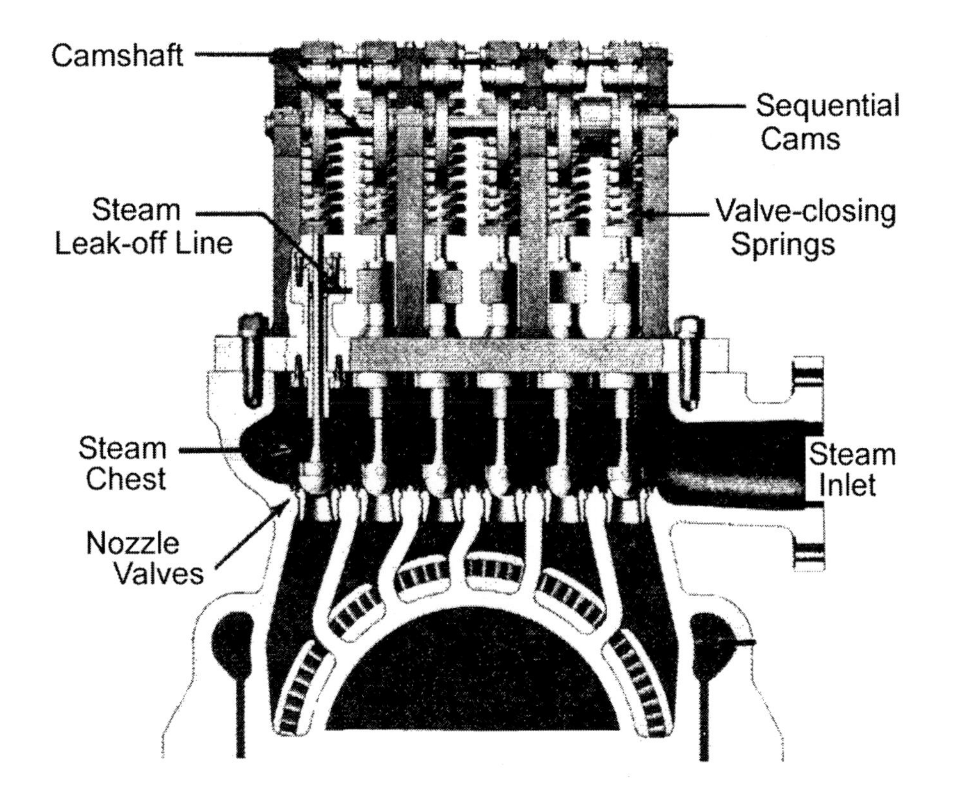

FIGURE 10

Cam Lift Nozzle Control Gear

Throttle Governing

An example of throttle governing is shown in Figs. 11 and 12. Here, a single valve at the inlet to the turbine adjusts the steam flow into the turbine casing and, from there, it is directed to the nozzles equally by the internal design of the turbine. The inlet, or throttle valve, responds to the governor to increase the steam flow for more speed or reduce the steam flow for less speed. In some larger turbines, there may be two throttle valves, arranged in parallel in the steam line.

This type of governing is always used with reaction turbines since the pressure drop in the moving blading requires steam admission to the full circumference, and the multi-valve arrangement supplying steam to nozzle groups cannot be used. With throttle governing ,one or two control valves control the load from 0% to 100%.

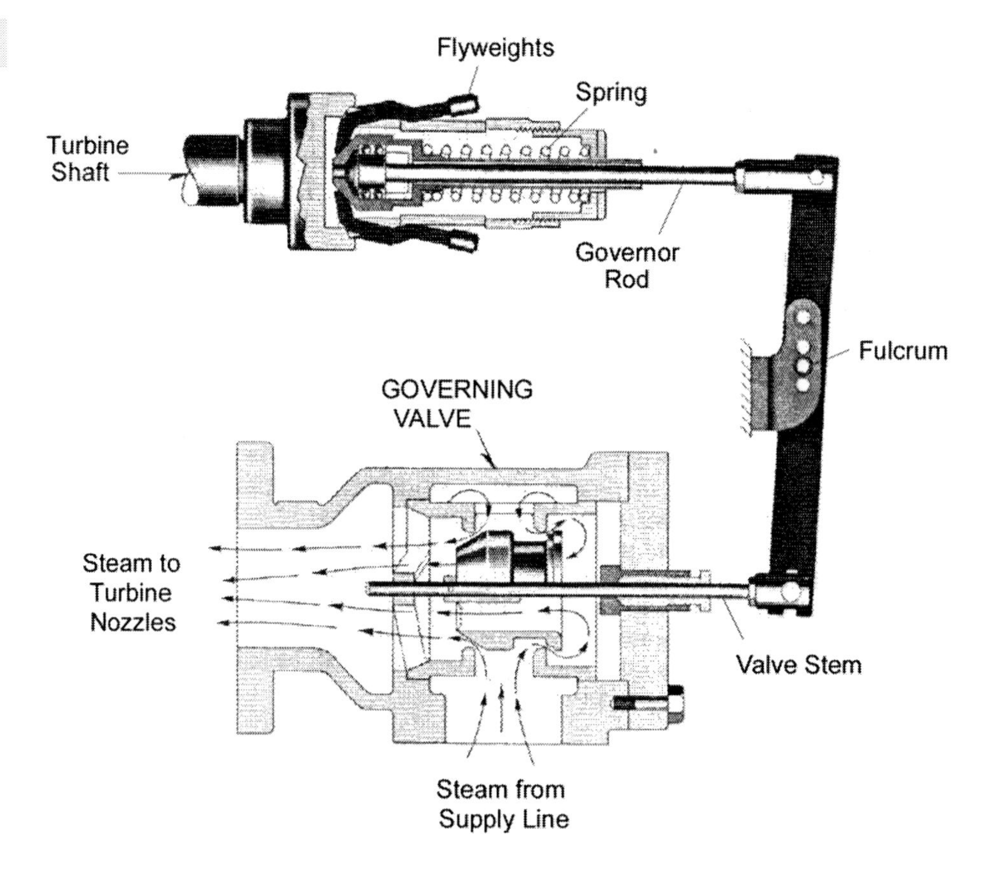

FIGURE 11

Simple Throttle Governor

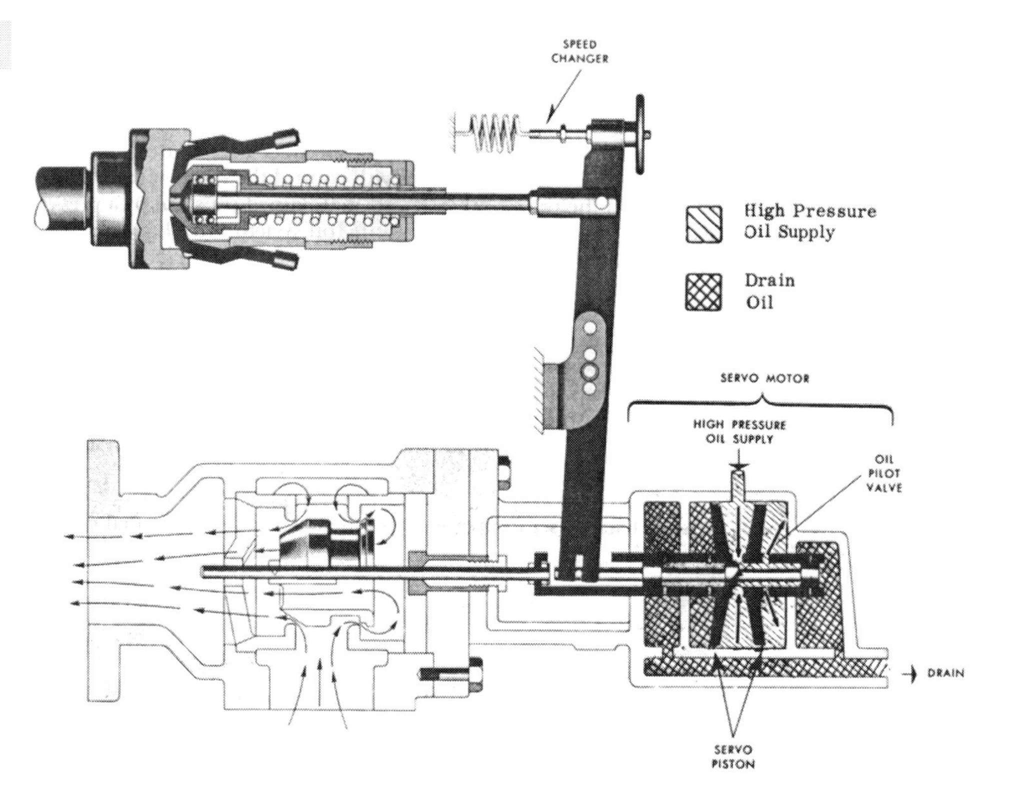

FIGURE 12

Mechanical-Hydraulic Governor With Servo

Bypass or Overload Governing

This system is used on both impulse and reaction turbines. It consists of two throttling valves, one at the inlet of the first stage of the turbine and the other at an inlet located downstream of the first few stages. The purpose of the second inlet point is to allow the turbine to maintain speed while producing extra power, during high load or overload conditions.

Fig. 13 shows a steam chest with a stop and trip valve (on the left), followed by the main steam throttle valve and the bypass throttle valve (on the right). This steam chest/valve arrangement is mounted on the turbine so as to direct steam to the appropriate nozzles, as shown in the turbine cross-section of Fig. 14.

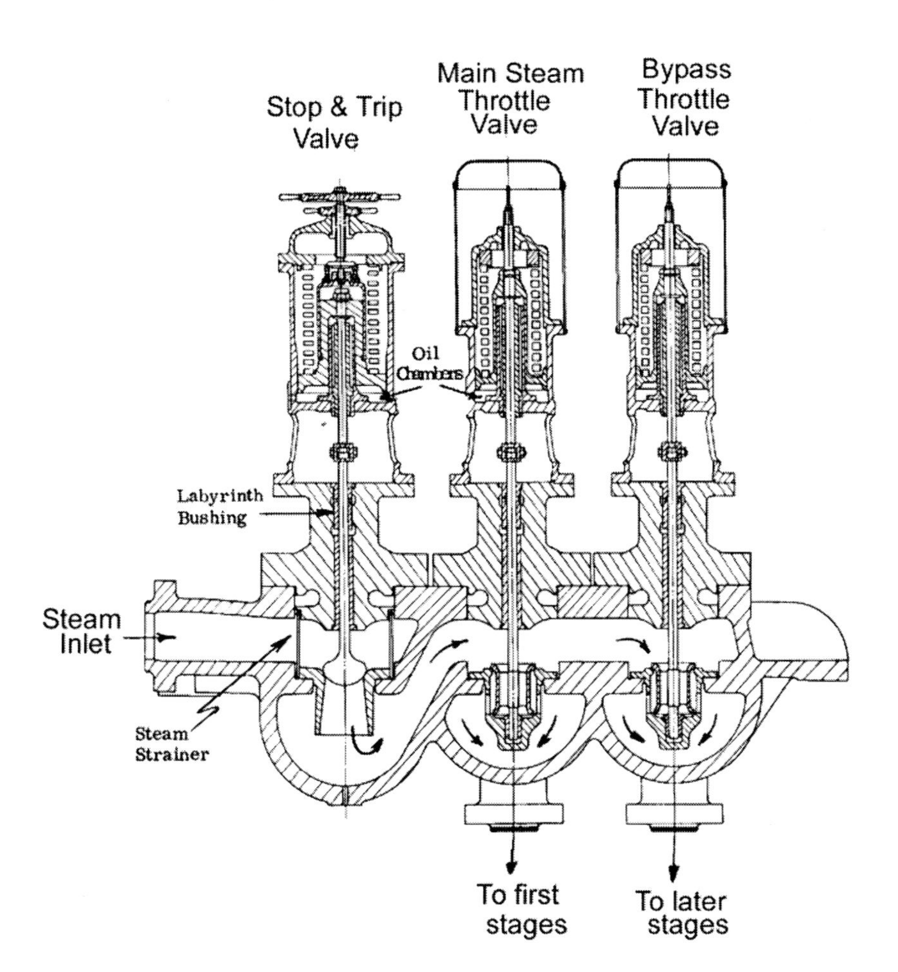

FIGURE 13

Steam Chest with Stop, Trip and Throttle Valves *(Courtesy of C.A. Parsons)*

FIGURE 14

Bypass-Governed Turbine

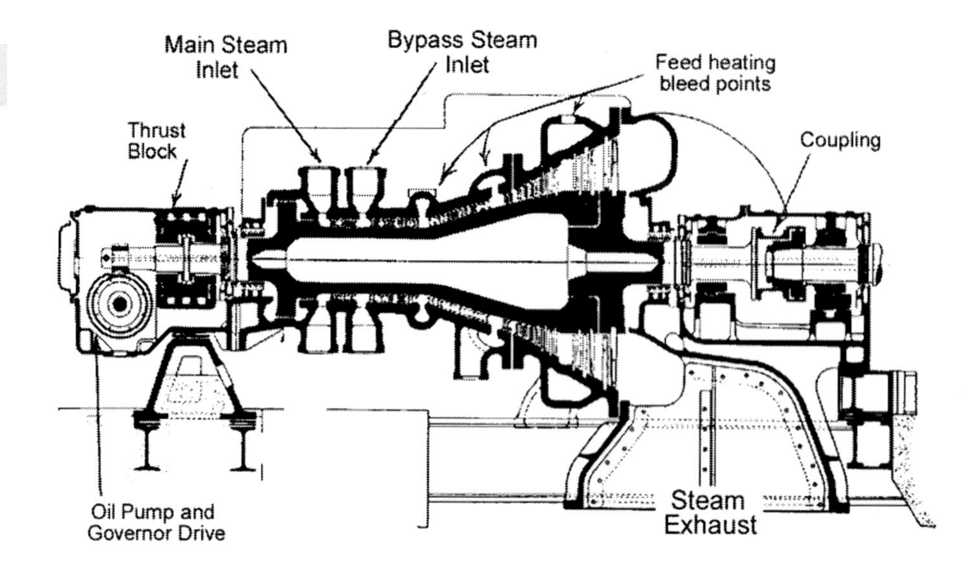

PRESSURE SENSITIVE GOVERNORS

Pressure sensitive governors either control a steady backpressure at the steam exhaust (outlet) of the turbine or they extract steam from part way through the turbine and discharge it at a controlled pressure, from that point. There is usually a combination of speed and pressure control to assure relatively steady turbine operation.

Backpressure Governing

This system uses a pressure-sensing element on the exhaust steam line from the turbine. A setpoint is entered into the controller, which then adjusts the position of the inlet steam throttle valve. If pressure is low, the throttle valve will open further to admit more steam and raise the exhaust pressure. If pressure is high, the throttle valve will close further. This system is commonly used with condensing turbines, where the pressure to the condenser should be as steady as possible. It is also used in processes where the exhaust steam from the turbine is used for heating and where the pressure must be steady to ensure good heat control.

The efficiency of the backpressure turbine is very high because there are no exhaust steam losses. The disadvantage of this system is that the load output of the turbine is completely dependent on the demand for process steam.

Extraction Governing

Process steam can be supplied by extracting steam, at controlled pressure, from intermediate stages of a turbine. The control systems for extraction turbines are complicated, as they must allow changes in the turbine load without affecting the steam extraction. They also must allow changes in the quantity of steam extracted without affecting the turbine output.

A schematic of such a system is shown in Fig. 15. When the extraction steam demand increases, the extraction pressure decreases and this forces the pressure regulator piston downwards. This moves point "G" down, and since point "D" is kept stationary by the speed governor, the linkage makes point "F" move the extraction valve down and point "E" move the steam inlet valve up. The result is that less steam can get through the extraction valve, so increased extraction steam flows at constant pressure.

If the load on the turbine increases, the speed will decrease and the speed governor will force point "A" downwards. Since point "B" is fixed and point "G" is held stationary by the pressure regulator, points "C" and "D" will move upwards and points "E" and "F" will move their respective valves upwards. This results in more high-pressure steam being admitted. The extra steam goes via the more open extraction valve to the low pressure stages of the turbine, giving increased load with no change in the extraction flow and pressure.

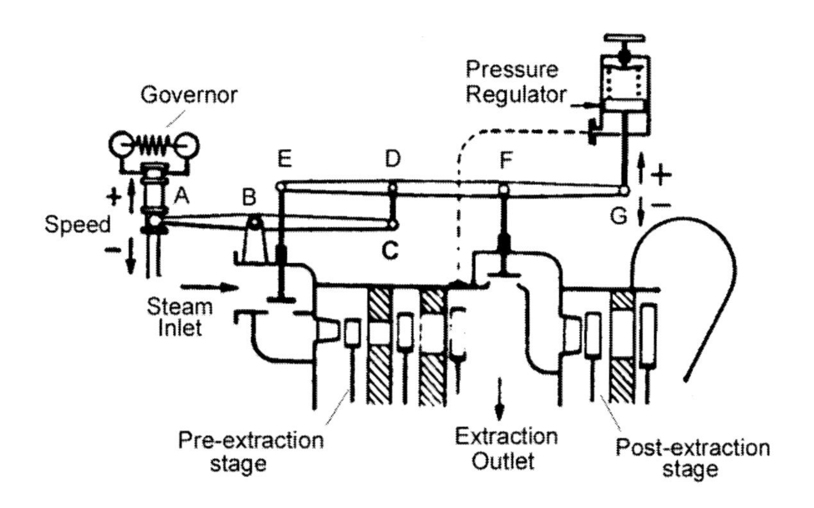

FIGURE 15

Combined Speed and Pressure Governor

GOVERNOR DROOP

Speed droop is the change in speed that results from an increase in load. An ideal governor will have the ability to maintain a constant speed at any load. However, there are mechanical losses within most governors that prevent achievement of this speed control. If the load on a turbine changes from zero (no-load), to maximum (full-load), the turbine will slow down and the governor may not be capable of restoring it to set speed.

The difference between the no-load and full-load speed, expressed as a percentage of the set speed, is called the "droop" of the governor. As the load increases, the speed will "droop" below the set speed.

For example, if the set speed of a turbine is 5 000 r/min, which is what it operates at with no load, and the governor system can only achieve 4 500 r/min, when the turbine becomes fully loaded, the droop of the governor is (500/5 000) x 100 = 10%.

Governors with low droop are more sensitive to load changes and generally have more accurate control than governors with high droop.

ISOCHRONOUS CONTROL

Isochronous governing gives perfect speed regulation with zero speed droop. An isochronous governor regulates the turbine to a constant speed at all loads so that the speed regulation or droop is zero percent. Isochronous governing is used when prime movers are operating alone. If turbines are sharing load in a parallel operation, an action called "hunting" can occur in which each turbine attempts to pick up the change in load and they begin "fighting" each other for control. This creates an uncontrollable cycling of the load and of the turbine speeds and the end result may be that one machine ends up fully loaded while another machine may have no load.

SPEED SENSITIVE GOVERNORS

The speed governor is a proportional-action controller, in that each change in power causes a change in the turbine speed. The governor controls the opening of the control valves as a function of this speed change. Due to the governor speed droop, the frequency is not constant over the full range of load, without an external adjustment.

The speed sensitive governor may be:

a) Mechanical
b) Mechanical – hydraulic
c) Electronic – hydraulic

Mechanical Governors

Fig. 16 shows the components and arrangement of a simple, mechanical governor. Attached to the end of the turbine shaft is a set of weights, called flyweights that pivot and have the ability to move in and out. The shaft ends of the flyweights contact the end of a governor, which is free to move to the left or right, but which is also acted upon by a counterspring. A governor valve, or steam inlet valve, is mounted at the inlet of the turbine and connected to the external steam supply line. The valve disc is double-seated and has a stem that extends out of the valve casing. Connecting the valve stem to the governor rod is a lever that is pinned to and free to pivot on a fixed fulcrum. This allows movement in the governor rod to be transmitted to the valve steam.

The governor functions, as follows. Rotation of the turbine shaft causes the flyweights to pivot outwards, due to centrifugal force. The greater the speed of rotation, the greater the centrifugal force will be and the further outward the flyweights will move. Movement of the flyweights will cause movement of the governor rod, which, through the lever and fulcrum, will cause movement of the governor valve.

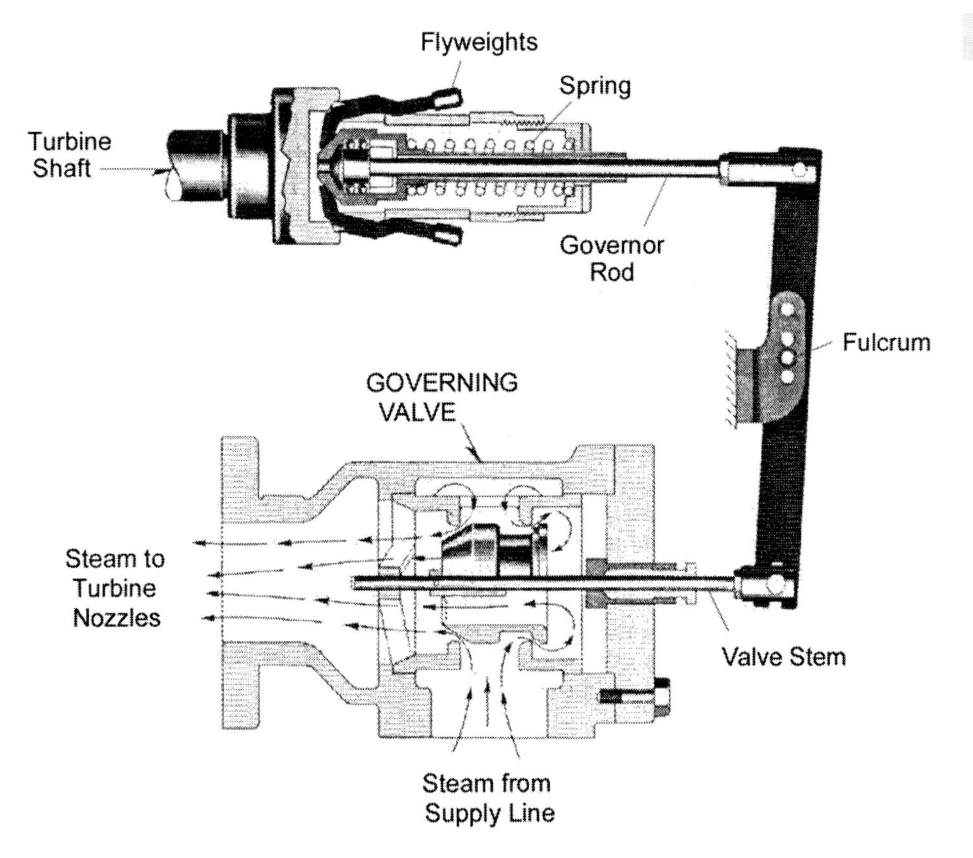

FIGURE 16

Mechanical Governor

For example, referring to Fig. 17, if the load on the turbine increases, it will slow down slightly. This will cause the flyweights to move inwards (due to less centrifugal force) and the governor rod will move to the left, due to the force of the counterspring. The lever will pivot at the fulcrum and the lower end will move to the right, thus opening the governor valve further. Now, as more steam enters the turbine, the speed will begin to increase. The flyweights will move outwards again until the system becomes balanced at the set speed, under the new load.

The disadvantage of simple mechanical governors is that they have a high-speed droop, usually around 10%. Therefore, they are not suitable for large machines or where control must be extremely accurate. Within limits, changing the pivot point at the fulcrum can reduce the effects of droop, so that the governor rod movement has more affect on the governor valve movement.

FIGURE 17

Simple Centrifugal Mechanical Governor

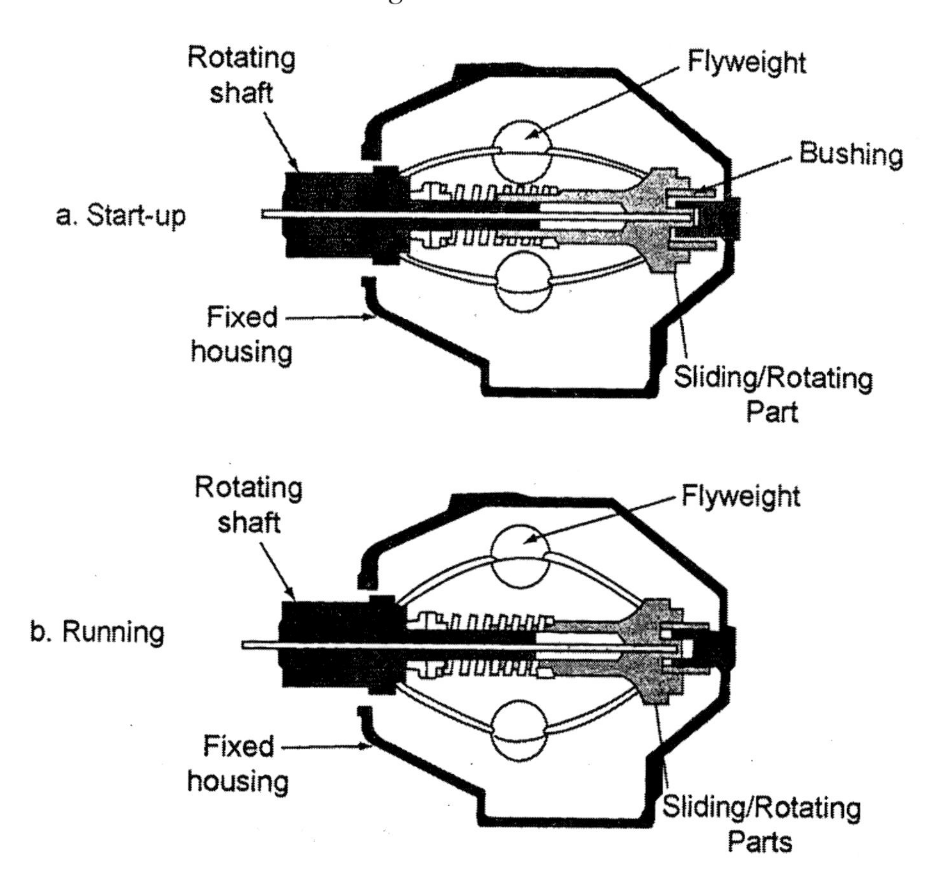

Mechanical-Hydraulic Governors

The mechanical governor has a pilot valve and a hydraulic amplifier. This arrangement removes the direct linkage of the flyweights to the governor valve. Instead, the flyweights position an oil pilot valve that admits high-pressure oil to a piston that moves the governor valve. The advantage of the design is that the mechanical losses of the governor are greatly reduced. The flyweights require less force to position the pilot valve and the pilot provides the power to move the governor valve. The droop of this governor can be reduced to almost zero.

Fig. 18 is a simple diagram of a mechanical-hydraulic governor. Oil, at approximately 72 psi, is continuously supplied to the center of the pilot valve, which at normal speed covers the oil ports to the amplifier cylinder so that oil cannot enter or leave the cylinder. If the load drops and the turbine speed increases, the flyweights move outwards. This pulls the pilot valve upwards, admitting oil to the top of the cylinder while allowing oil to drain from the bottom of the cylinder. The piston moves downward, forcing the steam valve to close further.

As the steam valve closes, the turbine speed decreases and the flyweights move inwards. At normal speed, the pilot valve will have returned to the central, or neutral, position and the turbine will continue to operate at the set speed, under the new load. Conversely, if the turbine load increases and the turbine speed drops, the pilot valve will admit more oil below the piston and cause the governor valve to open further.

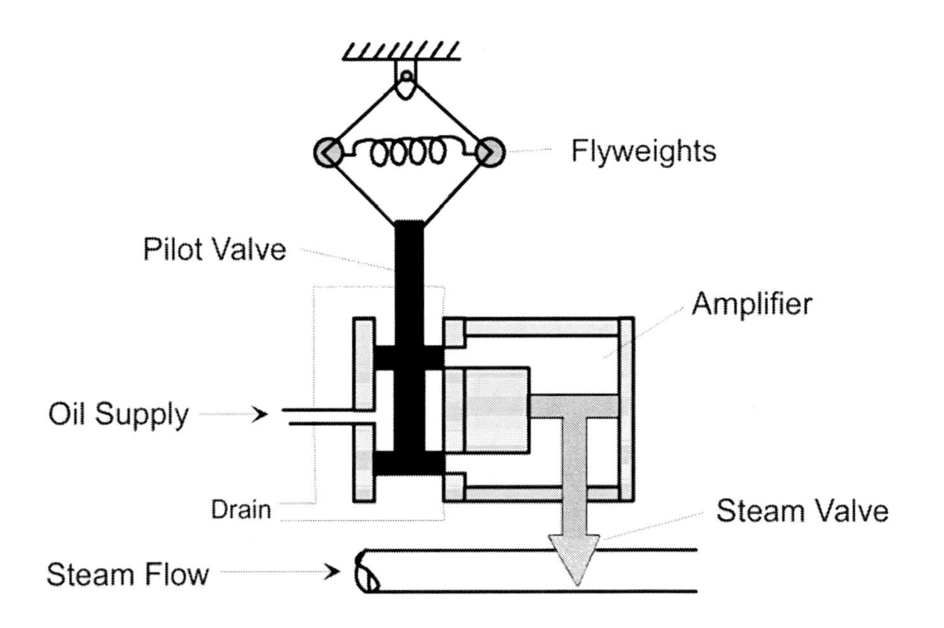

FIGURE 18

Mechanical-Hydraulic Governor

Fig. 19 shows the same governor as Fig. 18 with the addition of a hydraulic cylinder and piston. This hydraulic arrangement is often called a "servo" or "servo motor". Note that the lever positions the pilot valve, while the servo piston positions the stream valve. Also, notice the speed changer. Adjustment of this wheel creates a slight change in the positioning of the servo piston, which then alternates the internal hydraulics to cause a change in the operating speed of the turbine.

FIGURE 19

Mechanical-Hydraulic Governor With Servo

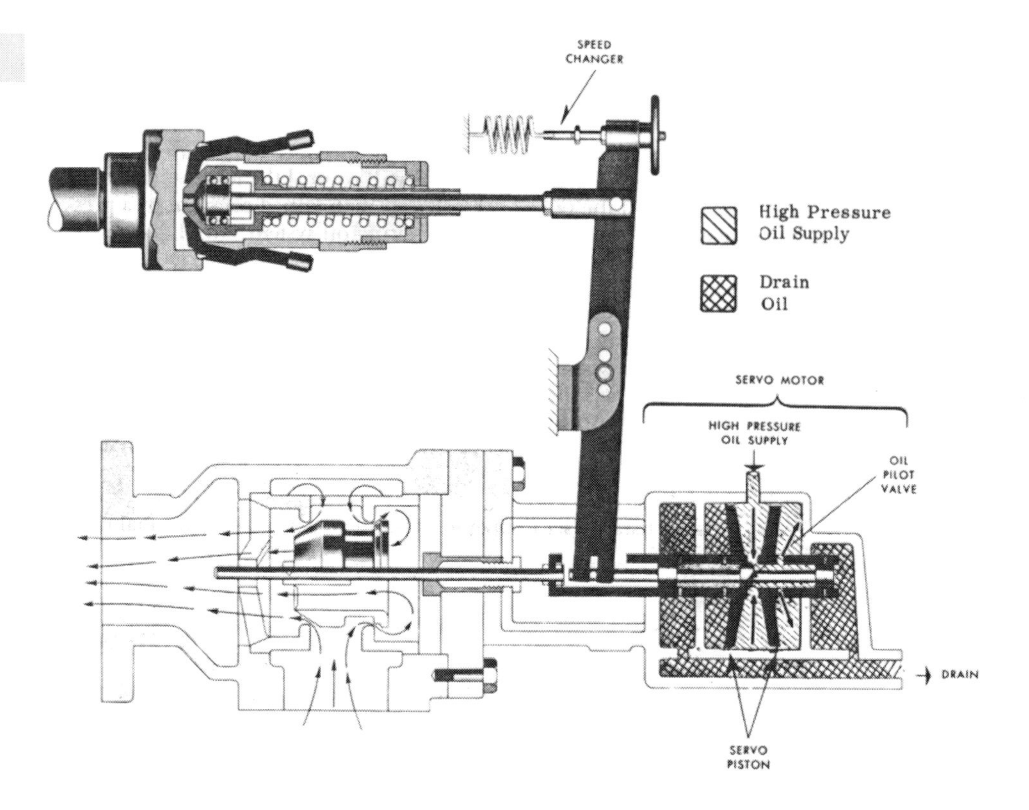

Therefore, the effort required by the governor, can be reduced to a relatively small force by the use of an oil relay, as illustrated in Fig. 21. In this case, the governor arm operates only the pilot valve. When the pilot moves, it opens an oil port admitting oil, which forces the servo piston to move with it. The steam valve spindle movement shuts off the oil when the piston has caught up with the pilot. The pilot movement then admits high-pressure oil to one side of the servo piston and connects the other side to drain, producing a positive control.

Mechanical-Hydraulic Governor System

The following diagram and description, Fig. 20, demonstrates how components relate to each other to provide a complete governor system. Referring to the diagram, the turbine shaft drives a main, gear-type oil pump, which supplies the hydraulic oil pressure to the various governor components. An auxiliary oil pump, driven by an electric motor, provides oil pressure during start-up of the turbine, until the main oil pump can provide sufficient operating oil pressure.

Before start-up, the overspeed trip assembly is manually re-latched so that the oil trip valve, “B”, is open, allowing oil pressure and flow to the other governor components. This includes the turbine stop valve, which is held open by the pressure under the operating piston in cylinder “C”.

When the turbine is running steadily, the spinning flywheels take a position, balanced by their counterspring. Flyweight movement controls the position of a plunger sliding within sleeve "G", which is part of the servo, or speed adjuster. The relative position of the plunger and the sleeve determines the opening of the oil ports in the sleeve.

Meanwhile, high pressure oil goes directly to the pilot valve, "K", in the control oil cylinder. The pilot valve regulates the oil pressure below the throttle valve cylinder, J, increasing pressure if the speed is high. The position of the throttle valve responds accordingly.

However, the droop, proportionally and speed control of the governor is affected by the positioning of the moveable governor fulcrum, which is determined by the piston in cylinder, "H". Oil to this cylinder is taken from the main oil supply, through valve "F". The pressure in the line, and therefore the pressure below piston "H," is determined by the position of the oil ports at "G", in the servo. Adjusting the handwheel, "L", will change the servo port openings, causing more or less oil to be drained, thus affecting the pressure to cylinder "H" and causing the speed of the turbine to change. The movement of "L" may be done manually or it may be activated by a small electric motor, with remote control.

In an overspeed situation, the overspeed trip will close the oil supply cylinder, "B". This will cause all oil pressure to be lost beneath the trip valve and the throttle valve. The turbine will come to quick stop, due to immediate loss of the steam supply.

FIGURE 20

Mechanical-Hydraulic Governor System

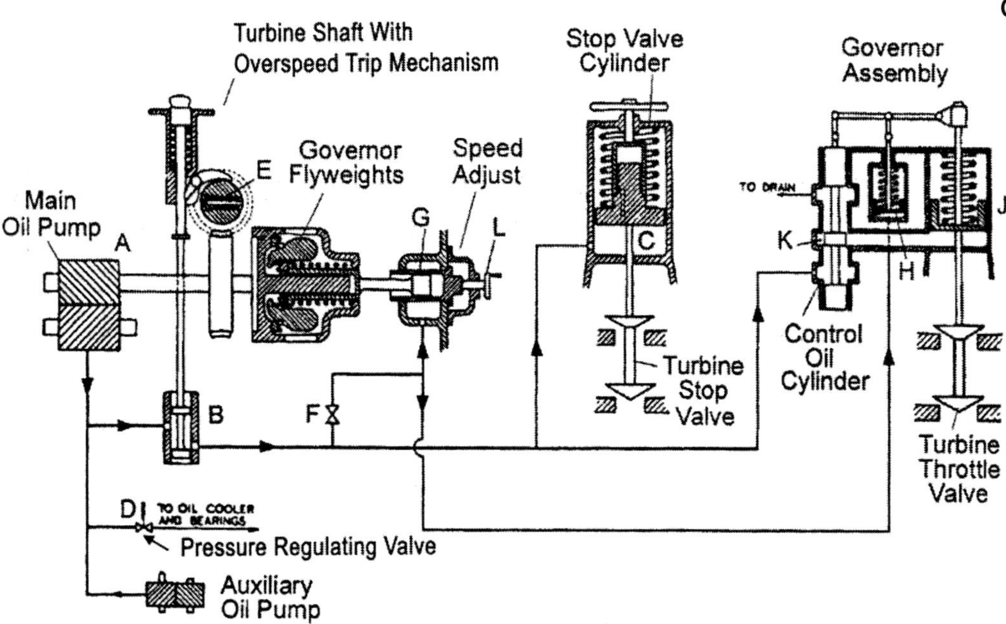

Electronic-Hydraulic Governors

Electronic-hydraulic governors use a combination of electronic and hydraulic controls. The turbine control console contains all the controls necessary for starting, accelerating, and loading the turbine, as well as for controlling the extraction steam flows and pressures if applicable.

Referring to Fig. 21, the speed-measuring device, a permanent magnet generator, produces an electrical output signal that is amplified and compared to a reference signal by the computer in the control console. The difference is then amplified and applied to a servo-valve, which hydraulically positions the servo-rams, moving the steam valves and controlling the steam flow. The valve position is measured and fed back to the control console, providing more exact control. Provisions are made for on-line servicing of the computer circuit cards while the turbine is carrying load.

Electro-hydraulic governor systems use a separate fluid power unit to provide high-pressure hydraulic oil to operate the servo-rams, rather than using part of the lube oil system. The fluid power unit supplies hydraulic oil, at pressures in the range of 1,200 to 1,600 psi.

FIGURE 21

Electro-Hydraulic Governor System

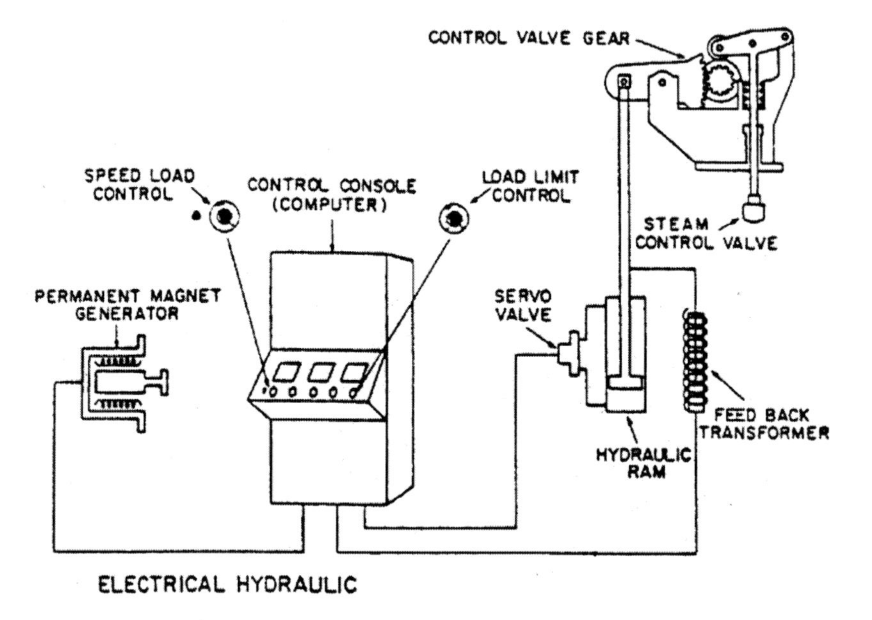

Fig. 22 shows a typical example of a basic electronic governor system for a turbine generator. The activator controls the pilot valve to readjust the position of the steam control valve and maintain the desired speed versus generator load changes. The force to move the throttle valve is usually hydraulic power acting through the servo piston.

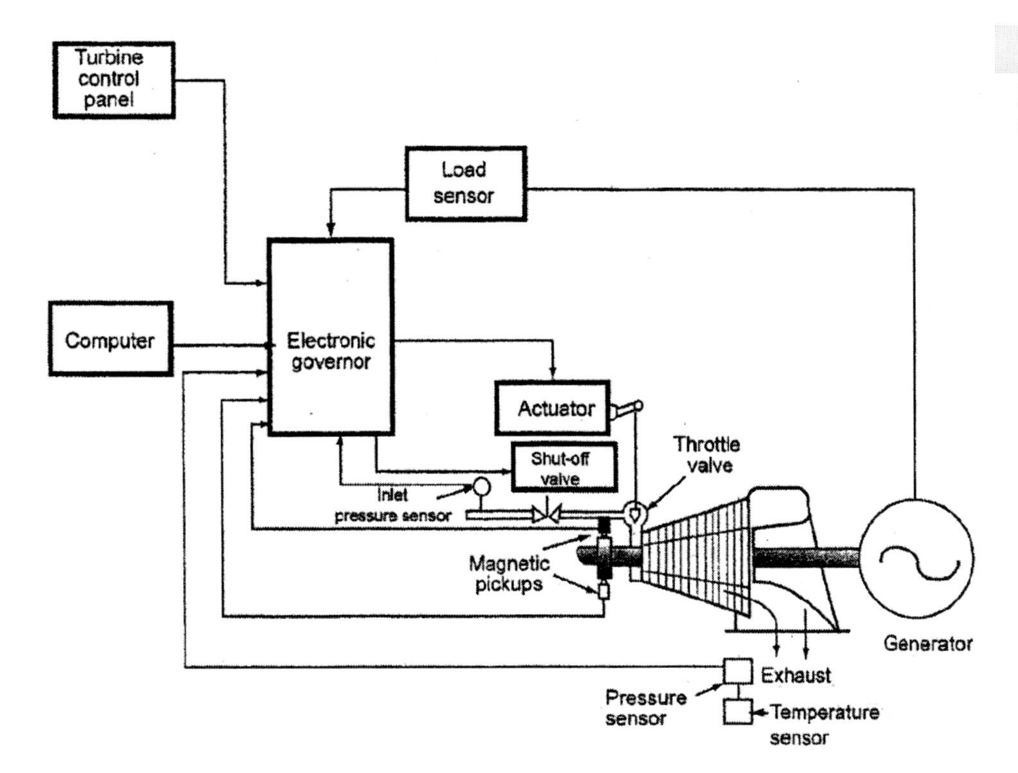

FIGURE 22

Electronic-Hydraulic Governor System

MECHANICAL OVERSPEED TRIP SYSTEMS

The mechanical overspeed trip on a steam turbine is an integral part of the governing system in that it prevents steam from entering the turbine, if the speed becomes dangerously excessive. The mechanical overspeed trip gear is generally located at the front end of the high pressure turbine shaft and is designed to shut off the steam supply to the turbine. The trip speed is usually 10 to 12% above the normal operating speed.

A basic trip bolt is shown in Fig. 23. It consists of a weighted bolt that is held inside a specially made hole in the shaft. A spring is held in compression to keep this trip bolt inside the shaft during normal operating conditions, as shown in Fig. 23. If the turbine shaft reaches the overspeed setting, the spring compression is overcome and the bolt will be thrown out by centrifugal force, as shown in Fig. 24.

FIGURE 23

Overspeed Trip in The Normal Operating Position (Reset)

FIGURE 24

Overspeed Trip Position

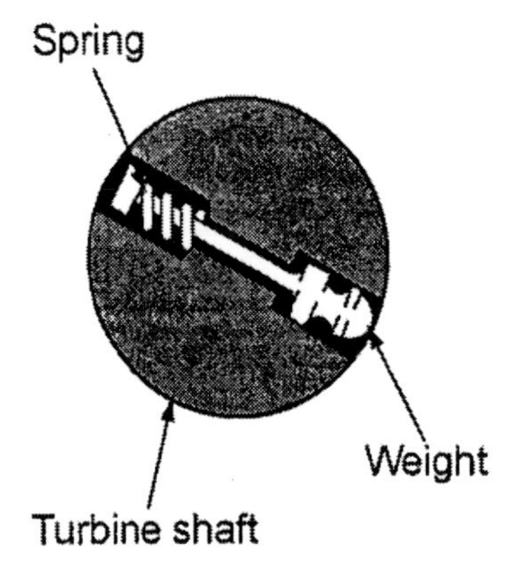

Figure 23

Figure 24

Fig. 25 shows a mechanical overspeed trip system using a mechanical linkage to control the flow of steam to the turbine, during normal running conditions.

FIGURE 25

Mechanical Overspeed Trip System (Turbine Normal Operation)

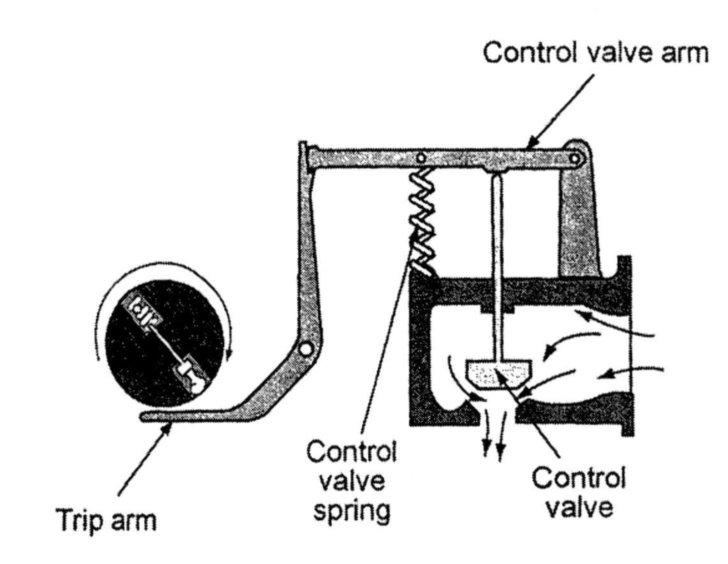

Fig. 26 illustrates an overspeed situation (movements are exaggerated for clarity).

FIGURE 26

Mechanical Overspeed Trip System (Turbine Tripped)

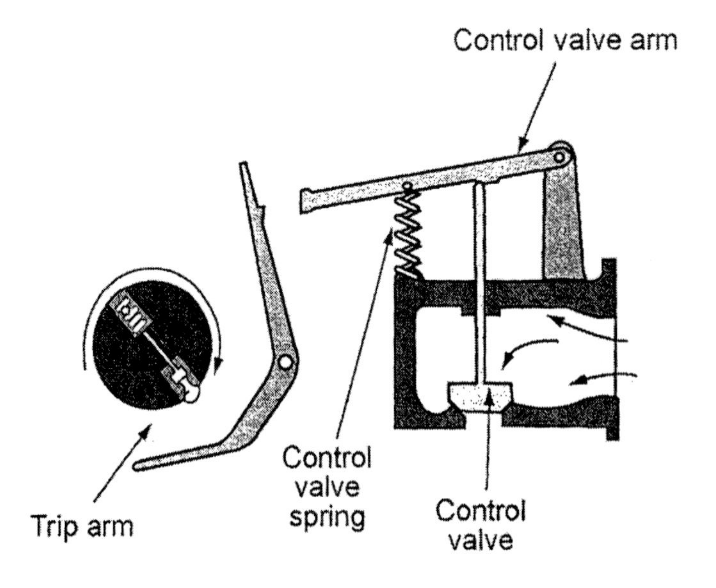

The overspeed trip can be manually operated, at any time, by using the trip lever. The overspeed trip, in Fig. 27, shows clearly the operating principle of all overspeed trips for turbines with hydraulic governor systems. The spring loaded tripping bolt, located in the turbine shaft, has the center of gravity slightly off the center of the shaft in the direction of the bolt head. The nut, at the end of the bolt, provides a stop for the bolt in the tripped position and for the tripping speed adjustment. During normal operation, the main spring holds the relay rod against the tripping lever. Piston "A" closes the oil drain and the high-pressure oil passes between pistons " A" and "B", to the stop valve. Note: The gear is shown in the set position.

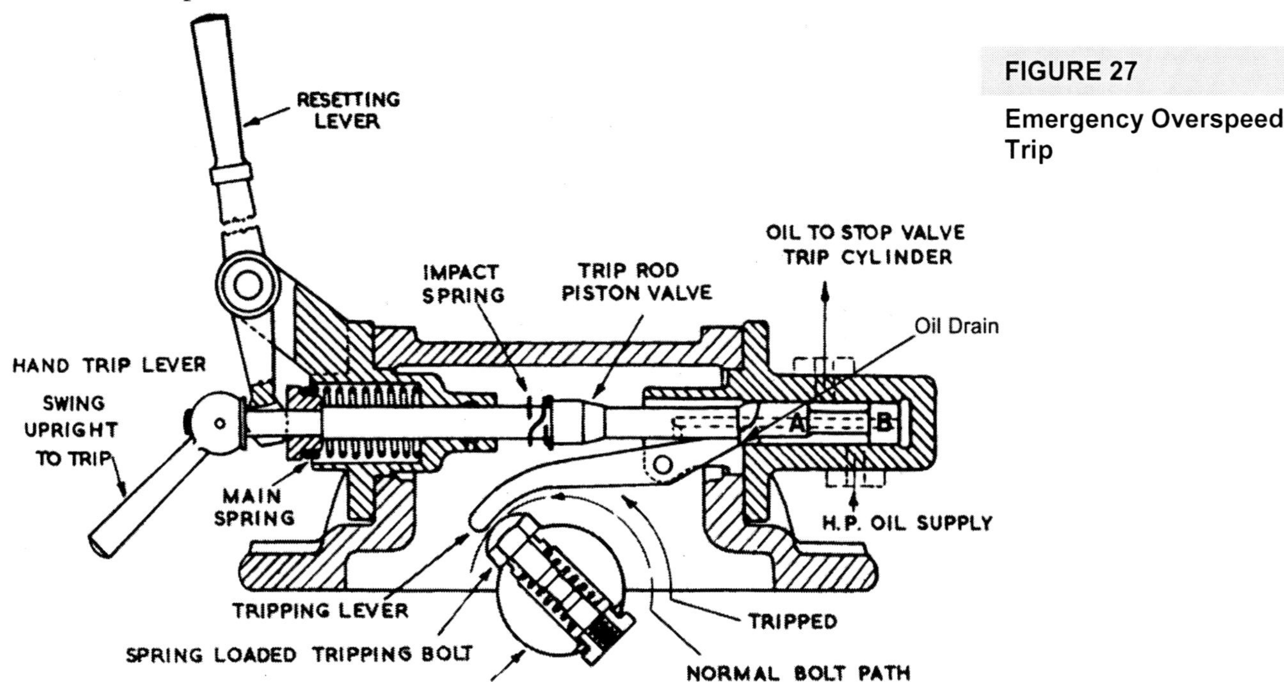

FIGURE 27

Emergency Overspeed Trip

When the turbine speed increases to the trip setting, usually 110% of operating speed, the following occurs:

- Centrifugal force overcomes the bolt spring tension
- The bolt moves to the trip position and strikes the tripping lever
- This unlatches the relay rod
- The main spring moves the relay to the tripped position
- Piston "A" opens the stop valve oil-port to drain
- Piston "B" closes off the high-pressure oil inlet port

Fig. 28 shows a bolt type overspeed trip located in the high-pressure turbine shaft end. The bolt is eccentric in the shaft, but is held in position by the spring, at normal speeds. The oil supply, maintaining the steam valves open, passes through ports "P" and "U" in the normal position. At an overspeed condition, the pin (bolt) trips the latch “R”. When “R” is tripped, the trip relay spring lifts the trip relay piston so that “P” is closed off and “U” is open to drain.

FIGURE 28

Overspeed Trip Gear

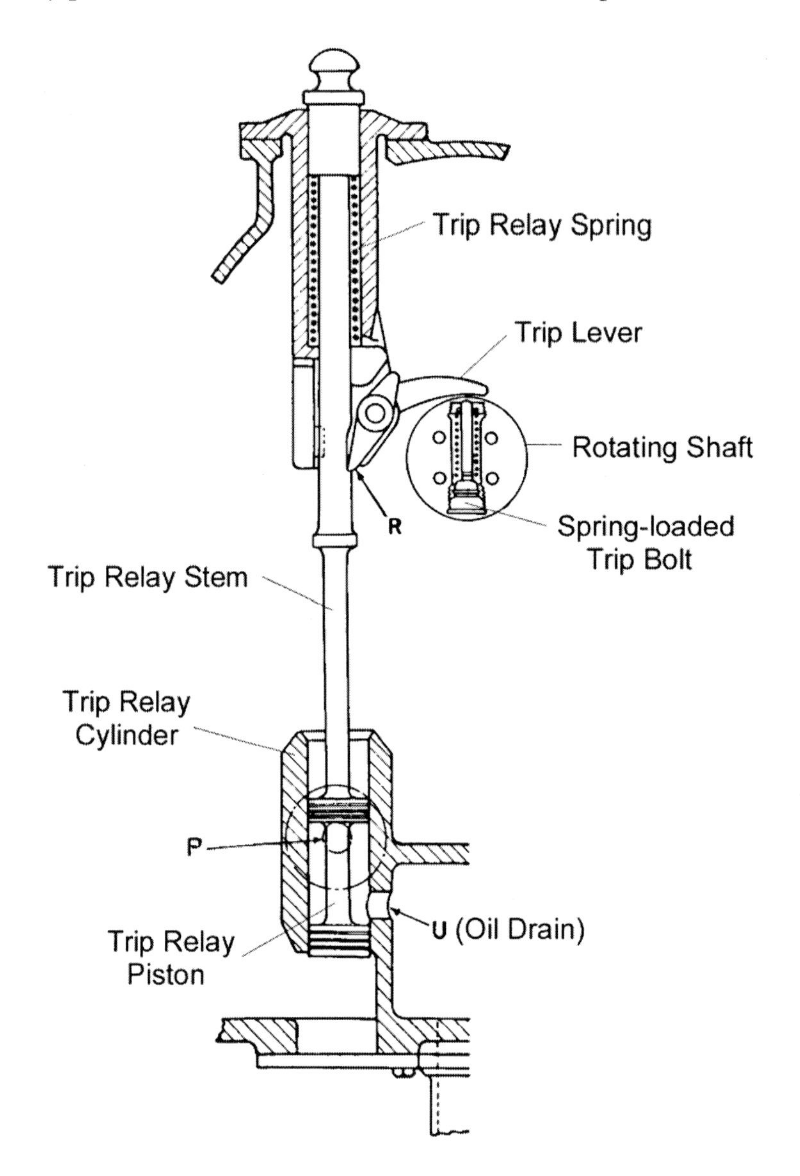

ELECTRONIC OVERSPEED TRIP SYSTEMS

Steam turbines are fitted with a shutdown system to prevent damage to the machine. In the event the speed governor fails to control the speed, the overspeed trip actuates to shut down the machine. When the shaft speed exceeds a desired safe level, generally 10% overspeed, a latching device or oil dump mechanism is actuated to close a special emergency stop valve. This system is totally independent of the governor.

Referring to Fig. 29, the turbine shaft contains a notched gear wheel. Inductive sensors, also known as magnetic speed pickups, are mounted to the turbine casing. As the gear teeth pass the sensors, the principle of magnetic induction generates an AC voltage that can be read by the ECM (Electronic Control Module), which contains pulse counting sensors. These units then convert the electronic pulse signals to revolutions per minute, for calculating the turbine shaft speed. Most modern steam turbines overspeed trip systems, installed with three magnetic speed pickups, require that two out of the three sensors agree that the unit has reached the overspeed condition, before a trip is initiated.

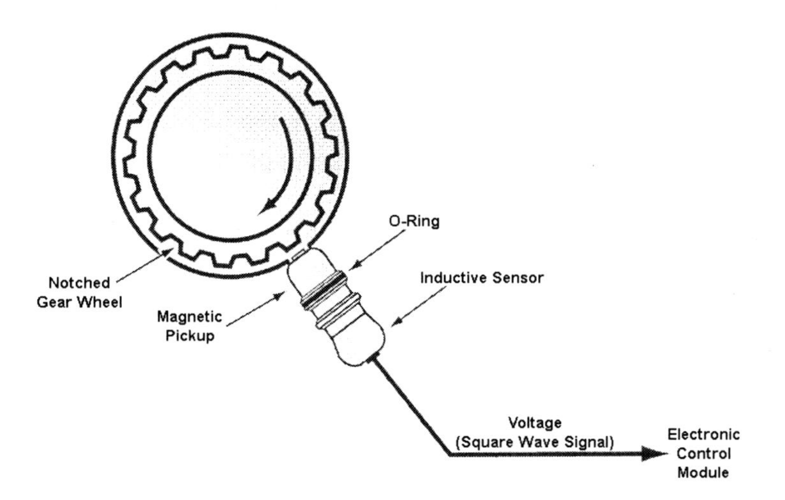

FIGURE 29

Magnetic Speed Pickup Sensor

When overspeed reaches the set point, an action is initiated to shut the emergency stop valve. Referring to Fig. 30, electronic signals are sent from the electronic control module to the trip block that shuts off the supply of hydraulic oil that normally maintains the stop valve in an open position. Another signal is sent from the electronic control system to close the control valve, which also stops the flow of steam to the turbine.

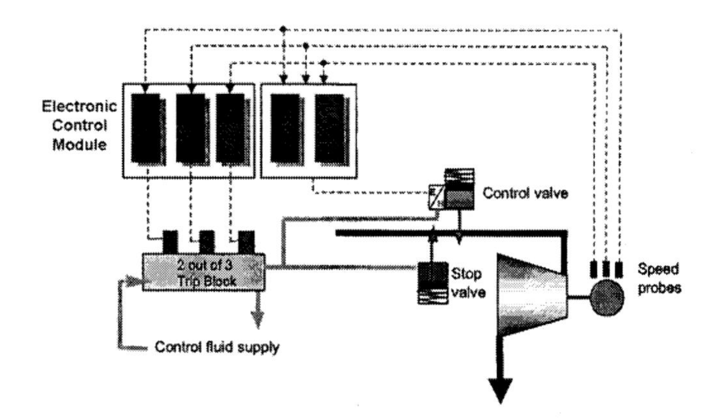

FIGURE 30

Electro-Hydraulic Control System

STARTING A NONCONDENSING TURBINE

1. Check that the governor linkages are well lubricated, and grease cups, if used, are filled.

2. If the bearings use a ring oiler, check oil levels in the bearing sumps. If a pressure lubrication system is used, check the oil level in the main oil reservoir.

3. Make sure all condensate is drained from steam and exhaust lines. If these are drained by traps, open the bypass lines around the traps.

4. Slowly open the shutoff valve between the turbine and the exhaust line.

5. If the turbine is equipped with a pressure lubricating system operated by a separately driven oil pump, then start the pump. Verify that sufficient oil pressures and flows are established.

6. If bearing oil sumps or oil reservoirs are water cooled, then turn on the cooling water system.

7. Commission the unit that the turbine is driving, as per the manufacturers recommended procedure.

8. Open the throttle valve part way to start the turbine rotor turning. Close the valve again to the point where the rotor turns slowly. Listen carefully for any noise indicating that the rotor is rubbing against the casing. If oiler rings are used, check to see that the rings are operating.

9. If no unusual noises or problems are detected, increase the turbine speed to 200-300 r/min. Maintain this speed for about half an hour to allow rotor and casing to approach operating temperature. For small turbines, warm-up time will be less, for large turbines, the time could be longer.

10. Slowly increase the rev/min until the governor takes over, and then open the stop valve completely.

11. Slowly adjust the governor to increase the speed until the turbine trips on overspeed, and then adjust the governor back to minimum speed.

12. When the turbine speed has decreased to about 20% below normal operating speed, reset the stop valve and the trip gear.

13. Slowly open the stop valve until the governor take over, open the stop valve completely and adjust the governor to operating speed.

14. If a main oil pump driven by the turbine is installed, the separately driven auxiliary oil pump may now be shut down. Check oil pressures and flows again.

15. Close steam line drains and trap bypasses.

16. Gradually increase the load on the turbine.

17. Enter in the logbook the date, time, and trip rev/min of the turbine.

STOPPING A NONCONDENSING TURBINE

1. Reduce the turbine load to zero.

2. If a separately driven auxiliary oil pump is used, start it.

3. Shut off the steam supply to the turbine by manually closing the throttle valve.

4. Shut off the cooling water to the oil coolers.

5. When the turbine has come to a rest, close the exhaust line valve.

STARTING A CONDENSING & EXTRACTION TURBINE

1. Make sure the main oil tank contains sufficient high quality turbine lubricating oil.

2. Commission the external heating system for the lubricating oil supply tank, if so equipped. The lube oil should be at the minimum temperature recommended by the turbine manufacturer, usually in the 95°F to 105°F range.

3. Start the lubricating oil pump two to three hours before steam is admitted to the turbine. The pump supplies lubricating oil to the bearings in the range of 20 – 25 psi. Check the lube oil return sight glasses to make sure that each bearing is receiving a good supply of oil.

4. Warm up the main supply and extraction steam lines to the turbine by opening drain valves. If slugs of water are admitted into the turbine at high velocity, they can cause severe damage to the rotor.

5. Establish a level in the surface condenser by adding demineralized water. Commission the surface condenser level control system. Continue adding demineralized water until the turbine is operating and producing steam condensate.

6. Start the cooling water pump and establish cooling water flow through the surface condenser, gland steam condenser and the air ejector condenser.

7. Start the extraction (condensate) pump and circulate condensate through the surface and gland steam condensers.

8. Start the jacking oil pump which supplies lubricating oil, at 1,160 to 1,450 psi, to the bottom of the bearings to float and lift the turbine shaft.

9. Commission the turning or barring gear.

10. Commission the unit that the turbine is driving.

11. Admit sealing steam to the turbine glands.

12. Put the air ejector into operation and draw a partial vacuum (-14.7 inches of mercury) on the condenser or start the mechanical vacuum pump.

13. Verify that all the turbine trips have been satisfied and then reset the governor. Watch to make sure that the extraction valves go wide open, which will allow full steam flow to the condensing section of the turbine.

14. Unblock the extraction steam block valve.

15. Open the throttle or steam admission valve just enough to start the turbine rotating. The barring gear will now disengage and automatically shut down.

16. Increase the turbine speed to 200 – 300 r/min. Maintain this speed while checking around the turbine, listening and looking, for any unusual noises or vibrations. Follow the manufacturer's recommended startup procedure.

17. Gradually admit more steam to the turbine to slowly increase the speed. If any unexpected vibrations do occur, then decrease the speed and continue warming up the turbine until it runs smoothly, when the speed is increased again. Monitor the turbine vibration panel, if so equipped.

18. Shut off the supply of demineralized water, once a normal level is established in the surface condenser.

19. When the governor takes over, open the throttle valve completely.

20. When the oil has reached normal operating temperature, admit cooling water to the oil coolers to maintain the desired oil temperature. Shut off the external heating system for the lubricating oil supply tank, if so equipped.

21. All drain valves may now be closed.

22. Adjust the extraction valve to give the desired extraction and condensing flows.

STOPPING A CONDENSING & EXTRACTION TURBINE

1. Gradually reduce the turbine load to zero.

2. Shut off the supply of steam to the turbine by manually closing the main inlet and the extraction block valves.

3. Shut off the air ejectors and break the condenser vacuum.

4. Shut off the gland condenser steam.

5. Open the demineralized water supply and verify that a normal level is being maintained in the surface condenser.

6. Open the steam drain valves.

7. Start the jacking oil pump.

8. Start the turning or barring gear.

9. When the barring gear is up to normal barring speed, shut off the jacking oil pump.

10. When the machine has cooled off, stop the cooling water pump.

11. Keep the turbine barring for 24 hours, then shut down the barring gear. It should disengage automatically, but check for proper disengagement.

12. Shut off the lubricating oil pump.

UNIT 6

Turbine Condenser Systems

Learning Objectives

Here is what you will be able to do when you complete each objective:

1. Explain the purposes of a turbine condenser in a steam plant cycle and describe a typical condensing circuit, with operating temperatures and pressures.
2. Explain the design, operation and applications of the jet condenser, including the ejector type.
3. Explain the design, operation and applications of the surface condenser, including air-cooled and water-cooled, down flow and central flow.
4. Describe construction details for surface condensers, including shells, tube attachment, supports, and allowances for expansion.
5. Explain the effects of air in a condenser and describe the design and operation of single and two-stage air ejectors. Explain the detection of condenser air leaks.
6. Explain the devices and operating considerations used to protect a condenser against high backpressure, high condensate level, and cooling water contamination. Describe a cooling water leak test.
7. Describe the operating conditions and corresponding design considerations for condensate extraction pumps.
8. Describe a feed water heater system in conjunction with a steam condenser and explain the designs of low-pressure and high-pressure feed water heaters.

SIMPLE STEAM PLANT

A large percentage of the electricity generated in the world is produced in power stations using generators driven by steam turbines. Fig. 1 shows a diagram of a simple steam plant. The boiler uses fuel to generate steam and the turbine converts the energy in the steam into mechanical work.

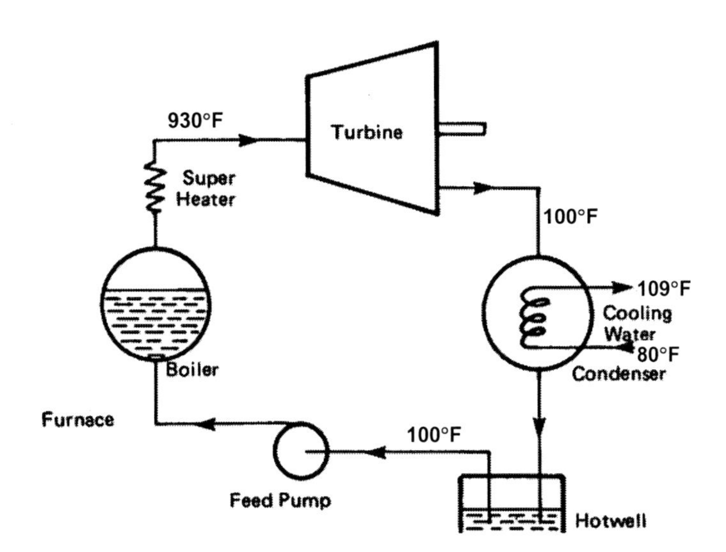

FIGURE 1

Simple Steam Plant Cycle

In a power plant, it is frequently necessary to change the temperature of some substances. In the case of fluids like water, steam, gas, or air this is done by the transfer of heat from one substance to another in a heat exchanger.

In almost all cases, the heat exchanger works on the surface heat transfer method. The two fluids are separated by a good conducting material like brass, copper or cupronickel, and do not come in direct contact with each other.

The basic principles of heat exchange are:

- There is a temperature difference between substances.
- Heat is always transferred from a warm substance to a colder substance.
- The rate of heat transfer depends upon the temperature difference, the area of the transferring surface, and the resistance to the heat transfer of the material separating the two substances.

This can be written as $Q = k \times A \times \Delta T$ where

Q	=	heat transfer, Btu
A	=	area, ft^2
k	=	thermal conductivity, Btu/sq feet hr °F/in
ΔT	=	temperature difference, °F

Consider the case of a condenser receiving the exhaust steam of a turbine. Here the terms of the equation become:

Q	=	heat transfer from steam to cooling water
A	=	area of the condenser tubes heat passes through
k	=	thermal conductivity of condenser tube walls (including scale, etc.)
ΔT	=	temperature difference between exhaust steam and cooling water

CONDENSERS

The largest heat exchanger in a steam plant is the condenser. It is necessary to condense the steam back to water, after completion of its work in the turbine, because it can only be returned to the boiler as a liquid.

The necessity of condensing the steam is the cause of the largest single heat loss in the steam power cycle. The latent heat of the steam entering the condenser is transferred to the cooling water and dissipated to the atmosphere via the cooling tower, river, lake or ocean.

The above statement applies to a plant using a condensing cycle. When the exhaust steam can be used for heating or process work, the overall plant efficiency is considerably higher. Typical figures for plant thermal efficiencies are 20% when exhausting to atmosphere, 30% when condensing, and 80% or better when the exhaust steam is used for heating or process work.

These figures indicate that the efficiency of a turbine exhausting to the atmosphere may be increased by 50% with the addition of a condenser. The figures also show that in the turbine with a condenser, one third of the work is done by the low-pressure turbine, at pressures below atmospheric pressure.

When the load on the turbine increases, the steam flow also increases and therefore the heat to be transferred (Q) increases. In order to balance the increase in (Q) there must be an equal increase on the other side of the equation. The thermal conductivity (k) of the tubes is fixed and so is the area (A); the only variable is the temperature difference (ΔT) and this must therefore increase.

The cooling water inlet temperature will remain constant, so the necessary increase in the temperature difference can only be an increase in the turbine exhaust temperature. Increased turbine exhaust temperature is the same as saying that the turbine exhaust pressure in increased, or that the condenser operates at a reduced vacuum.

Condensation of the steam in a steam plant cycle must take place at the lowest practicable absolute pressure to enable the prime mover to extract the maximum amount of work from each lb of steam before being condensed. Thus the condenser must be capable of maintaining a vacuum while handling a full load of exhaust steam flow from the prime mover. It will do this most efficiently if only the latent heat is removed and none of the sensible heat, that is, the condensate temperature should be as near as possible to the entering steam temperature.

Further, the cooling water, which is circulated through the condenser, will be most efficiently used when there is a minimum difference between its leaving temperature and the temperature of the entering steam. The condenser, in addition to its function of condensing exhaust steam, can be said to conserve pure feed water by returning all of the condensate to the feed system and also to act as a very efficient deaerator in the condensate circuit.

CONDENSER TYPES

Condensers can be divided into two main groups "Contact" and "Surface". The first, generally called "Jet" condensers, operate by bringing exhaust steam and cooling water into *direct contact* with each other. The steam mixes with the cooling water, condenses, and the resulting condensate leaves the condenser with the cooling water.

The most common is the *surface condenser*. The second type interposes a surface between the exhaust steam and the cooling water so that they are never in contact with each other. The cooling water is circulated through large numbers of small diameter tubes. The exhaust steam flows over and around the tubes, and the condensate is collected from the bottom of the condenser shell. Both of these condenser types can be subdivided, with each type having a specific application.

Jet Condensers

Jet condensers use the principle of spraying cooling water into direct contact with the incoming exhaust steam in order to condense it. The combined cooling water (coolant) and condensed steam (condensate) drain to the hotwell.

FIGURE 2

Jet Condenser

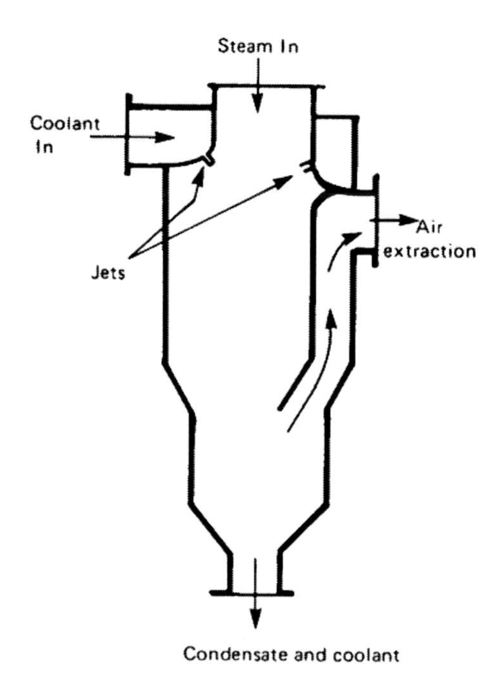

The feed pump takes suction from the hotwell the quantity of feed required by the boiler. The remainder overflows into the cooling pond where it is cooled and returned to the condenser as cooling water. This arrangement has the definite disadvantage that the entire cooling water quantity must be chemically treated to maintain boiler feed water purity. For this reason there are very few jet condensers in operation today.

Fig. 3 shows two different applications of jet condensers. Fig. 3a is direct contact condenser called a low-level jet condenser, using a pump to remove the water from the condenser. The air and condensate are pumped from the condenser. The cooling water flow is induced to flow by the condenser vacuum.

FIGURE 3

Jet Condenser Applications

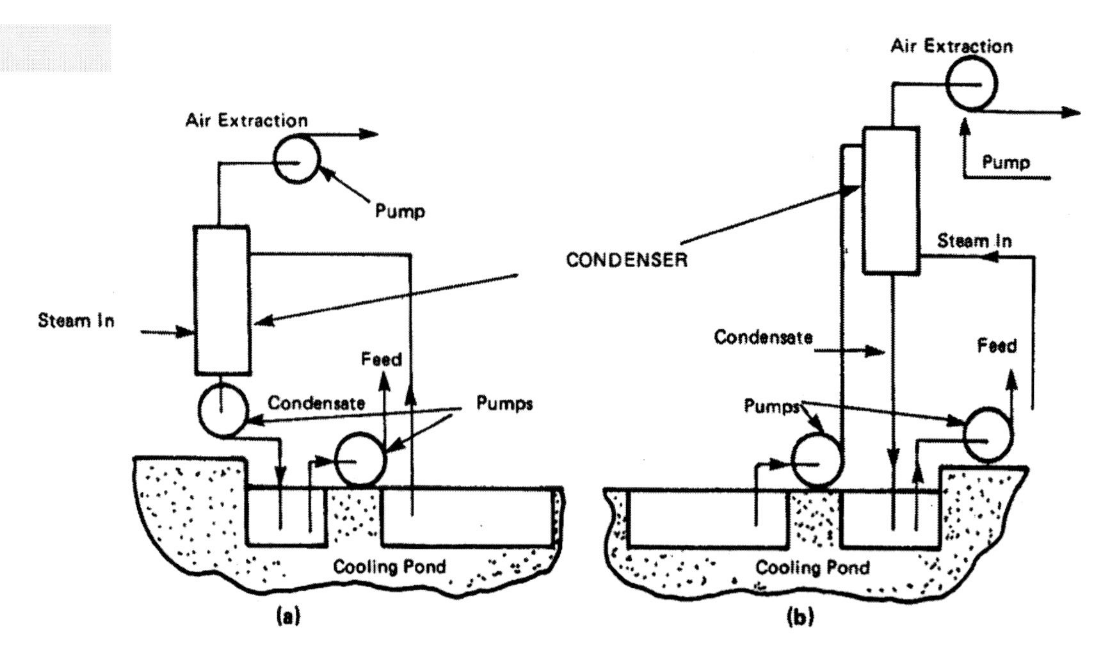

In Fig. 3b the condenser sits about 34 ft above the level of the hotwell. The head of water (condensate and coolant) in the discharge pipe is sufficient to cause it to fall into the hotwell against the vacuum in the condenser, without pumping. This is a so-called "barometric leg". The cooling water must be pumped into the condenser and the air pumped out.

Barometric Jet Condensers

Condensers operating with direct contact between steam and water (jet condensers) may use a pump to remove the water from the condenser body. They are called low-level jet condensers. The body may be set at sufficient height above the hotwell that the water will flow out by gravity, in which case they are known as barometric condensers.

The necessary length of tail pipe for a barometric condenser will depend upon atmospheric conditions, and the vacuum carried in the condenser, but will be about 34 ft between body and hotwell. Fig. 3b shows the layout of a barometric condenser. Cooling water flows through jets from the cooling-water inlet and falls at right angles to the steam inlet.

Fig. 4 illustrates a variation of the barometric condenser. The tail pipe carries the cooling water and the condensate as before; the air and non-condensable gases, however, are drawn from the top of the condensing space by steam ejectors.

FIGURE 4
Barometric Condenser

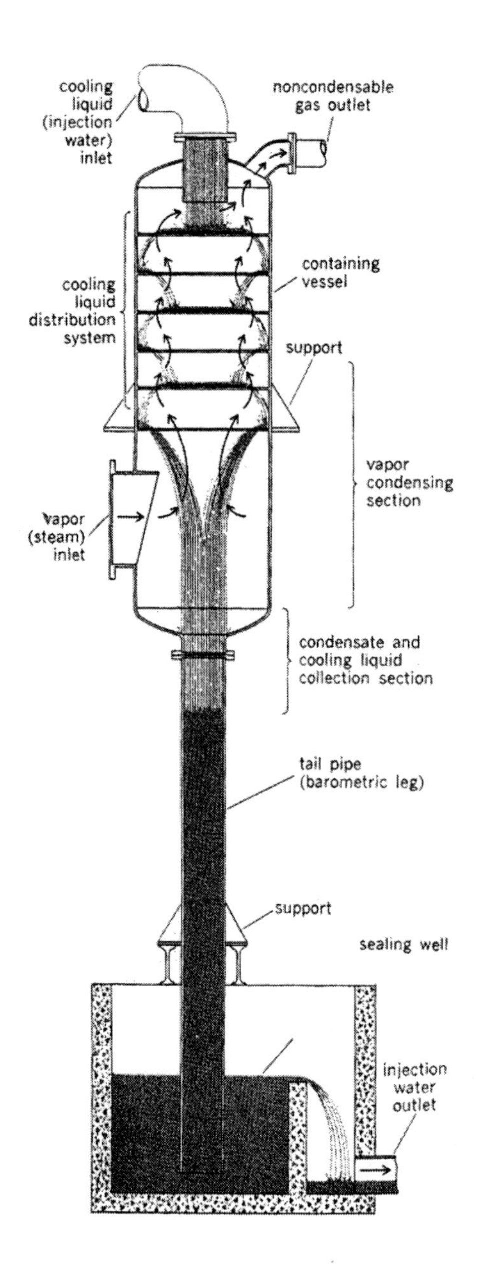

Ejector Condenser

Another direct contact type of condenser is called an *ejector condenser*, which is a special form of jet condenser. The cooling water flows into the condenser body through a series of convergent nozzles, which increase its velocity; steam exhaust is induced into this cooling water flow and condensed by direct mixing. The ejector condenser is suitable only for moderate vacuum. Fig. 5 illustrates the ejector condenser.

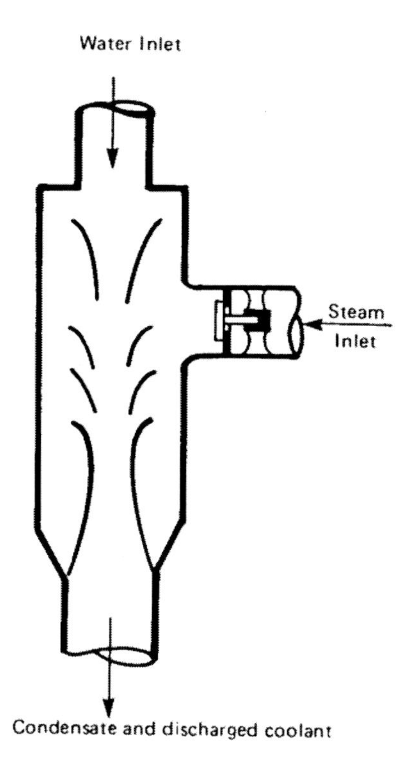

FIGURE 5

Ejector Condenser

THE SURFACE CONDENSER

The main purposes of a surface condenser are:

- To produce and maintain a vacuum at the turbine exhaust, allowing the steam to expand to a lower pressure and do more work.
- To conserve pure water for boiler feedwater, by condensing the exhaust steam to feedwater for the boiler.
- To act as a deaerator, by removing air and other gases from the condensate.

Fig. 6 shows a facility with a surface condenser, using river water for cooling. Fig. 7 shows the layout of the condenser circulating cooling water in a plant using cooling towers.

The condenser shown in Fig. 8 is air-cooled using finned tubes. The steam flows inside the tubes and air flows around the tubes. Finned air cooled tube construction is shown in Fig. 9.

FIGURE 6

River Water Cooled Condenser

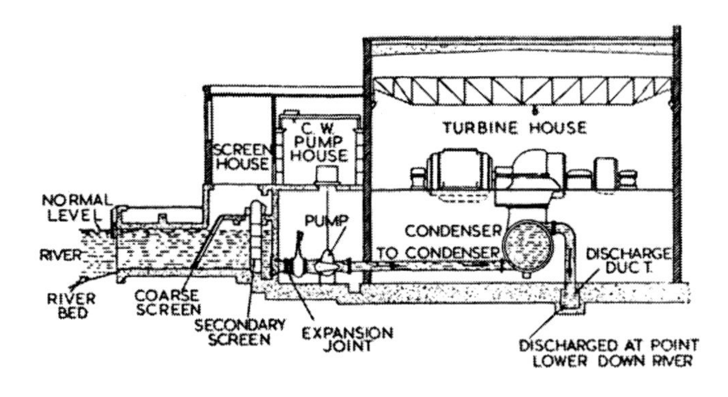

FIGURE 7

Condenser Using Cooling Water from Cooling Tower

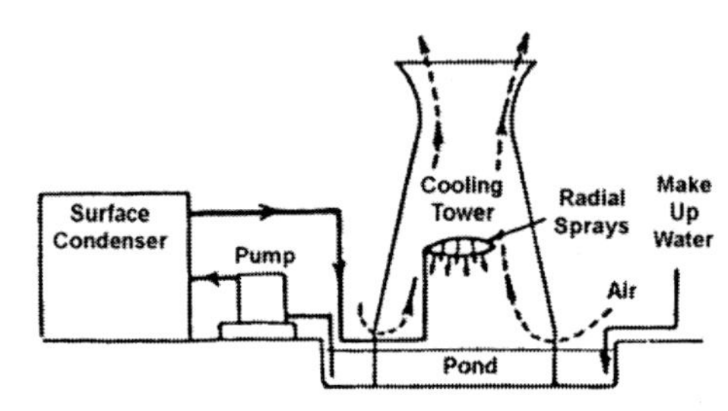

FIGURE 8

Air Cooled Condenser

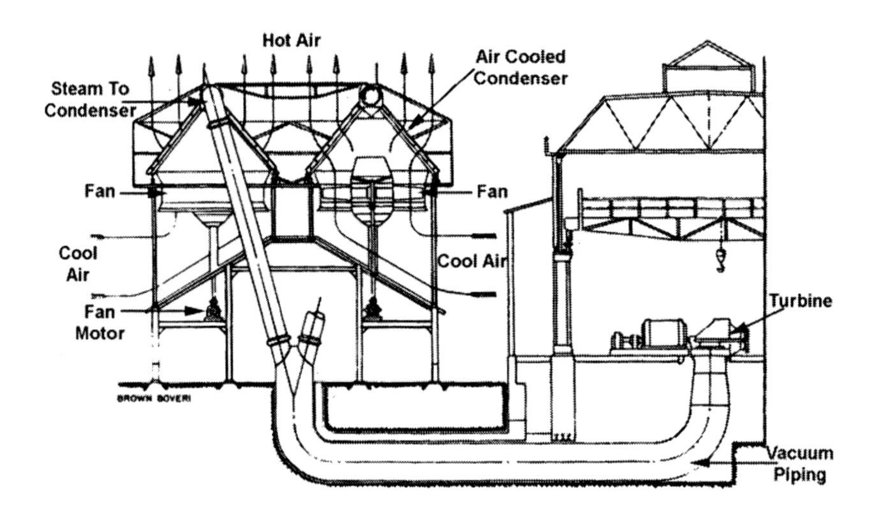

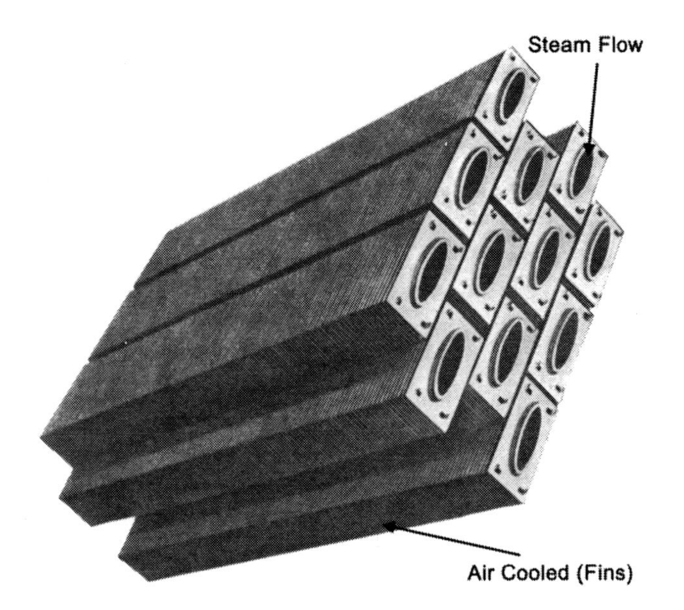

FIGURE 9

Nest of Finned Air Cooled Tubes

Down Flow Condensers

The downflow condenser illustrated in Fig. 10 has the vapor inlet at one end and the noncondensable gas outlet at the other end. The steam flow is directed through the tubes by baffles. Condensate drains into the hotwell. The cooling water enters the top of the water box. The cooling water makes four passes through the exchanger before exiting at the bottom of the shell. The tubes are the U-tube design.

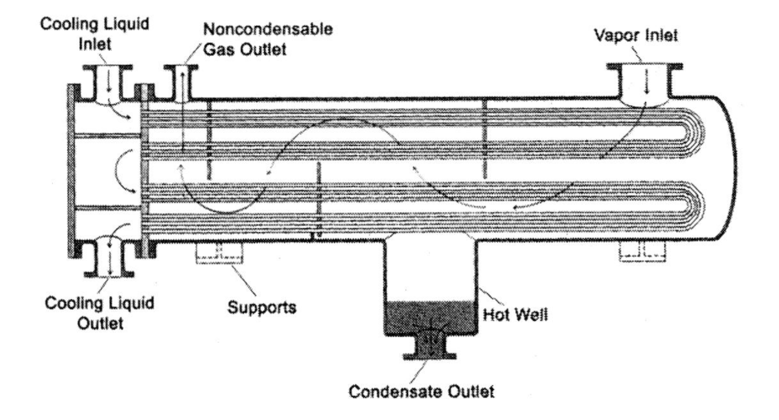

FIGURE 10

Surface Condenser (Downflow Design)

Fig. 11 shows a downflow condenser, where the steam enters the center of the shell. It has vertical steam lanes supplying the hot well with steam for heating, and deaerating the condensate cascading into the hotwell. Note that in downflow condensers, the descending steam is forced into the center by the air extraction baffles, and the rising air and gases are forced in under the baffles.

The heavy construction of tubes, under the air suction baffles, prevent the steam from entering the air removal equipment (ejectors or mechanical pumps). This can cause poor vacuum when starting the turbine.

FIGURE 11

Downflow Condenser

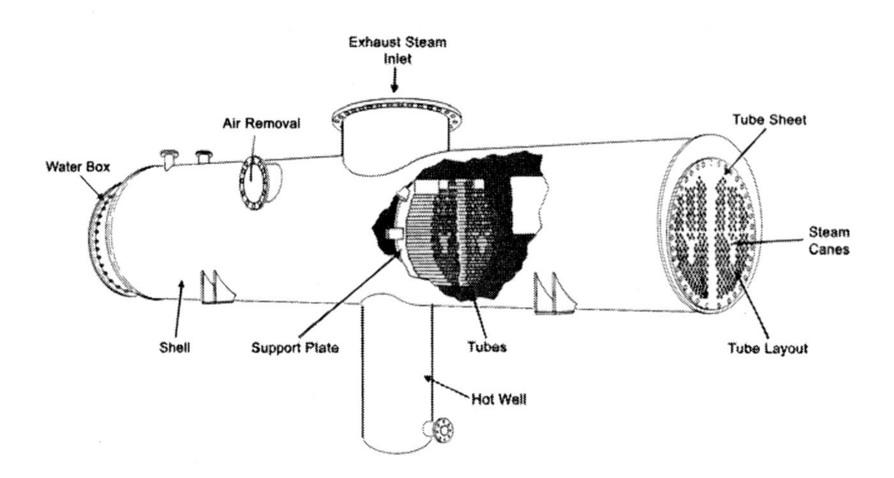

The exhaust steam is admitted to the top of he condenser in Fig. 12, which is a shell and tube type cross flow heat exchanger. Cooling water flows through the tubes and extracts heat from the steam, which is on the shell side. The steam condenses on the surface of the water tubes. The condensate formed falls to the hotwell. A controlled water level is maintained in the hotwell. This cross-section shows the steam lanes, which allow steam to the bottom areas of the condenser. Air outlets are under baffles near the bottom of the condenser. This design has a center steam lane allowing steam to reach the hotwell and maintain the condensate temperature near the saturation temperature.

FIGURE 12

Downflow Condenser

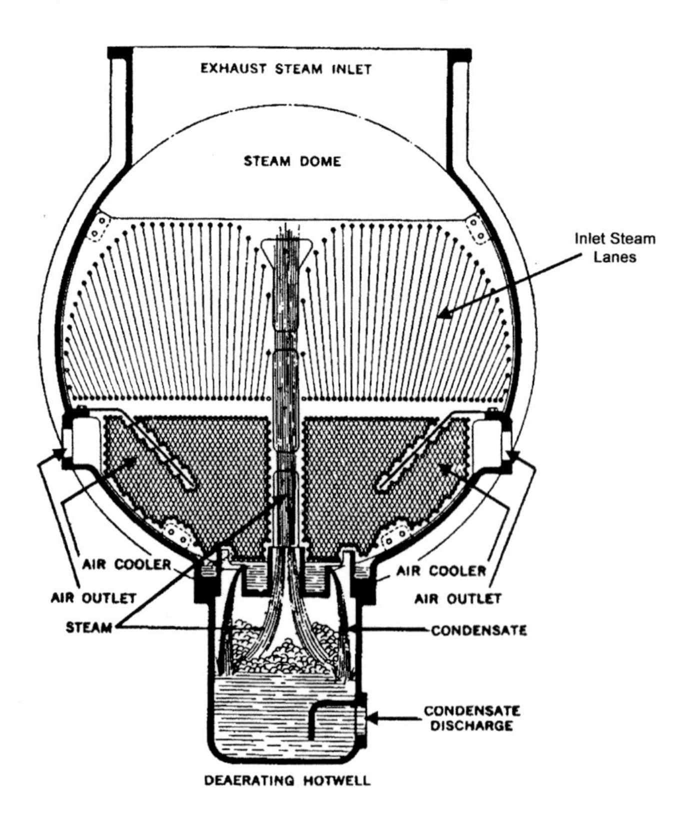

Central Flow Condensers

Fig. 13 shows a central or radial flow condenser where the steam flow is toward the center of the condenser. Steam will always flow toward the coldest area, as it has the lowest pressure. For this reason, the central flow condenser will have the first pass of the cooling water at the center. The condenser has two passes; the first under the inverted "V" shaped baffle and the return pass outside the baffle. Air extraction is from the center of the tube nest in which case the steam flows radially through the tubes, giving the type of the name "central flow".

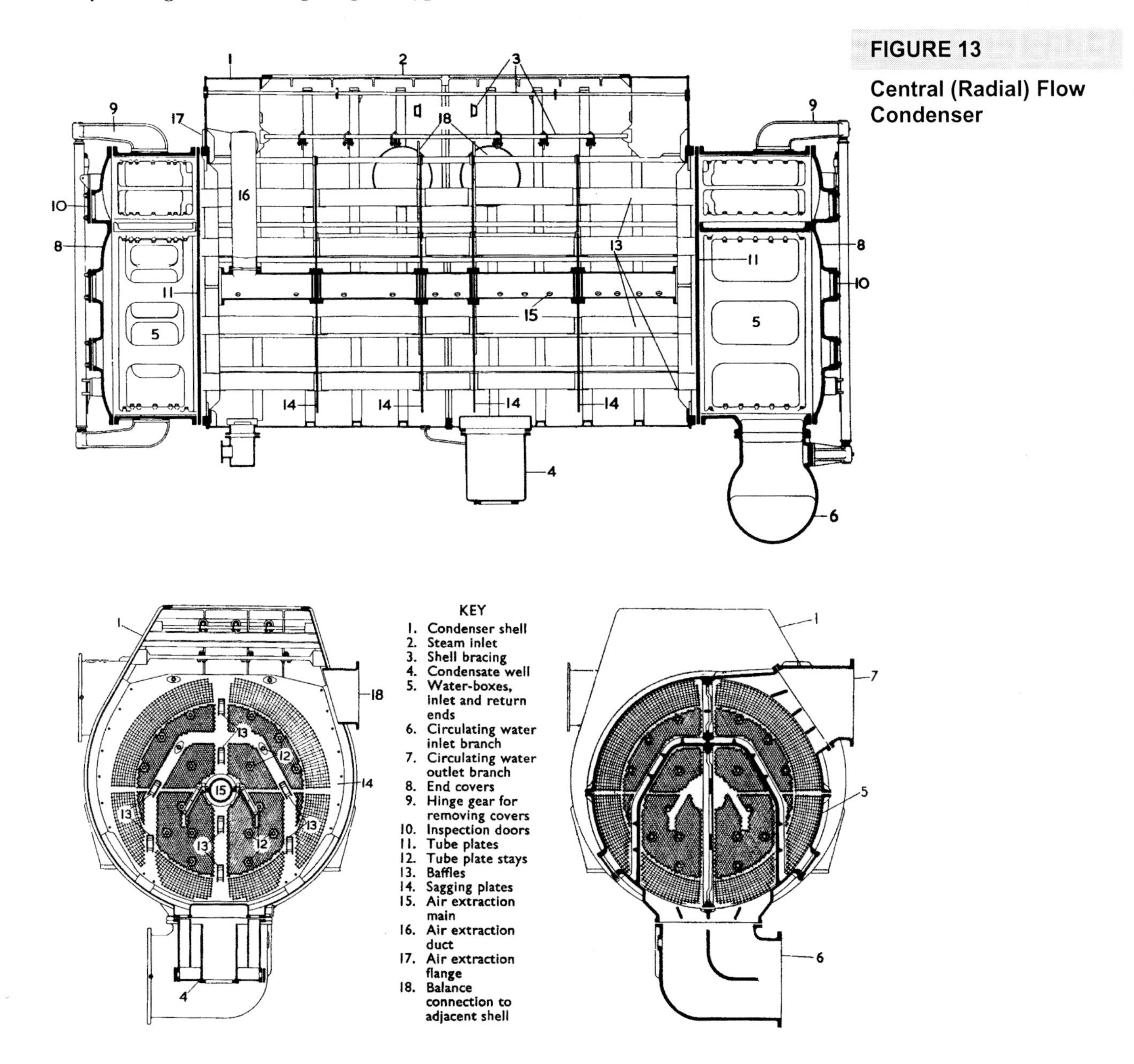

FIGURE 13

Central (Radial) Flow Condenser

Fig. 14 shows a large, single pass, radial flow condenser. The wide spacing between and around the tube banks prevents subcooling. Air extraction is from the center of each tube bank.

FIGURE 14

Tube Bank Pattern of Large Radial Flow Condenser

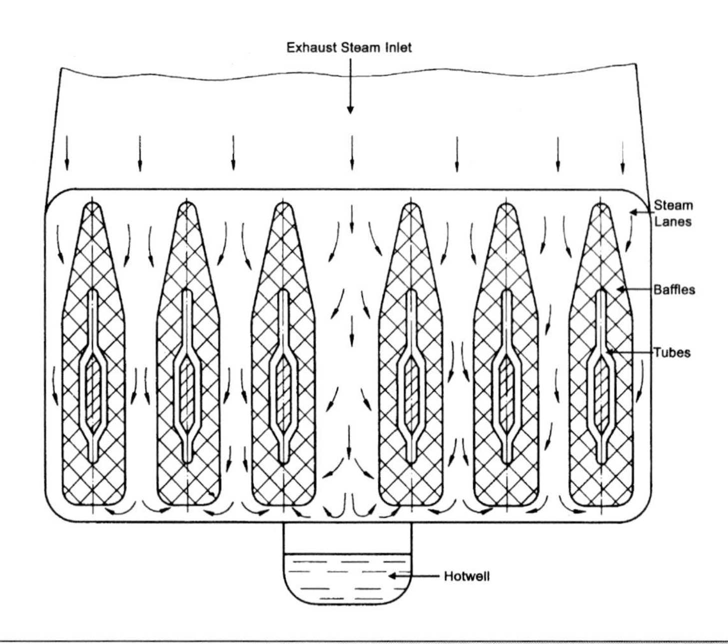

CONDENSER CONSTRUCTION

Fig. 15 shows a surface condenser and its components. This is a downflow design with steam entering at the top. The hotwell is at the bottom, with two condensate pump connections. Each side of the condenser has an air ejector connection. The cooling water enters at the top of the water box and exits the same end at the bottom of the water box.

FIGURE 15

Surface Condenser

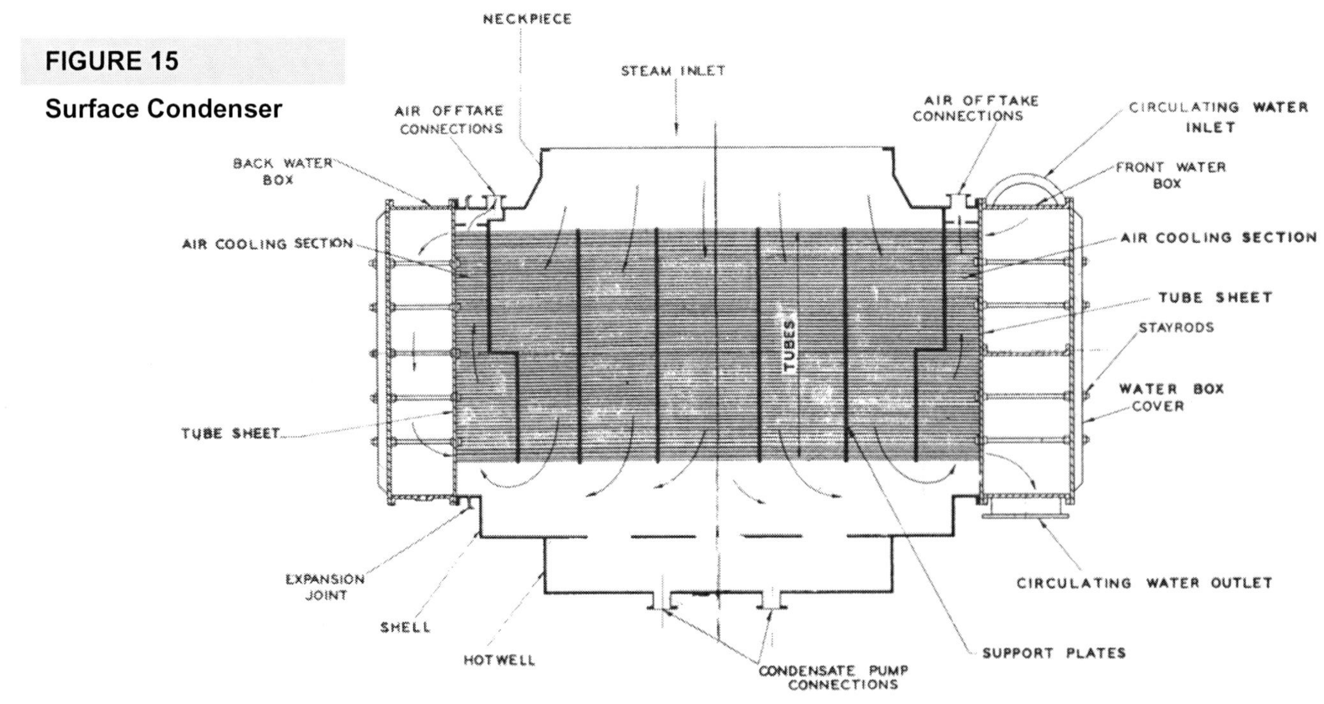

The Condenser Shell

The shape of the shell can be cylindrical, oval, or rectangular (for large shells). The shell is welded steel and reinforced with external ribs. The exhaust neck and hot well are welded steel and reinforced with external ribs. The exhaust neck and hot well are welded to the shell. The support plates, welded to the shell, support both the shell and the tubes, and dampen the tube vibrations.

Provision must be made for relative movement between the exhaust flange and the machine foundations. In the smaller designs, this is done by bolting the condenser feet rigidly to the foundations and fitting an expansion joint, such as a corrugated bellows piece between the exhaust flange and the condenser inlet flange. Larger designs bolt the condenser directly to the machine exhaust but support the condenser feet on springs.

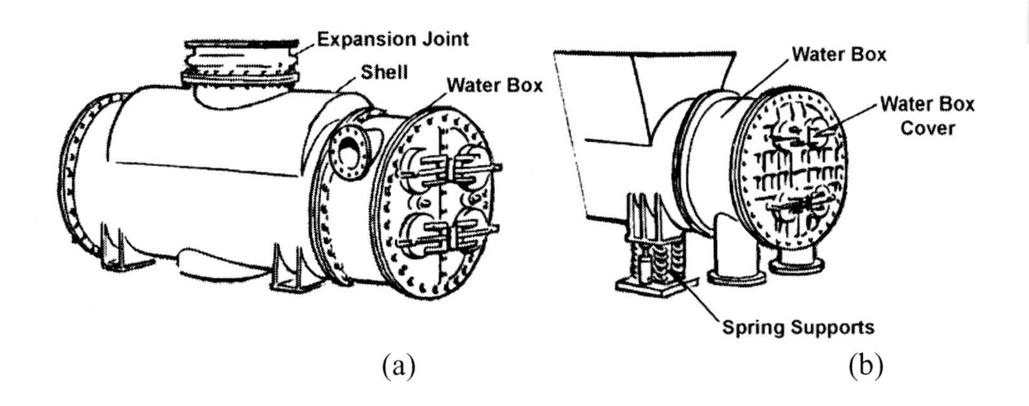

FIGURE 16

Condenser Expansion Joint and Spring Supports

The condenser shell in Fig. 16(a) sits on a solid foundation has an expansion joint between the shell and the turbine. The condenser in Fig. 16(b) is mounted on spring support feet.

The shell may also be fitted with an expansion joint to allow longitudinal movement. This is done when the design calls for the tubes to be expanded into their tube sheets at both ends and relative movement between shell and tubes must be accommodated. Fig. 17 shows how a tube is attached to condenser tube sheets. In this case, an expansion joint in the shell is used.

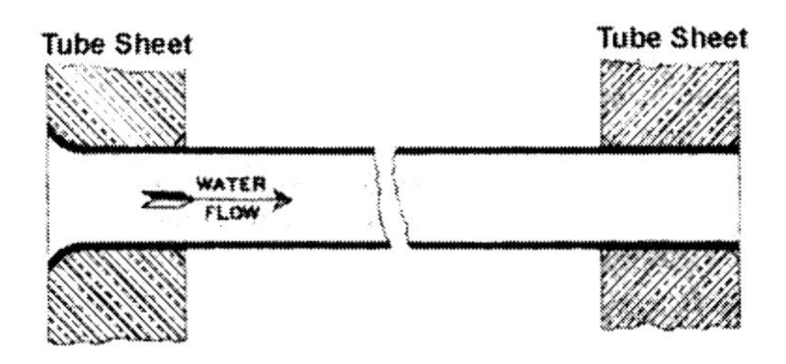

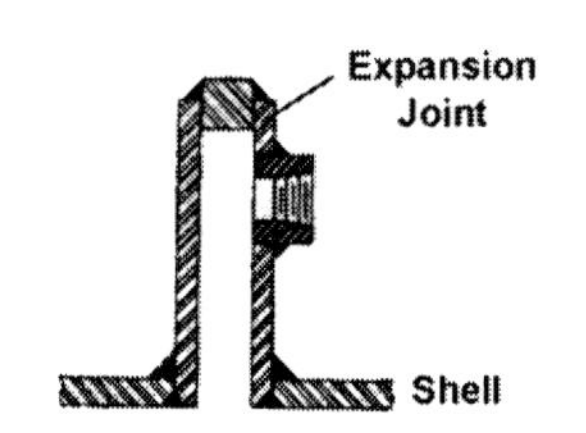

FIGURE 17

Expanded Condenser Tube and Condenser Shell Expansion Joint

Condenser Tube Plates

Condenser tube sheets or plates are usually Admiralty brass or Muntz metal, 1 to 1 ¾ inches (25 to 40 mm) thick. They are bolted to the shell flanges with collar bolts (Fig. 18). Rubber gaskets are used between the shell and tube plate, and between the tube plate and water box. The collar bolts fasten the tube plates, and when the tubing is finished, the water box is placed over the collar bolts and fastened. The collar bolts allow opening of the water box, without disturbing the shell and tube plate joint.

FIGURE 18

Collar Bolt

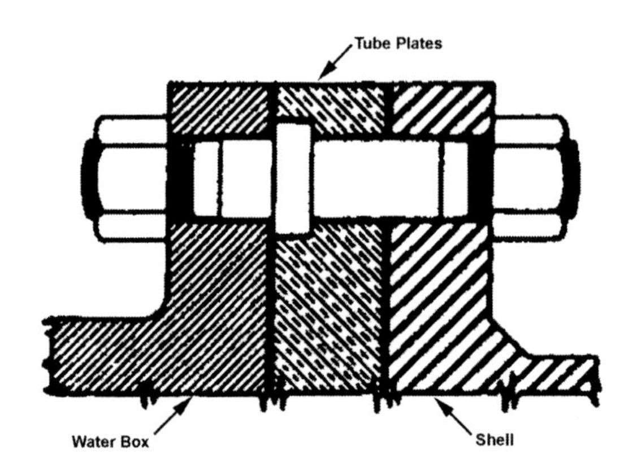

Tube plates of brass or Muntz metal, for large condensers, are very expensive and may not be available in the required sizes. The problem has been solved with the use of welded steel plates with stainless steel cladding. A welded water box showing the tube plate welded in position and the protective coating on the waterside is shown in Fig. 19. The tube plate is clad with stainless steel on the waterside.

FIGURE 19

Water Box Construction

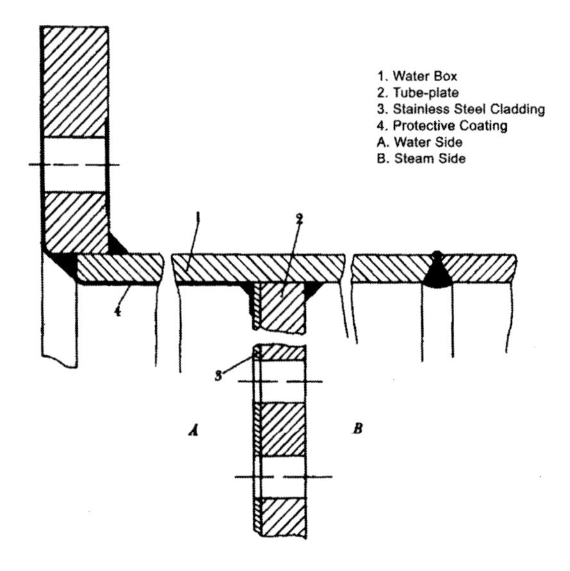

Condenser Tubes

A large heating surface can most easily be obtained with small diameter tubing, which also gives the best heat transfer, as the required wall thickness is very small. The tubes may be of Stainless Steel, Admiralty brass, aluminium brass, or cupronickel. The tubes are available in a variety of sizes up to an 1 inch. The larger condensers use the larger tubes.

The tubes can be installed with ferrules, metallic and fiber packings, by roll expanding, or with combinations such as inlet end expanded and belled and the outlet end packed or ferruled (Figs. 20 and 21). In some condensers, the tubes are welded into the tube plate, when plates and tubes are of essentially the same material.

Allowance must be made for differential expansion of tubes and shell. Packed tube ends may allow the tube to move axially in the packing. For expanded or welded tubes, the shell may be equipped with an expansion joint or some other method of allowing for expansion, as shown in Fig. 17.

FIGURE 20

Tube End Fastening Methods

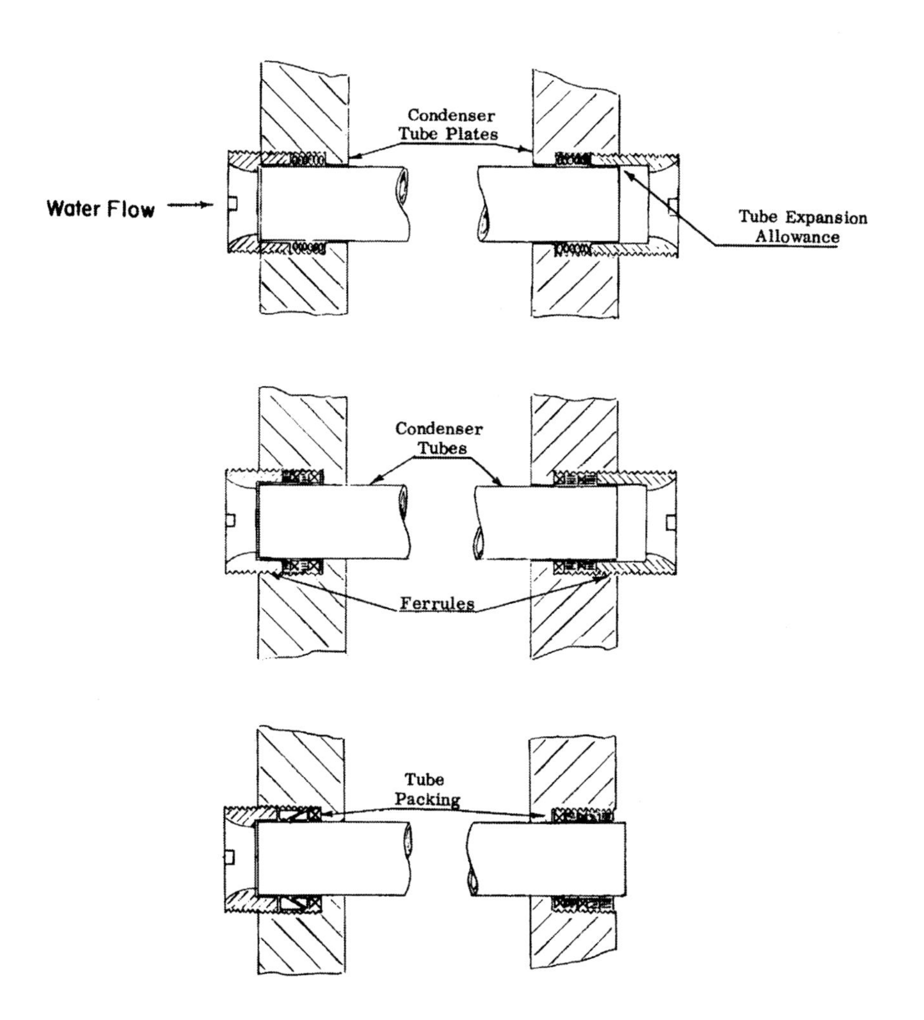

FIGURE 21

Tube End Fastening Methods

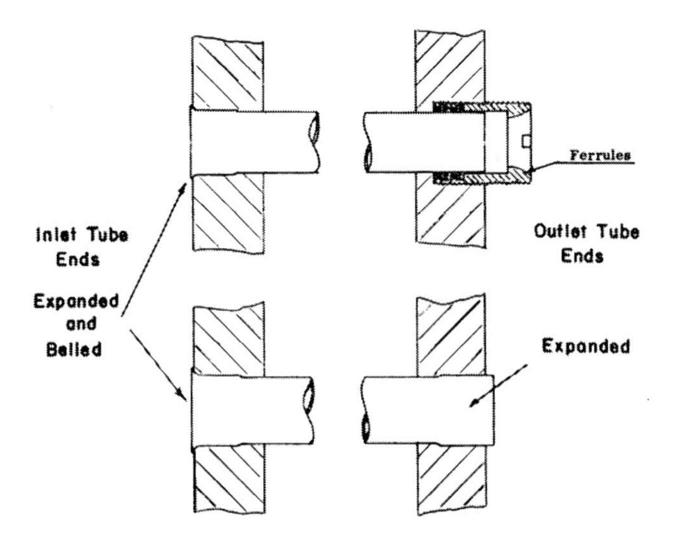

Water Boxes

The classic material for water boxes is cast iron. Water boxes are usually bolted to the shell with the tube plate collar bolts (Fig. 18). Hinged end covers allow tube replacement. Large water boxes have inspection doors for inspection, tube cleaning and tube plugging.

The water boxes of large condensers are, for both economical and practical reasons, of fabricated steel, and either welded to the shell or an integral part of the shell as shown in Fig. 19. Because seawater is used for cooling water in this condenser, the water box has a coating of rubber or glass-fiber reinforced epoxy resin as corrosion protection.

The main purpose of the stay bolts, or stay rods in the water boxes (Fig. 15) is not, as it might seem, to support the water box cover and the tube sheet against the pressure of the cooling water, but to support the tube sheet against the condenser vacuum.

AIR EJECTORS

The pressure within a condenser shell is well below that of the surrounding atmosphere and this induces atmospheric-air leakage through glands, joints, and flanges. Other non-condensable gases may be carried in with the steam from the boilers although modern dearators and chemical feedwater treatment has reduced these to a minimum. All gases are poor heat conductors and, if allowed to accumulate, will soon blanket the condenser tube surfaces.

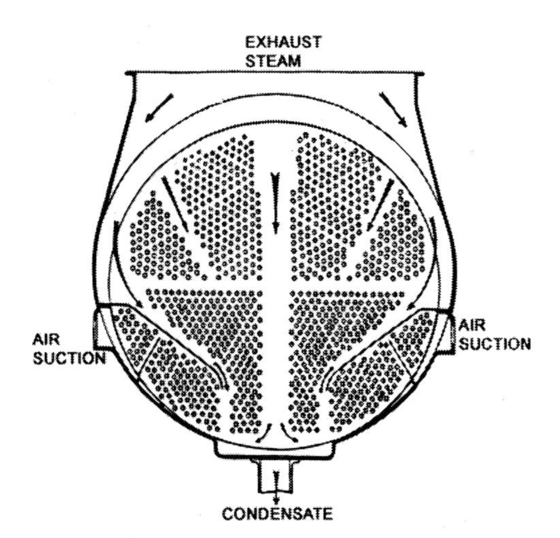

FIGURE 22

Typical Surface Condenser

These small air quantities accumulate in the steam space of the condenser and must be removed continuously as the absolute pressure in the condenser according to Dalton's Law is the sum of all partial pressures or the sum of the steam pressure and the air pressure; thus the air increases the condenser pressure and may air blanket part of the cooling surface.

The usual means of extracting such air is by means of an air ejector, although in some cases an air pump, either reciprocating or rotary, may be used for this purpose. The condenser in Fig. 22 shows the air extraction points. These are taken from below baffle plates specifically located to trap these gases. One of the most commonly used items of equipment for continuous removal of these gases is the steam-jet ejector. Fig. 23 shows an external view, and Fig. 24 a cross-sectional view of a single-stage ejector.

In the air ejector, high-pressure steam is allowed to expand through a nozzle, thus converting its heat energy into kinetic energy and producing a high velocity jet at the nozzle discharge. This jet is used to entrain air and other non-condensables and draw them from the condenser space. Most condensers have baffle plates to guide the air to special air coolers at the air extraction points.

FIGURE 23

Single-Stage Steam-Jet Ejector

FIGURE 24

Sectional View of Ejector

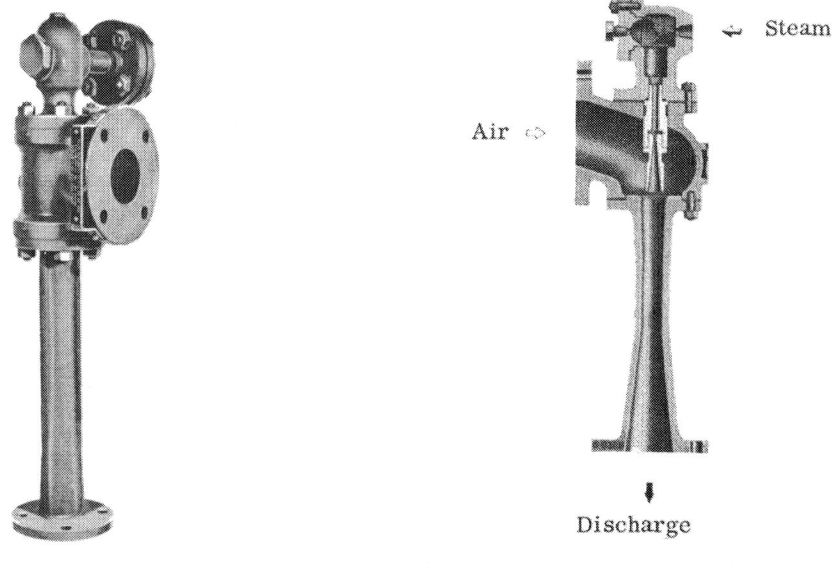

Figure 23 *Figure 24*

Fig. 25 shows a two-stage steam-operated air ejector. High-pressure steam is supplied to both nozzles and allowed to expand through a small orifice. The resulting high velocity steam entrains gases from the condenser and carries them into the first stage shell-and-tube condenser. Here the steam is condensed and the remaining gases are drawn off again by being entrained in the steam jet from the second stage nozzle.

FIGURE 25

Two-Stage Steam Ejector

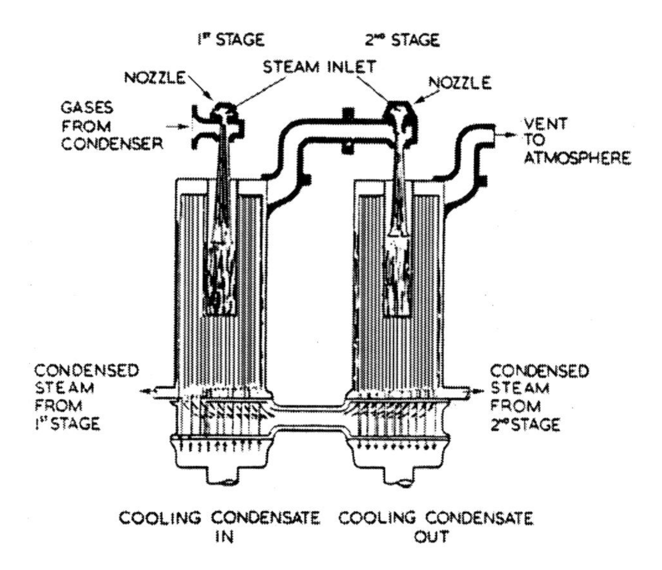

The steam is condensed in this stage but here the pressure is slightly above atmospheric. The remaining air and other gases are vented to atmosphere.

The water used to cool the ejector steam is often boiler feedwater. It can also be cooling water. When feedwater is used, the heat gained by condensing the ejector steam is absorbed into the feed water (or condensate) in its passage between the extraction pumps and the boiler feed pumps. Thus the ejector becomes, in effect, another feed heater; so the heat in the steam used is not wasted.

The orifice in the ejector nozzle is small and care must be taken to see that it does not become choked with foreign matter from the steam supply pipes. A fine mesh steam strainer is usually fitted upstream of the nozzles for this reason.

Referring to Fig. 26, high-pressure steam enters at A and passes through nozzle B. The high-pressure steam passing through C and the venturi section (E), draw the gases from the condenser into the ejector through D. The steam and condenser gases are directed over the outer tubes (F) several times by the baffles (K). The steam is condensed by the cooling water and the gases from the condenser leave the first stage and enter the second stage through G. This process is repeated in the second stage, with the gases being vented to atmosphere through L.

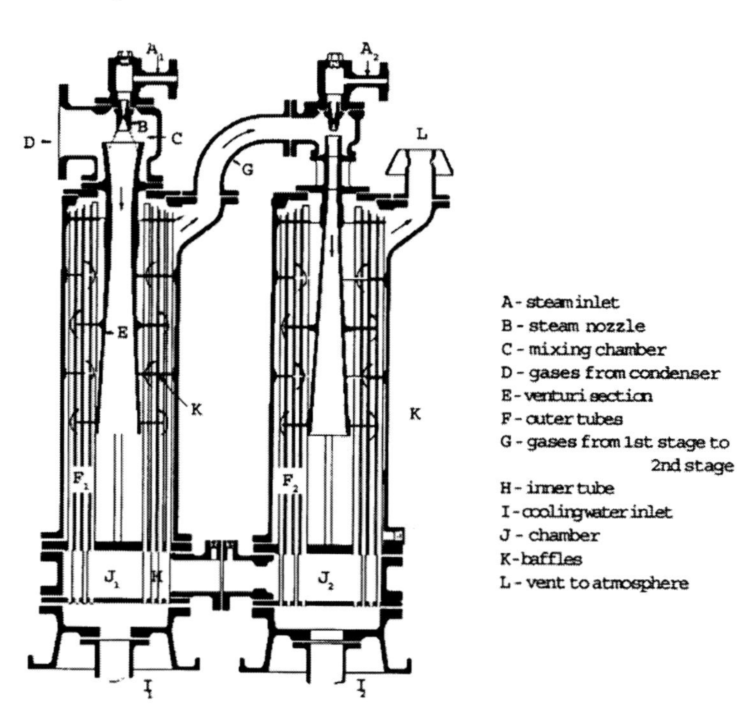

FIGURE 26

Two-Stage Steam-Jet Air Ejector

The cooling water for the ejector cooler in Fig. 26 is condensate from the extraction pump. The cooling water enters at I_1, and flows up through the inner tubes (H) to the top of the outer tubes (F). The closed top sends the water back down through the outer tubes (F), to the first chamber (J_1), and then to the second chamber (J_2). From J_2, the water flows up the outer tubes and down the inner tubes, leaving the second stage at I_2.

The use of condensate makes the ejector coolers function as feedwater heaters recovering heat losses from the steam jet.

FIGURE 27

Flow Diagram

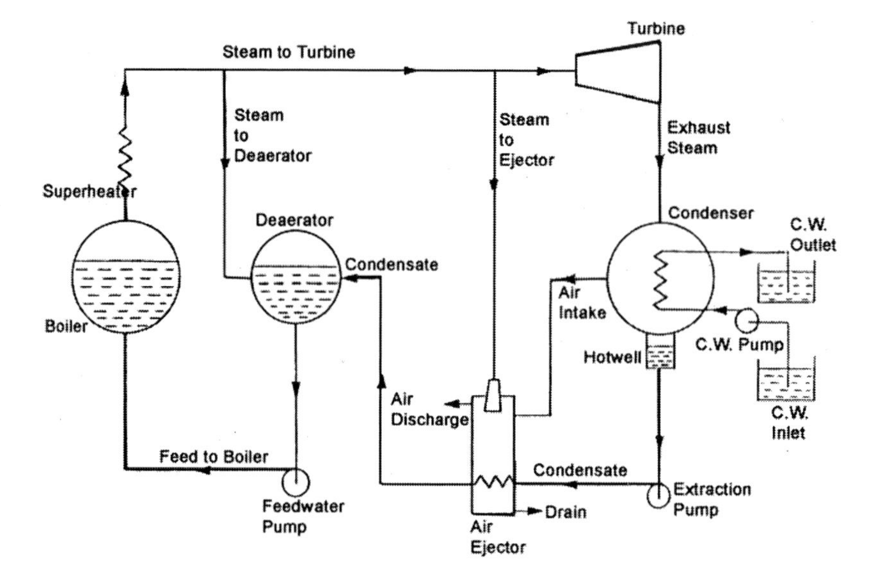

Fig. 27 is a simplified flow diagram showing the arrangement of the various components, including extraction pump and air ejector. In this example, condensate from the extraction pump is used to cool the air ejectors. Steam is supplied from the turbine supply line. This is a simplification as steam pressure to ejectors is usually 50 psi to 145 psi.

For high vacuum, three-stage ejectors (Fig. 28) are used. Each stage has its own condenser. The condensers may be separate heat exchangers or they may be contained in a single heat exchanger, as in Fig. 28.

Separate drains drain condensate from the three stages of the air ejector condenser to the hotwell of the main condenser. To prevent air being sucked into the hotwell, a steam trap is provided in the third stage drain line, and 6-foot U-bends are provided in the 1st and 2nd stage drain lines.

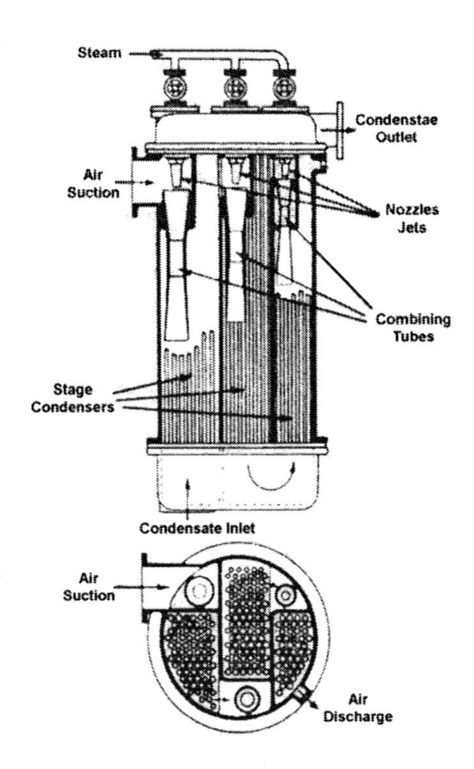

FIGURE 28

Three-Stage Steam-Jet Ejector

AIR LEAKS

Air leaks can be quite large, up to 5 mm in diameter, before they interfere with the vacuum, as the air ejector can usually handle the air from smaller leaks. Air leaks can only be detected by shutting down both turbine and condenser, and filling the low-pressure heaters and the condenser steam space with water. The size of the leaks will usually make them easy to locate.
Common locations for air leaks are:

- Flanges with vacuum on one side and atmospheric pressure on the other
- Valves under vacuum. Their flanges or packing glands may leak
- Suction side shaft packing or seals on extraction pumps
- Turbine shafts under vacuum pressure, with low seal steam pressure

Methods of identifying air leaks while the equipment is running include:

- Taping all suspect flanges
- Tightening all valve packing
- Using smoke or shaving cream to detect leakage points
- Using ultrasonic listening devices

Air leaks will affect condenser performance as indicated by increased condenser pressure but little or no increase in condensate temperature. These small air quantities accumulate in the steam space of the condenser and thus decrease the plant efficiency.

CONDENSER SAFETY DEVICES

A condenser would not be complete without certain safety devices, designed to protect both the condenser and the turbine exhausting into it, against possible operating troubles. The main dangers to be guarded against are: an increase in backpressure, a rise in condensate level, and contamination of condensate.

Atmospheric Relief Valve

The condenser is a closed vessel and therefore it would be possible for the backpressure to rise until it was above atmospheric pressure if, for example, the cooling water flow stopped while the condenser was on load. A condenser shell is not designed to withstand a pressure from the inside and would soon fail.

The atmospheric relief valve is designed to open if the pressure in the condenser rises above atmospheric and allows steam to escape from the shell. Under normal operating conditions this valve is held closed by the difference in pressure between the atmospheric pressure outside and the vacuum in the shell. In order to ensure that air does not leak past the valve into the condenser, it is usually fitted with a water seal. It usually has a test lever and should be tested at frequent intervals when the machine is off load. This ensures the valve is operating freely.

Since the purpose of the atmospheric relief valve is to vent the full flow of exhaust steam to atmosphere, it is very large.

For large condensers the atmospheric relief valve is replaced with explosion diaphragms or rupture discs on all L.P. turbine exhausts. Other protective devices for condenser pressure are: vacuum pay-off relays and vacuum trip relays. The vacuum pay-off relay is incorporated in the turbine governor system and is usually set to operate between 1.5 psi and 6 psi absolute pressure. Unloading of the turbine begins at 1.5 psi and the turbine is fully unloaded at 6 psi. The vacuum trip relay is set to trip the turbine at 7 psi.

Condenser gauge Glass

The gauge glass gives a clear indication of the level of the condensate in the condenser hotwell. The top and bottom of the glass are connected above and below the water level and the whole of the fitting operates under condenser vacuum.

Care must be taken to see that there are no air-leaks in the fitting, particularly through the cocks or valves.

High Water-Level Alarm

The gauge glass is often supplemented by a float operated, high water-level alarm.

A steadily rising condensate level would seal off the air outlet, fill the vacuum space with noncondensable gases, increase the back pressure of the exhaust steam, and decrease turbine output by activating the vacuum unloader relay.

DETECTION OF COOLING WATER LEAKS

If a condenser tube is damaged or a ferrule begins to leak, cooling water may leak into the steam space and contaminate the condensate. Leaks must be quickly detected and corrected. Several methods can be used to detect leaks, with the electrical purity method (conductivity) being the most common.

Very pure water, like condensate, is a nonconductor of electricity, while impure water, like cooling water, is a good conductor. A conductivity meter can detect changes in the conductivity of the condensate and so detect leaks.

Sodium chloride in water can be detected by the silver nitrate test. The addition of a few drops of silver nitrate to salt water immediately creates a milky-white silver chloride precipitate. This is a simple and sensitive test for leakage of salt water into a condenser and is used when the cooling water is salty.

Very small leaks can be tolerated, if the condensate is cleaned up condensate polishers. When the leak is larger than the polishers can handle, the leak must be repaired.

REPAIR OF COOLING WATER LEAKS

Single flow type condensers must be taken out of service for repairs. When the turbine is shut down, the water boxes can be drained and the inspection doors opened.

The steam space is filled with clean water, after the supporting or jackscrews are applied to carry the weight of the condenser. When the steam space is full of water, the water will leak out of the leaky tube. Since leaks detected by the conductivity meter may be very small, fluorescein dye (about 10 ppm) can be added to aid detection. The dye glows a fluorescent green in the light of an ultraviolet ray lamp.

Large condensers are usually double flow, with tubes expanded at both ends. They can be repaired at half load or less. Usually one side is drained and a measurement of conductivity indicates if the leaky side is the side still in service or not.

EXTRACTION OR CONDENSATE PUMPS

The extraction or condensate pump continuously pumps condensate from the condenser hotwell, through the air ejector coolers and low-pressure heaters, into the deaerator.

Extraction pumps are usually centrifugal pumps with two or three stages. Fig. 29 is a two-impeller horizontal extraction pump with opposed impellers. The opposed impellers work in parallel. Extraction pump suction side seals are usually supplied with pump discharge water to seal the shaft.

Extraction pumps must operate under severe conditions, as they must maintain a near constant level in the hot well, while pumping nearly boiling water at near zero absolute suction pressure. They must also handle a large range of capacities due to the varying loads of the turbine, which is exhausting to the condenser.

FIGURE 29

Horizontal Extraction Pump

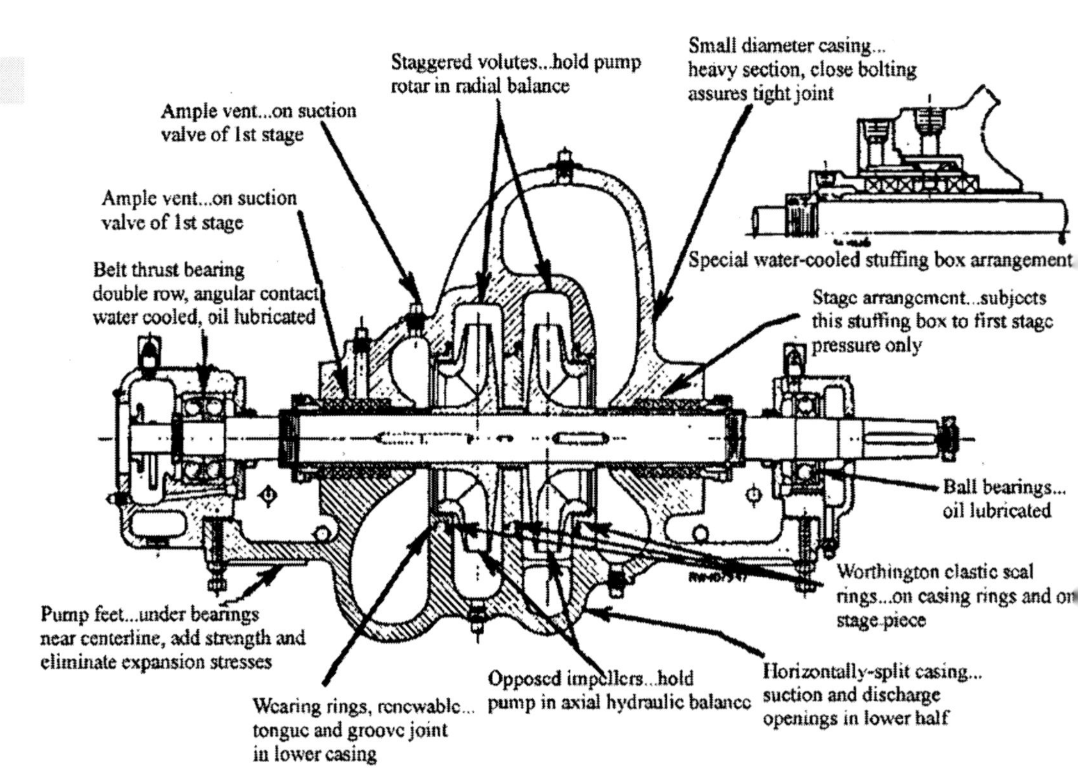

The extraction pump must pump water close to boiling, a condition that requires a very low NPSH (net positive suction head), and exposes the pump to much more cavitation than other pumps. To reduce cavitation the vertical well type extraction pump (Fig. 30) is often used. The flange of the well is level with the floor to increase the suction head. The well is airtight with an air-release line to the condenser. These pumps have better performance and less cavitation than the horizontal pumps.

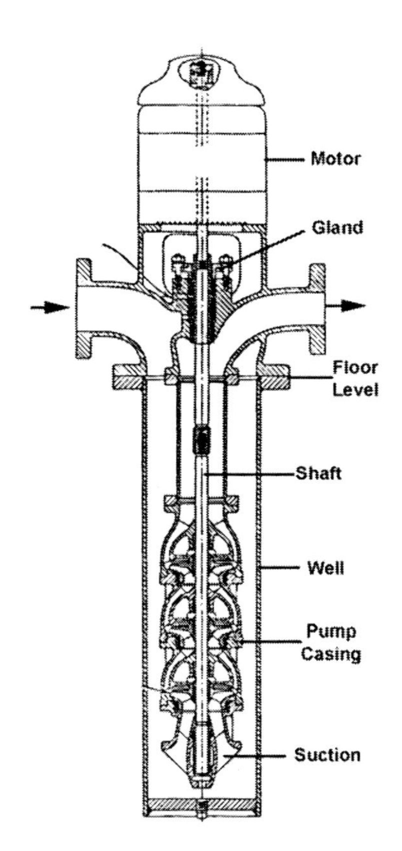

FIGURE 30

Vertical Multistage Extraction Pump

FEEDWATER HEATERS

As explained previously the latent heat of the turbine exhaust steam is lost to the condenser cooling water. The application of feedwater heaters, where the latent heat of bleed steam is used for heating feedwater, reduces the quantity of steam exhausted to the condenser and increases the efficiency. The feedwater heaters are divided into low-pressure and high-pressure heaters.

FIGURE 31

Low Pressure Feedwater Heater

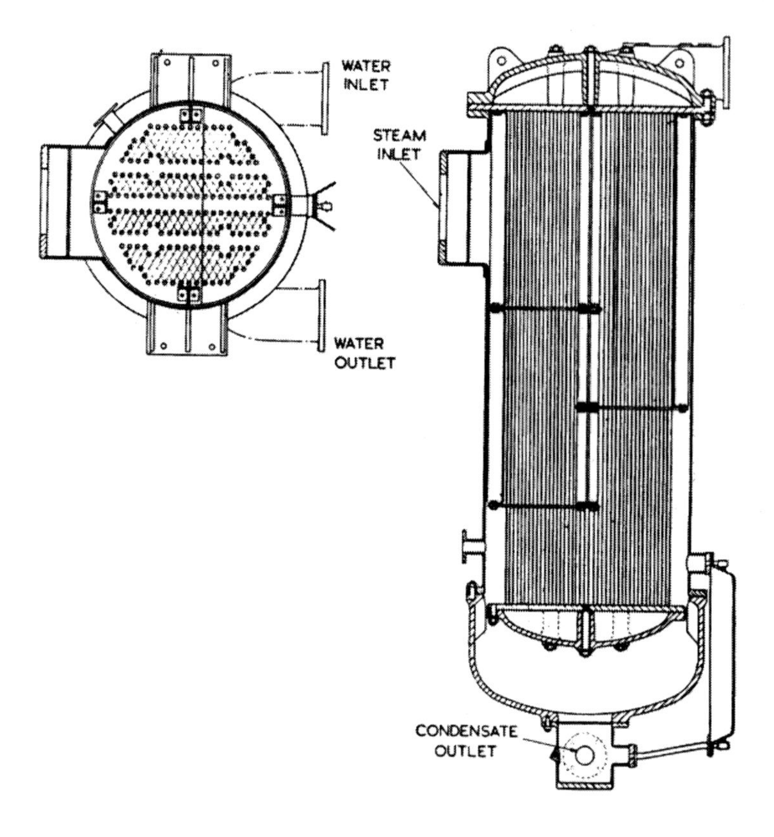

The low-pressure heaters (Fig. 31) have the waterside exposed to the discharge pressure of the extraction pump, while the high-pressure heaters have the boiler feedpump pressure on the waterside.

Low-pressure heaters are often of the straight-tube design. Tubes and tube-sheets are constructed brass, the shell of mild steel, and the waterboxes are of steel or cast iron. The shell may have an expansion bellows or a floating waterbox as in Fig. 31, which allows for expansion and contraction.

The boiler feed pump forces the feedwater through the tubes of the high-pressure heaters. These tubes are of carbon steel and the "U" tube design is general due to the excellent and simple solution for expansion and contraction. (Fig. 32) The tubes may be expanded or welded to the tube sheet.

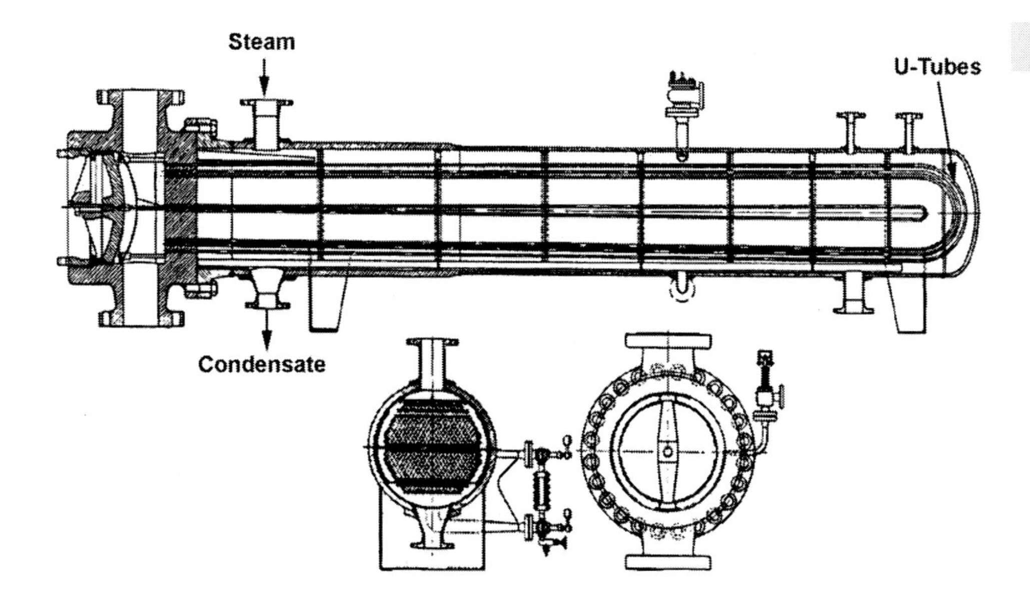

FIGURE 32

High Pressure Feedwater Heater

Heaters vary in shell design, channel layout, and end enclosures. They may be vertical or horizontal. The shell has an expansion joint when the tubes are welded into the tube sheets, or a floating head.

Fig. 33 illustrates a single pass heat exchanger with an internal floating head. The floating head, which is connected to the tube bundle, fits snugly against the outer pressure shell. It can however, move enough to allow for the expansion of the tubes.

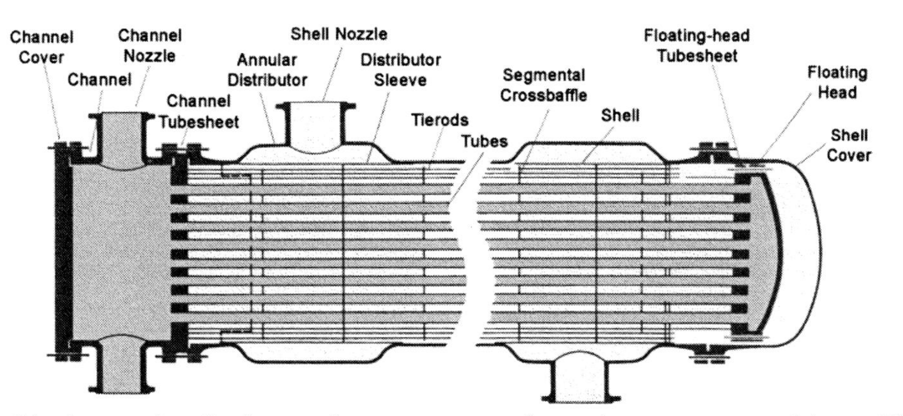

FIGURE 33

Heat Exchanger with Floating Head

Fig. 34 shows the feedwater heater system for a large steam turbine. The condensate passes through the air-ejector coolers, drain-cooler, low-pressure heaters into the deaerator heater. The boiler feed pump then pumps the deaerated water from the deaerator through a series of three high-pressure heaters to the boiler. The feedwater heaters, both high-pressure and low-pressure, and the deaerator are all supplied with steam bled from various stages of the turbine.

FIGURE 34

Feedwater Heater System

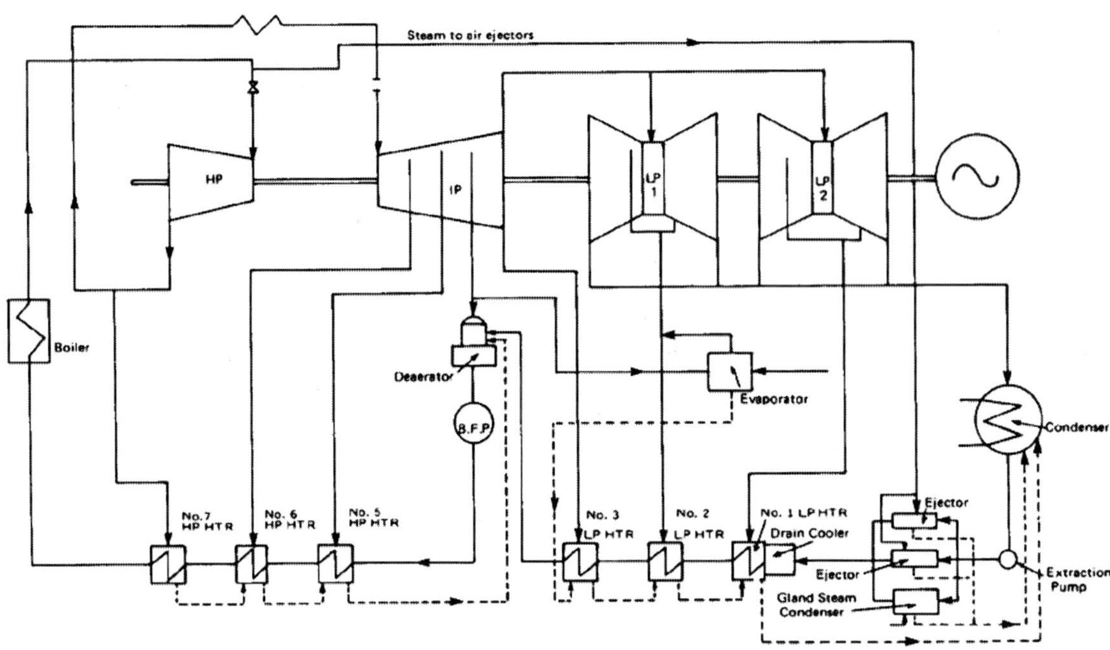

A six-stage feedwater heating system is shown in Fig. 35. The temperature of the condensate as it makes its way through the system is shown. The bleed steam supplying the heaters is not shown. The dotted lines indicate steam that is flashed condensate from one heater to the next lowest pressure heater. The deaerating heater is the 3rd stage of feedwater heating. The water temperature is raised from 100°F at the condenser hotwell to 490°F entering the steam generator economizer.

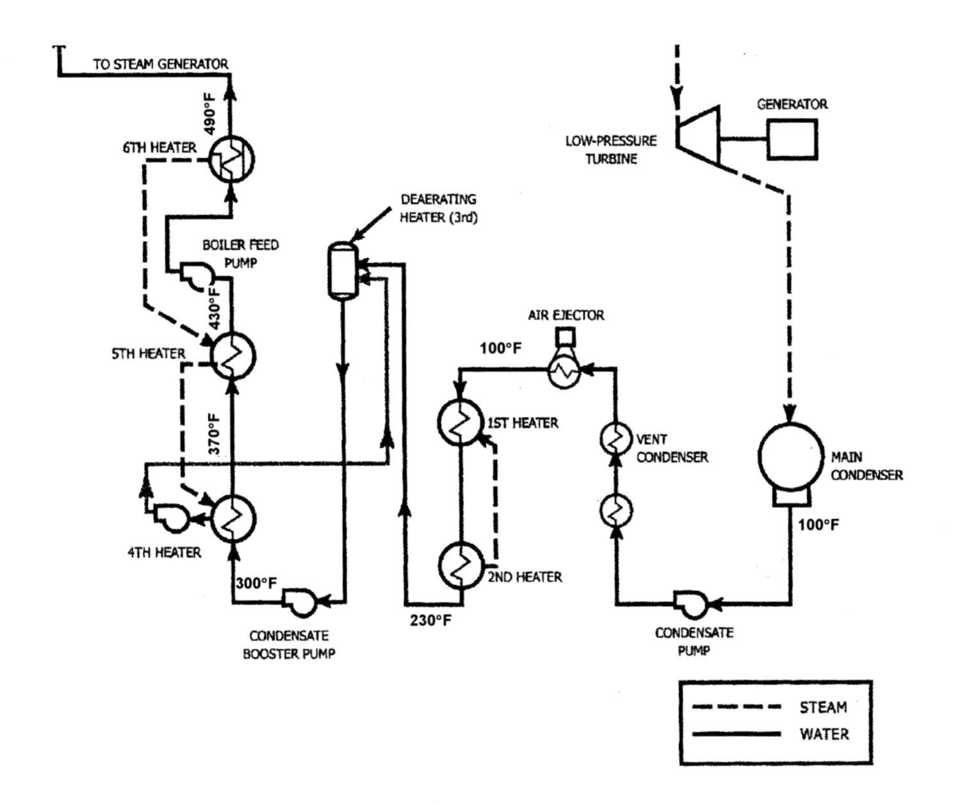

FIGURE 35

Six Stage Feedwater Heating System with Temperatures

UNIT 7

Rotating Equipment Monitoring

Learning Objectives

Here is what you will be able to do when you complete each objective:

1. Describe the purpose, importance and types of rotating equipment monitoring.
2. Explain the concept and significance of turbine thermal expansion, the general principles and placement of measuring devices, and the procedures to control.
3. Explain the concept and significance of turbine differential expansion, the general principle and placement of measuring devices, and the procedures to control.
4. Explain the concept and significance of turbine eccentricity, the general principle and placement of measuring devices, and the procedures to control.
5. Explain the concept of vibration, including typical causes, effects, and locations of vibration in rotating equipment and how it is measured.
6. Explain the concept and significance of turbine critical speed.
7. Explain the concept and significance of oil whirl, oil whip, and steam whirl, and the design and operational considerations to counter oil whirl.
8. Describe common oil problems and their effects on rotating equipment and a typical oil sampling and testing program.

PURPOSE AND IMPORTANCE OF ROTATING EQUIPMENT MONITORING

Effective monitoring is a critical factor in the successful operation of all types of rotating equipment. Monitoring systems are varied and include: vibration, thermal expansion measurement, temperature monitoring, pressures, performance, and oil condition. This module will focus on monitoring techniques for steam turbines, but many of these techniques are used for all types of rotating equipment.

The primary purposes of monitoring are to:

- Ensure that operating limits are not exceeded

- Minimize wear and deterioration on rotating components, especially during startup and shutdown

- Maximize equipment performance

- Extend the life of equipment

- Provide warning of potential problems that can lead to major failure

- Assist with diagnosis of equipment condition in order to plan maintenance activities

- Ensure that equipment condition and performance has been restored after maintenance

The importance of monitoring relates to all aspects of operation and maintenance including:

- Minimizing operating and maintenance costs
- Achieving high reliability
- Obtaining maximum availability
- Maintaining high levels of performance and efficiency

TYPES OF ROTATING EQUIPMENT MONITORING

For rotating equipment, monitoring is largely integrated with the control system and highly computerized. This integration allows instrumentation to be used for monitoring equipment condition, controlling rotating equipment operation, and providing protection from abnormal conditions.

In general, monitoring for rotating equipment can be grouped into the following types:

- Performance such as power output, process flows, steam flow, and amount of heating or cooling
- Vibration monitoring
- Oil monitoring
- Temperature monitoring of components such as bearings
- Process readings including temperatures, pressures, and flows
- Thermal expansion including differential expansion and eccentricity
- Condition monitoring of auxiliary systems using pressures, temperatures, and fluid levels

The specific monitoring used and the way it is applied is naturally dependent on the type of rotating equipment. Its size is a factor since larger rotating equipment justifies more extensive monitoring due to the consequences of failure. In critical applications, close monitoring is also necessary because of the impact a failure will have.

STEAM TURBINE MONITORING SYSTEMS

In this module, a large steam turbine generator is used to illustrate the major types of monitoring that are used for rotating equipment. The system that performs monitoring and control of a steam turbine is known as a turbine supervisory instrumentation (TSI) system. These systems feature highly accurate instrumentation converted at source to digital signals that are transmitted over high-speed networks to computerized control systems.

A TSI system monitors the following indicators of equipment condition:

- Rotor eccentricity
- Rotor/casing differential expansion
- Steam/metal differential temperature
- Shell or casing expansion
- Shaft vibration
- Bearing cap vibration
- Rotor axial position
- Rotor speed and acceleration
- Steam valve position

It is important to recognize that these parameters are interrelated and deal mostly with the effects of temperature changes that occur primarily on startup and shutdown.

CONCEPT OF THERMAL EXPANSION

Thermal expansion occurs whenever a turbine is heated, as in a startup, and contraction occurs whenever it is cooled as in a shutdown. Problems arise mainly because of what is called **differential expansion** which is the result of different components, especially the casing and the rotor spindle, expanding at different rates during startup. Differential expansion occurs because the turbine casing contains a much greater mass of metal than the rotor does, so it expands and contracts more slowly than the rotor when steam temperatures change. This expansion causes effects such as rubbing and rotor bowing which become evident in higher vibration levels. The limiting factors to heating are the thermal stresses due to temperature gradients, distortion arising from these stresses, and the risk of rubbing due to excessive differential expansion.

Monitoring of these thermal effects can be broken down into three categories:

- Shell (or casing) expansion
- Differential expansion between the casing and the rotor
- Eccentricity of the shaft

Stresses and distortions set up in the turbine depend upon the temperature difference between the heating medium (steam) and the metal being heated. When a turbine has been shut down for only a short period, the metal retains a considerable amount of heat and reaches its operating temperature again much more quickly than when starting cold. Some authorities give a metal cooling rate of about 55°F per hour. This varies considerably depending on the size of the machine, the initial temperature, and the amount of insulation used.

Starting and stopping increases wear and can induce high stresses in materials used in the casing of a steam turbine and the drum of a boiler, both of which have thick walls to withstand the high pressure of the steam. When steam is first admitted into the turbine during startup, the inner surface of the casing becomes hotter than the outer surface and expands more than the outer surface. This differential expansion creates stresses in the casing and could produce fatigue cracking with consequential reduction in the life of the casing material. Differential expansion, during startup of thick walled vessels and pipes subject to high temperature, restricts the ability of a steam-driven power station to quickly startup from cold.

The best steam-to-metal temperature difference is thought to be about 100°F - 175°F (inlet steam to inlet belt metal); the safe rate of increase of metal temperature about 400°F per hour. Larger machines require a slower heating rate, down to 100°F, and the manufacturer's operating instructions should be closely followed. Where the HP cylinder cover joint is secured with clamps, the temperature differential between flange and clamp must be kept to a safe maximum to prevent straining of the clamps. Using these temperature guides, with the assistance of instrumentation to monitor eccentricity and vibration, very rapid running up and loading rates have been developed. For example, a 60 MW machine operating at 850 psi and 900°F, having been shut down for 8 hours, might be run up to speed in 15 minutes and loaded to 60 MW in a further 15 minutes.

A gas turbine can start up much faster because it does not have these thick-walled vessels or pipes and because it is made of more exotic alloys. However, the rate of increase in temperature of the rotor shaft and the blades is still critical to avoid differential expansion overstressing and thus still places a limit on the startup time of a gas turbine. The reduction in life of the gas turbine blades associated with a startup is considered to be equivalent to the reduction in life caused by several hours of standard operation.

SHELL EXPANSION

Starting a turbine means heating it and heating entails expansion. The turbine is designed to allow the supports to slide easily to give axial and radial expansion while at the same time maintaining the fixed and moving parts concentric with each other.

Figure 1 gives an example of this thermal expansion on an HP and IP cylinder where the cylinders are anchored at the exhaust end and expand towards the inlet, and the spindle thrust bearings are at the inlet of the cylinders.

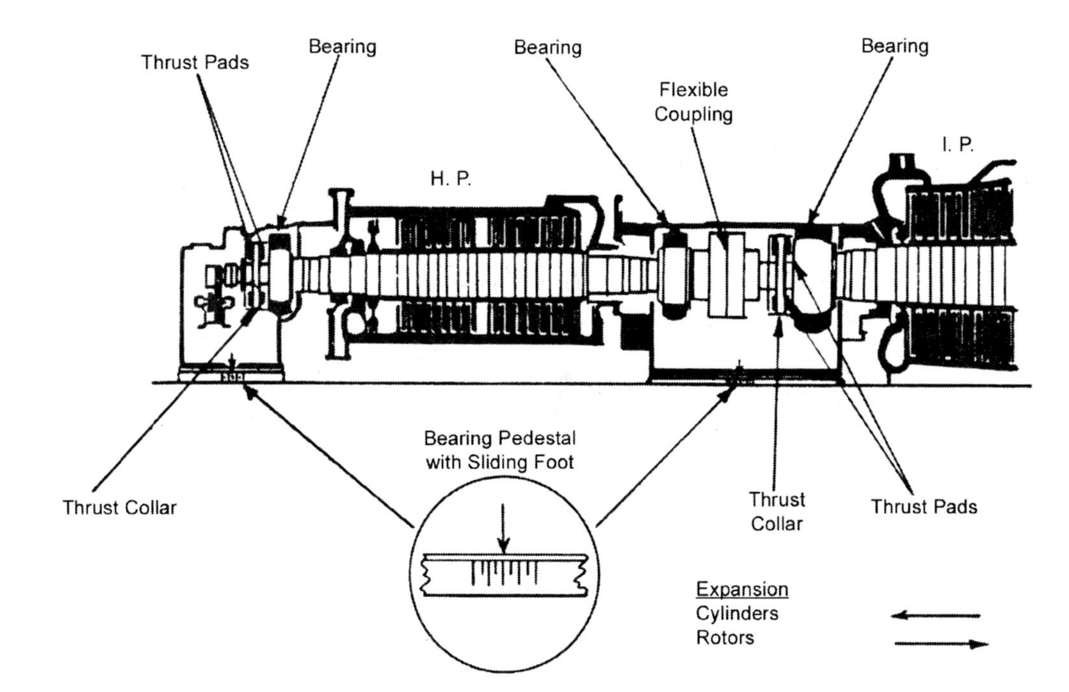

FIGURE 1

Expansion of a Steam Turbine

Occasionally, due to improper turbine shell preheating, maintenance or location of the steam inlets being used to preheat the turbine, the turbine shell may become distorted causing internal damage.

Turbine cocking (see Figure 2) occurs when the turbine slider hangs up or sticks on one side of the foundation and continues to grow or slide on the other. This condition sometimes corrects itself by breaking loose quite dramatically. If the turbine case does not grow evenly, it is allowed to cool and is then reheated with more even heat distribution.

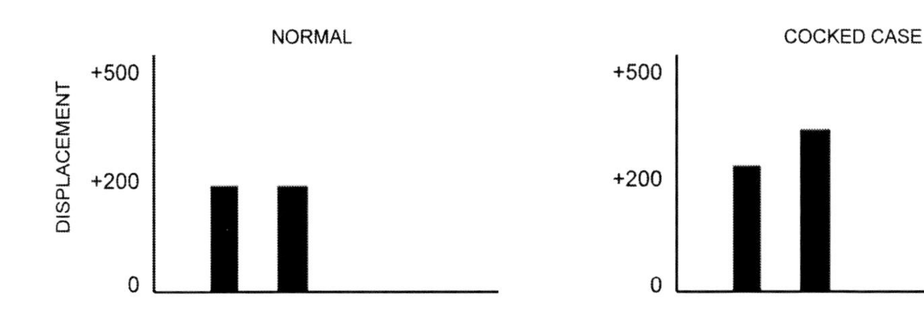

FIGURE 2

Cocking of a Turbine Case

MEASUREMENT OF EXPANSION

Measurement of expansion and monitoring for distortion or cocking is accomplished by installing a device on either side of the turbine case. In some cases, coil induction detectors operate on an electromagnetic inductor principle and consist, in essence, of a variable impedance element in a Wheatstone bridge circuit. These detectors are now being replaced by linear variable differential transformer transducers.

As seen in Figure 3, LVDTs are electromagnetic devices that have three coils of wire wound on a hollow tube with a metal rod moving inside the tube. The primary coil of wire is excited by a supply voltage which induces a voltage in the other coils as the rod or plunger travels throughout its range. When the plunger is centered in its range, the induced voltage of the two secondary coils is equal in magnitude, but opposite in polarity. As the plunger moves to either side of the centre position, the voltage of one of the secondary coils increases while that of the other secondary coil decreases. Direct current (DC) LVDTs differ from alternating current (AC) LVDTs in that they are manufactured with an internal carrier generator/signal conditioning module and only require DC power to operate.

FIGURE 3

Layout of a LVDT

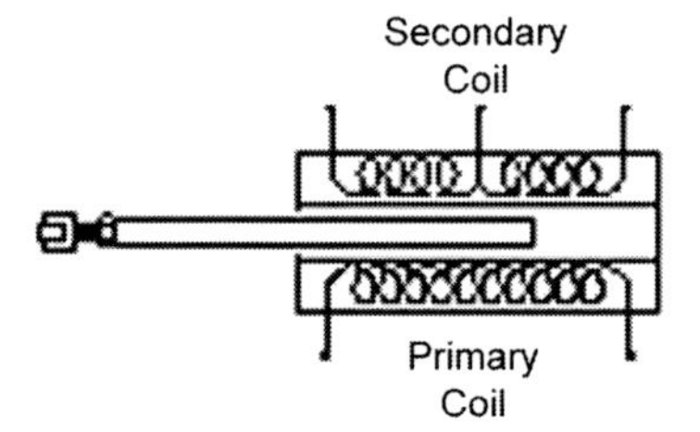

The body of the LVDT is designed to be rigidly attached to the turbine foundation the spring-loaded roller tipped plunger presses against a bracket that is attached to the turbine case. The bracket must be designed not to interfere with turbine operation and to allow the roller tip of the plunger to ride freely against it throughout the entire range.

A standard LVDT has an operating range of 1.0, 2.0 or 4.0 inches (25, 50, or 100 mm). The most commonly used is 0-2 inches (0-50 mm) with an output of (-7.5)-0-(+7.5) volts direct current (VDC) and an accuracy of ±0.5 % full scale. A shorter range may be selected by using the centre portion of the LVDT standard operating range.

The standard instrument convention indicates that as the plunger or rod is compressed into the LVDT body (motion towards the transducer), the signal output increases. The LVDT may be installed in either direction so that thermal growth causes a more positive going signal or a negative going signal. The monitoring system can usually be configured for either direction.

If a turbine casing does not expand as it should during initial heating, it may be that the sliding surfaces are binding. This can sometimes be corrected with additional lubrication, such as applying grease to the grease nipples.

Large turbines are often constructed with longitudinal channels inside the flanged surfaces of the casing half joints. Steam can be admitted to these channels to heat the casing metal that is not directly exposed to turbine steam. This process is called **flange warming**. It must be used sparingly, because the steam used tends to force the flange surfaces apart, and it will eventually stretch the studs.

DIFFERENTIAL EXPANSION

Whereas shell expansion deals with axial movement of the turbine casing with respect to the foundation, differential expansion describes the movement of the rotor with respect to the case.

Differential expansion monitoring measures the change in axial clearances between the machine rotor and casing caused by thermal changes inherent in most machines. The primary purpose of a differential expansion monitor is to guard against axial rub between rotating and stationary parts. This measurement is typically performed on larger steam turbines. Excessive differential expansion can produce catastrophic failures of rotary machinery resulting in very expensive repairs and possibly machine replacement.

The differential expansion measurement should not be confused with other axial position measurements such as rotor position and thrust position. These are designed to measure the axial position of the rotor within the machine train, with minimal or no effect from machine thermal changes. The parameters are equally important for proper machine protection. However, the location and application of these measurements are completely different from those of differential expansion.

When discussing differential expansion, there are two basic machine conditions that can occur during machine operation:

- The rotor long condition
- The rotor short condition

Rotor Long

When high-temperature steam is applied to the machine (during startup), the rotor thermally expands at a faster rate than the machine casing because of the rotor's smaller mass and different metallurgy. When the rotor grows faster than the casing, the condition is referred to as a **rotor long** condition (the rotor is growing long with respect to the case). If the rate of rotor growth in relation to the rate of casing growth is not controlled, the moving and stationary parts of the machine come into contact.

Figure 4 shows a typical turbine double flow low-pressure stage. As the rotor grows longer, clearances between the rotor-mounted blade rows and the case-mounted diaphragms diminish. Attention should be given to seal steam temperatures applied to the unit, as excessive seal steam temperatures have been known to cause excessive differential expansion values during machine startup procedures.

FIGURE 4

Rotor Long Differential Expansion

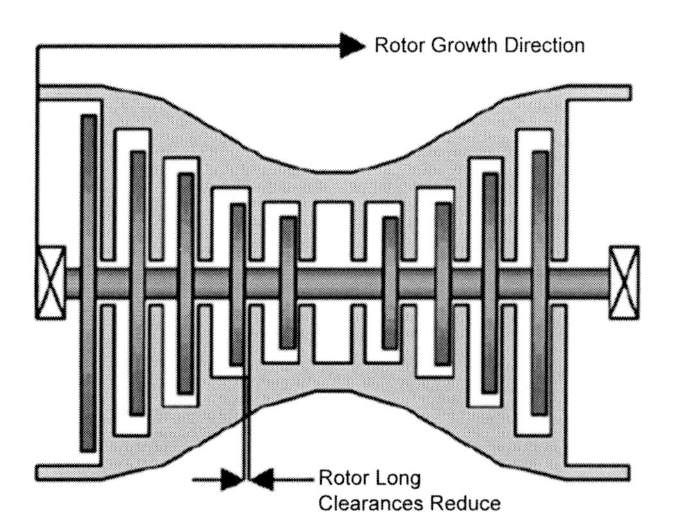

To control the system's rate of expansion, steam temperatures and flows must be controlled. Turbine soak periods further control the expansion process. **Soak period** is a term that describes the amount of time that the machine's speed is controlled to allow the machine's casing to thermally expand and catch up to the rotor assembly. During these periods, steam temperatures and flows are strictly maintained to prevent diminishing the machine's internal clearances.

Rotor Short

The **rotor short** condition typically occurs during steady state operation. Rotor short describes the condition where the rotor shrinks with respect to the machine case. As with the rotor long condition, when the machine is subjected to a sudden temperature change, the rotor reacts first due to its smaller mass and differing metallurgical properties.

Figure 5 shows a typical turbine double flow low-pressure stage. As the rotor contracts, as in a short rotor condition, clearances between the rotor-mounted blade rows and the case-mounted diaphragms diminish.

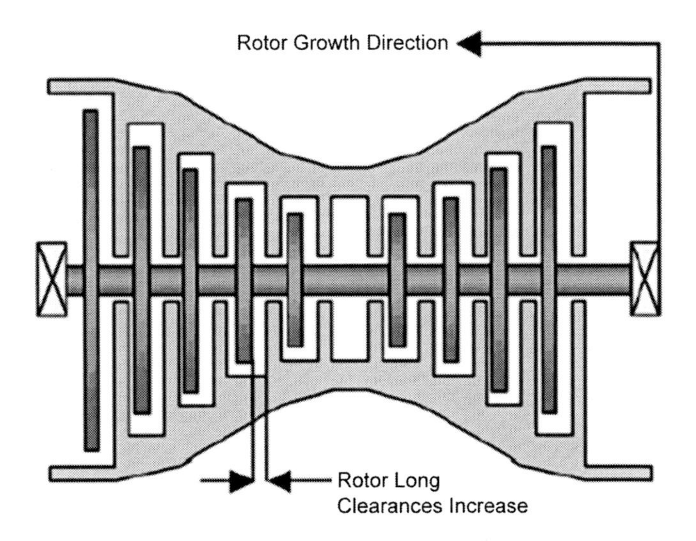

FIGURE 5

Rotor Short Differential Expansion

To cause a rotor short condition, a cooling force must be applied to the rotor assembly. This cooling effect is typically caused by a drastic reduction in steam temperature or flow within the machine and is usually called **quenching the rotor**. Subjecting the rotor to this cooling effect causes the rotor to shrink with respect to the machine case, thus diminishing internal clearances in the rotor short direction. If this quenching action exceeds acceptable limits, the rotor short condition can occur very quickly. Acceptable limits in the rotor short direction are typically small when compared to those for the rotor long direction. The standard machine is designed to have larger internal clearances in the rotor long direction, as this condition is typical during the machine startup process. The rotor short condition, however, is designed to have smaller clearances to increase unit efficiency as this condition should not occur during normal operation. Turbine seals that use water as a sealing medium can cause this condition if excessive seal water is applied. The excess water will leak into the turbine producing quenching.

MEASUREMENT OF DIFFERENTIAL EXPANSION

To accurately measure differential expansion, it is important to understand the machine's basic thermal characteristics. Without this, a full understanding of how to set up the differential expansion system or how to retrofit the unit cannot be achieved. Although each installation is configured slightly differently, understanding the machine and how it is designed to move ensures a successful installation.

The first and most important thing to understand is that the metal alloys and castings used in the fabrication of turbine rotors and cases expand or grow as a temperature increase is applied to them. Restricting the thermal growth of either the case or the rotor may cause internal damage to the turbine. To prevent an increase in stresses placed upon the turbine casings and rotor assemblies, all machines are designed to allow unrestricted growth of these parts.

The actual location of differential expansion transducers is dependent on the configuration of the turbine and specifically where the casings are constrained or able to move. Figure 6 illustrates a layout where sensors are located on the couplings.

FIGURE 6

Layout of Differential Expansion Transducers

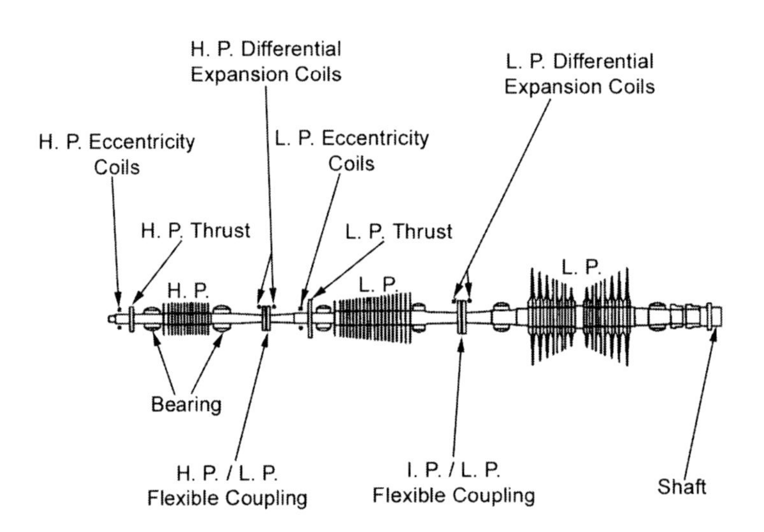

Sensors based on coil capacitance or inductance systems are being replaced by eddy current probes which are more reliable and accurate.

Eddy probe systems operate on the proximity theory of operation. The signal sensor generates a high frequency oscillating RF - radio frequency signal that is sent through the extension cable to the pickup tip. The pickup tip, containing a wound coil of fine wire, radiates an electromagnetic field. As the radiated field is bisected by the rotor surface, eddy currents are created on the rotor surface. As the rotor surface moves closer to the pickup tip, a greater number of eddy currents are created proportional to the gap between the surface and the pickup tip. The signal sensor contains a demodulator which measures the increase in eddy currents and generates an equivalent DC voltage proportional to the gap.

Because the eddy probe tip radiates a high frequency signal which is basically in a conical shape of 45° from the probe tip, the target area must be about three times the tip diameter. Care must be taken to ensure that the eddy probe transducer is mounted perpendicular to within a few degrees of the target or viewing area. Excessive mounting error will change the calibration factor of the installation. However, the transducer is not affected by oil or other non-conductive material that may come between the target area and the transducer.

An eddy current probe is usually mounted close to a collar on the turbine as shown in Figure 7. Dual transducers with a probe on either side of the collar are often installed to extend the range of the expansion that can be measured. They can be set up in a complimentary fashion so that as the rotor moves out of the range of one transducer, it enters the range of another. The best locations are typically located as far from the thrust assembly as possible because this is the location where the maximum rotor growth can be observed.

Differential expansion is derived by the monitoring system by comparing the signals from the eddy current probe (motor position) and LVDT (casing position).

FIGURE 7

Installation of an Eddy Probe Transducer

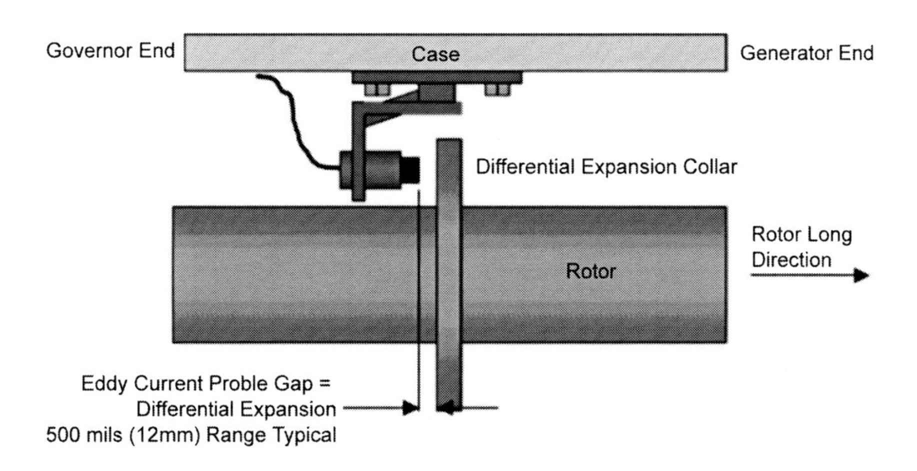

Some turbines have machined conical surfaces or ramps on the turbine shaft at one or more locations. Ramps increase the operating range of the measurement transducer by the sine of the ramp angle allowing larger measurements or the use of shorter range transducers.

ECCENTRICITY

In a turbine which has just shut down, the top and bottom halves of the cylinders tend to cool at different rates. If the spindles are kept rotating slowly at this time (usual barring gear speed about 20 r/min), the halves retain an even temperature at all points on their periphery and are prevented from **hogging** or **sagging.**

FIGURE 8

Rotor Eccentricity: Hogging or Sagging

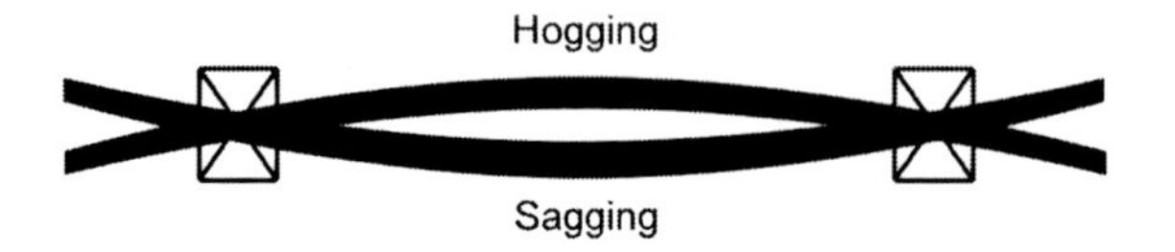

The same principle is applicable to the warming up period, when the steam entering tends to rise to the top of the casing. A stationary spindle would become hotter at the top than at the bottom and would tend to hog. Rotation of the spindles during these periods produces a fan action from the blading which promotes circulation and helps to even out the cylinder heating or cooling.

Further, by slowly turning the shaft journals and supplying oil to the bearings at the same time, damage to the white metal linings of the bearings, due to heat conducted along the shaft, may be prevented.

It is interesting at this stage to have a quantitative idea of the spindle eccentricity problem; the following generalizations will help.

In extreme cases of thermal/gravity bow, caused by a sudden trip of the unit and failure of the turning gear to engage, the rotor may be positioned and stopped 180° out of phase (bow up) to allow gravity to work entirely on the bow and substantially shorten the time required to reduce the bow.

The purpose of barring gear is to make sure that the turbine spindles remain straight during the time that the machine is off load.

Example, a turbine spindle for a typical high pressure turbine having a mass of 5.0 tons; it is 9.0 ft between bearings and the inlet steam temperature is 900°F. If this spindle is bent sufficiently to displace the centre of mass by 0.003 in. (0.08 mm). from the axis of rotation, then at 3600 r/min the centrifugal force produced will be due to the mass of the rotor. Further, if the spindle has a temperature all along one side 35°F higher than along the other side, then it will bend so that the centre of mass is displaced 0.00098 in..

These figures of 0.0031 in. bend in a 8.2 ft shaft and 35°F temperature difference, with 900°F inlet steam, serve to show the small differences that produce vibration.

MEASUREMENT OF ECCENTRICITY

Mechanical means have been used in the past to measure the amount of shaft eccentricity and the relative expansion between spindle and casing, these being the two major contributors to running up to speed.

Figure 9 shows a dial gauge for shaft eccentricity which gives good indication at low up to about 2000 r/min. It is most important that a stationary bend is corrected before the turbine is run up to speed because of the danger of making it permanent. A gauge of this kind enables the development, or dissipation, of a bend to be closely watched at low speeds. The differential axial expansion of cylinder and spindle can be measured by a similar arrangement of dial gauge.

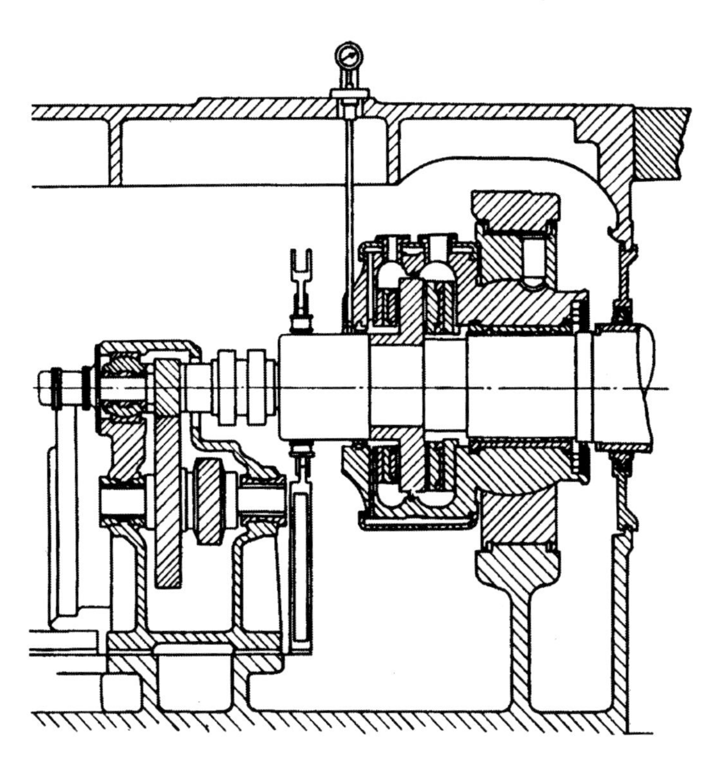

FIGURE 9

Dial Gauge (mounted on bearing pedestal) Indicating Rotor Eccentricity

Modern systems use eddy current probes similar to those used for differential expansion to measure eccentricity.

Eccentricity is measured while the turbine is on slow roll (1 to 240 r/min below the speed at which the rotor becomes dynamic and rises in the bearing on the oil wedge) and requires special circuitry to detect the peak-to-peak motion of the shaft. This motion is detected using circuitry with long update times selectable between 20 seconds (> 3 r/min) and 2 minutes (<3 r/min).

The eccentricity measurement is not required after a turbine is brought to speed; underload provisions are made to lock the measurement to zero. This condition can be accomplished without external contacts through the use of a speed measurement channel with underspeed or overspeed alarms.

As it is impractical to mount eddy probe transducers on the midspan of the rotor where the eccentricity measurement is the highest, the transducers are mounted outside the pressure case as far from the bearing as practical. The bearing should be avoided as a mounting location because, during slow roll operation, the rotor is turning in the bottom of the journal bearing and is not dynamic while the eccentricity measurements are being made. This effect forces the bearings to become nodal points.

Assuming uniform stiffness and weight, the rotor mid-span eccentricity may be expressed as the ratio of the transducer span from the bearing over the transducer measured eccentricity to 1/2 the bearing span over the midspan eccentricity or calculated using the following formula (see also Figure 10):

EQUATION 4.1

$$E_{ms} = \frac{1}{2} \times \frac{S_b}{S_t} \times E_t$$

where E_{ms} = eccentricity at midspan

E_t = eccentricity at transducer

S_b = span between bearings

S_t = span from transducer to bearing

FIGURE 10

Estimating Eccentricity at Rotor Midspan

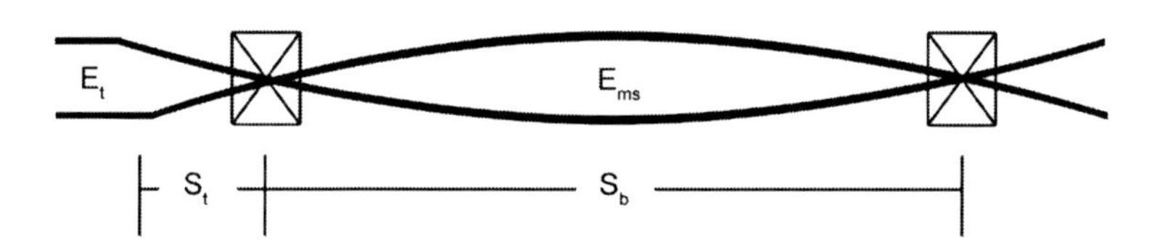

This formula yields an approximate calculation and original equipment manufacturers (OEM) should be consulted for actual calculations.

CONCEPT OF VIBRATION

Vibration is a fundamental aspect of rotating equipment. In its simplest rorm, vibration is a regular oscillation of an object. All rotating equipment produces vibration as a result of the energy that is being produced. A perfectly balanced rotating mass could, in theory, operate with no vibration, but imperfections, even slight ones, result in a certain level of vibration.

The most basic form of vibration can be illustrated by a sine wave which describes a regular oscillation about a centerline. The frequency of the oscillation is determined by the nature of the forcing function or the energy input. For rotating equipment, this force is almost always related to the rotation of a rotor or shaft where one period of the sine wave is equal to one rotation of the shaft. The most important force acting at a frequency that corresponds to rotational speed is unbalance which is caused by an uneven distribution of mass around the centerline of the shaft.

In real situations, other frequencies exist due to the different types of forces acting on the shaft. Misalignment shows itself mostly as a vibration at twice the rotating speed. In a turbine, there are vibration frequencies equal to the number of blades in a rotor stage times the rotating speed due to the excitation produced by the rotor blades passing the stator blades. In gear systems, vibration occurs at a frequency based on the number of gear teeth and the rotating speed.

A chart showing typical problems related to vibration frequency and rotating speed (RS) can be found in Table 1.

TABLE 1

General Vibration Frequency Chart

Vibration Frequency	Types of Problems	Cause See note
0-40% running speed (RS)	Oil-whip resonance, friction-induced whirl, loose bearing, loose seals, bearing damage, bearing-support resonance, case distortion, poor shrink fit, torsional critical speed	1
40-60% RS	Half-speed whirl, oil-whip resonance, worn bearings, support resonance, coupling damage, poor shrink fit, bearing-support resonance, rotor rub (axial), seal rub, torsional critical speed	1
60-100% RS	Loose bearing, loose seals, poor shrink fit, torsional critical speed	1,2
Running speed	Unbalance, lateral critical speed, torsional critical speed, transient torsional, foundation resonance, bearing-support resonance, bent shaft, bearing damage, thrust-bearing damage, bearings eccentric, seal rub, loose impeller, loose coupling, case distortion, shaft out-of-round, case vibrations	3
200% RS	Misalignment, loose coupling, seal rub, case distortion, bearing damage, loose coupling, support resonance, thrust-bearing damage	1,2,3
n x RS	Blade or vane frequency, pressure pulsations, misalignment, case distortion, seal rub, gear inaccuracy	3,4
Very high frequency	Shaft rub, seals, bearings, gear inaccuracy, bearing chatter, poor shrink fit	3,4
Non-synchronous frequencies > RS	Piping vibrations, foundation resonance, case resonance, pressure pulsations, valve vibrations, noise, shaft rubs, cavitation	5

Cause 1: Bearing-related problems

- Low-stability-type bearing
- Excessive bearing clearance
- Loose liners
- Impurities in oil
- Improper oil properties (viscosity, temperature)
- Frothing of oil due to air or process fluid
- Poor lubrication
- Worn bearings

Cause 2: Seal-related problems

- Excessive clearance
- Loose retainers
- Too-tight clearance
- Worn seals

Cause 3: Unit-design-related problems

- Critical speed
- Loose coupling sleeves
- Thermal gradients
- Shaft not concentric
- Inadequate support stiffness
- Pedestal or support resonance
- Case distortion
- Thrust bearing or thrust balance deficiencies
- Unbalance
- Coupling unbalance
- Bent shaft
- Loose shrink fits

Cause 4. System-related problems

- Torsional criticals
- Pedestal resonances
- Foundation resonances
- Misalignment
- Excessive piping loads
- Gear tooth inaccuracies/wear
- Piping mechanical resonances

Cause 5: System-flow-related problems

- Pulsation
- Vortex shedding
- Piping shell resonances
- Inadequate flow area
- Inadequate NPSH (for pumps)
- Acoustic resonance
- Cavitation (in pumps)

TYPES OF VIBRATION TRANSDUCERS

Most drivers and driven rotating equipment are fitted with vibration monitoring both for protection against and prediction of problems. In addition to permanently installed vibration sensors, some companies have vibration programs that entail manual vibration monitoring using handheld transducers.

A variety of transducer types are used in rotating equipment. Acceleration transducers are common on aeroderivative gas turbines, motors, gear reducers and pumps that use antifriction bearings. They are can be mounted on any accessible surface, but usually on the bearing housings. Measurements should always be taken in both the horizontal and vertical planes as support stiffness often varies. The major advantage of acceleration transducers is the ability to detect vibration with high frequencies.

Shaft displacement using proximity probes is used for industrial gas turbines, steam turbines, compressors, electric motors and pumps that utilize journal type bearings. Proximity probes, which can only be used for equipment with sleeve bearings, utilize a non-contacting eddy current to measure the actual shaft displacement; they are installed in the bearing housing and look directly at the shaft. Two probes at 90 degrees are used; the signals are integrated with a measurement of shaft phase angle so that the orbit can be examined.

USE OF VIBRATION IN PREDICTIVE MAINTENANCE

The importance of and reason for vibration monitoring is, first of all, to protect against high levels of vibration which will damage the machine. Whenever vibration transducers are installed permanently, they are almost always tied into the control system where the actual vibration is compared to an alarm level and sometimes a shutdown level. There may be a voting system between vibration transducers to eliminate nuisance alarms or shutdowns.

In addition, vibration levels may be trended so that longer term changes can be detected. Maintenance can then be planned and the impact of the repair can be minimized. This process is sometimes called predictive maintenance.

EXPLANATION OF CRITICAL SPEED

By its very nature, rotating equipment vibrates with a prime frequency that corresponds to its rotating speed. Mechanical analysis shows that the rotor responds in a certain manner depending on its physical characteristics. A simple model of a forced vibration system consists of a mass that has an oscillating force constrained by a spring force and a damping force as shown in Figure 11.

FIGURE 11

Forced Vibration System

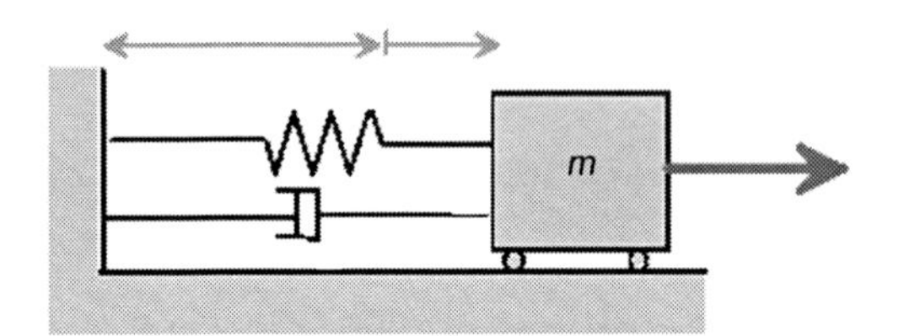

TURBINE CRITICAL SPEED

In a rotating machine, the shaft and rotor are the main vibrating elements and the forcing frequency is at the rotating speed. There is a speed where vibration will be higher than elsewhere in the speed range; this speed should be avoided.

Small rotating machines such as pumps involve light rotors usually with short shafts and high bearing stiffness. As a result, the machine operates below the critical speed.

Large rotating machinery is a different situation. The rotor is much heavier and the shaft is long and slender with low relative stiffness, resulting in what is referred to as a flexible rotor. If the supports are rigid and the bearings stiff, the rotor will respond with the bending modes shown in Figure 12. Each bending mode occurs at a specific critical speed.

FIGURE 12

Flexible Rotor and Rigid Supports

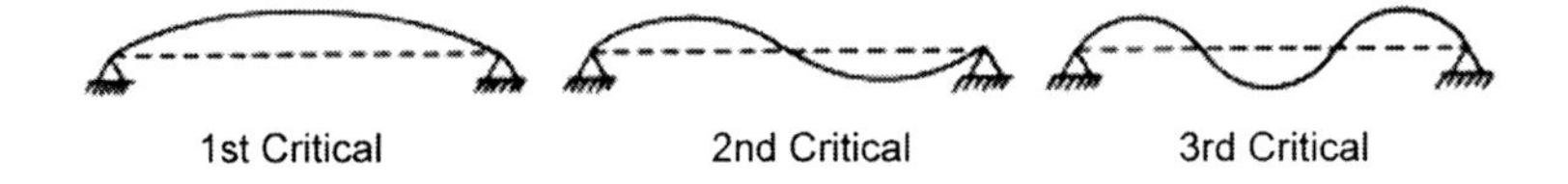

If the supports are flexible and the rotor is relatively rigid, the modes shown in Figure 13 apply. A real machine will exhibit a response somewhere in between these two types of bending moments. The calculation of the critical speeds for a specific rotor is very complicated because the rotor is non-uniform and bearing stiffness is not easy to determine.

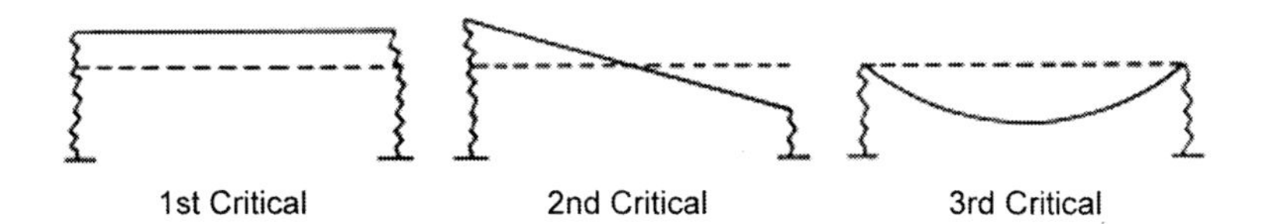

FIGURE 13

Flexible Supports and Rigid Rotor

The desirable operating range for a large rotating machine is normally between the first and second critical speeds. Design standards for the different types of rotating equipment specify the separation between the critical speeds and the operating speed range.

If the operator watches the vibration signal as a turbine is started, an increase in vibration and then a decrease as the rotor passes through the critical speed is seen. The control system typically suppresses alarm and shutdown levels during startup since vibration at the critical speed may well exceed these levels. As the turbine is started, it is desirable to accelerate more quickly at the critical speed to minimize the time spent at the peak vibration levels.

INSTABILITIES IN ROTORS

A number of instabilities can occur in rotating equipment. These result in an increase in vibration which can be severe enough to cause damage to bearings and rotating and stationary components such as rotor blades and stator vanes. The two major types of instabilities relate to:

- Oil bearings which can exhibit oil whirl and oil whip
- Cavities between the shaft and casing that become filled with a fluid such as steam

Oil Bearing Instabilities

The most common type of instability occurs with sleeve or journal bearings and is known as **oil whirl.** At the later stages of oil whirl, another condition called **oil whip** occurs.

Under proper operating conditions, the shaft rides on a stable oil wedge which supports the rotor with adequate damping to keep the rotor in a stable position as shown in Figure 14.

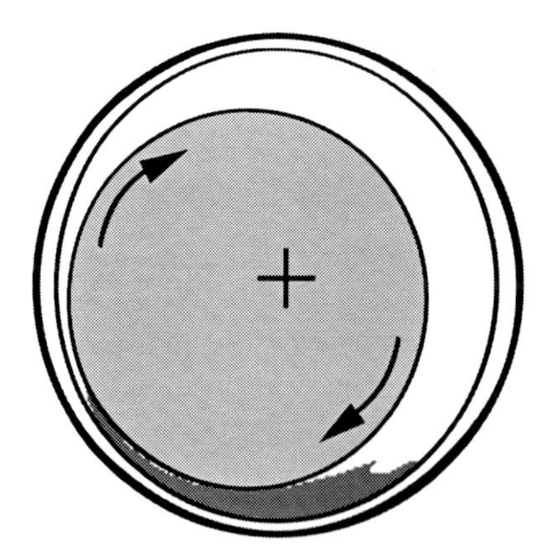

FIGURE 14
Shaft Riding on Stable Oil Wedge

Oil whirl occurs when the oil wedge supporting a shaft in a sleeve bearing becomes unstable. With specific fluid conditions and dimensional factors such as bearing clearance, fluid forces become unstable and the shaft starts to oscillate in a circle at a frequency that is just less than one-half the rotating speed. The shaft is forced into a rotation around the centre of the bearing in a direction that is opposite to the centre of rotation. It is estimated that the oil whirl frequency is between 0.42 and 0.48 of the rotating frequency and between 0.38 to 0.48. Figure 15 shows an example of a frequency chart.

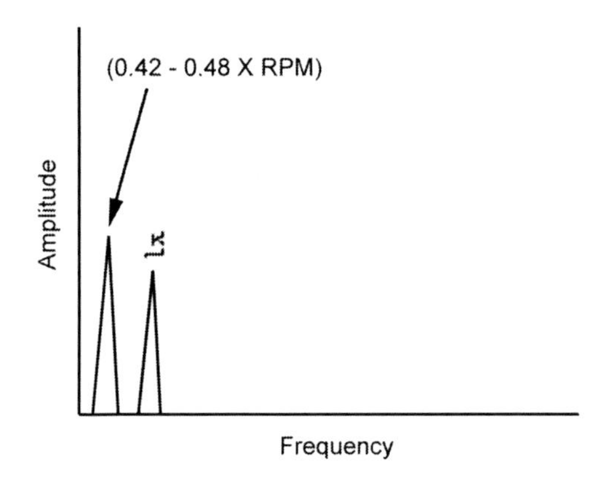

FIGURE 15
Shaft Riding on Stable Oil Wedge

If the rotor speed reaches a value twice that of the critical speed, oil whirl changes into a phenomenon called oil whip where the frequency seems to lock into the critical speed or one-half the running speed.

Oil whirl is often the result of a lightly loaded shaft or excessive bearing clearances. It can sometimes be reduced by changing the viscosity of the oil or the oil temperature.

Oil whirl is often associated with low oil temperature during a startup. It can be corrected by reducing the turbine speed until vibration is at a safe level, and soaking at that speed until oil temperature increases to normal operating temperature.

Tilt pad bearings are often used instead of sleeve bearings because the presence of individual pads seems to counteract the oil whirl mechanism. Some manufacturers put grooves into their bearing pads to add stability to the oil film.

Cavity Instabilities

A similar instability can develop if fluid such as steam collects in a cavity. This condition can occur if there is excessive leakage of steam across a labyrinth seal. The cavity then begins to act as a sleeve bearing. **Steam whirl** is therefore similar to oil whirl, but is much less common. It may be difficult to differentiate between the two phenomena.

OIL PROBLEMS

The lubrication system on major rotating equipment contains a large volume of high grade oil and in itself represents a considerable financial investment. It is essential that such oil be maintained in top condition to protect this investment and, of course, to ensure that it can adequately perform its lubricating and cooling duties in the complex machinery of the turbine and its controls.

In meeting the demands of reliability, continuity of operation, and economy from steam turbines, the turbine depends to a large extent upon the quality of the oil in its lubricating system, for unless this oil performs its functions properly, efficient turbine operation cannot be maintained. The oil must be suitable for continuous service for periods measured in years because complete replacement of the oil charge of a large turbine is a very expensive and lengthy process.

The main causes of deterioration in turbine lubricating oils are discussed in the following paragraphs.

Oxidation

When lubricating oils react with oxygen, materials are formed that impair the quality of the oil. Eventually they become insoluble in the oil, form sludges, especially with water and foreign suspended matter, and promote the formation of deposits. Because of continued oxidation, the oil develops organic acids and, in severe cases, the viscosity increases significantly.

The reaction between oil and oxygen is accelerated by: increasing the temperature, metallic catalysts, water, foreign suspended matter, and the oxidation products themselves. An increase of 50°F in the temperature of the oil approximately doubles the rate of oxidation.

Thus, an oil which gave satisfactory service life where the bearing outlet temperature was 150°F might show quite unsatisfactory life if the temperature was permitted to rise to 175°F. Therefore, operating temperatures should be held within the limits specified by the turbine manufacturers, usually 130°F to 160°F.

Oxidation is promoted by metals that act as catalysts. Copper, brass, bronze and zinc are particularly effective catalysts; their use is avoided as far as possible. Galvanized (zinc coated) iron piping and tanks are not recommended. The adverse effects of copper are overcome by tinning the surfaces that come in contact with the oil.

Moisture may enter the lubricating system through leaks at the sealing glands of steam turbines, at the oil coolers, and through condensation from the atmosphere in the sump tank. The lubricating oil is inspected periodically for the presence of water; and, if detected, its source should be determined and the difficulty eliminated as soon as possible.

The adverse effects of oil oxidation are addressed by using oxidation inhibitors usually incorporated in turbine oils by the refiner. Even under severe operating conditions very small amounts of these materials greatly prolong the useful life of the oil.

Foaming

The formation of foam on the surface of the oil in the sump tank indicates the presence of air in the oil. It is essential that most of the air entrained in the oil flowing through the lubrication system be eliminated before the oil is recirculated. Entrapped air reduces the flow of oil to the bearings and causes erratic operation of the governors. Turbine oils are manufactured so they free themselves of air very rapidly. In general, low viscosity oils dissipate entrained air more rapidly than oils of higher viscosity.

Air entrainment is promoted by the following mechanical and operational conditions:

- Air leakage into the suction line
- Low oil level, permitting the pump suction inlet to become exposed to air
- Insufficient venting of the lubricating system

- Excessive splashing from oil return lines to the sump oil level
- Oil return lines of insufficient size or capacity
- Discharge velocity from pressure regulating valve too high resulting in unnecessary splashing and spray above the oil level
- Operating the circulating oil pump at excessive capacity
- Wide difference in temperature between fresh oil added and the oil in the system.
- Vacuum conditions inside bearings

All of the above conditions are easily corrected by mechanical changes and adjustments.

When hydrogen-cooled generators are employed, the ability of the oil to free itself from entrained gas takes on added importance. The system oil is used to provide an oil film between the continuous babbitt seal face and the shaft flange to prevent the escape of the cooling hydrogen. Because the oil is supplied under a pressure greater than the hydrogen pressure, provisions must be made for the oil flowing through the seal to be returned to a hydrogen detraining tank where the oil and hydrogen are separated.

Emulsions

Water is, without doubt, the most prevalent of all the impurities which contaminate turbine lubricating systems. Steam from leaking shaft seals and condensation of humid air in oil reservoirs and return pipes are the most common sources of water. When water is churned up with a correct unoxidized turbine oil, an emulsion is formed which quickly separates back into oil and water.

Although limited oxidation is not in itself detrimental to the service value of a turbine oil, the products formed as oxidation continues will reduce the ability of the oil to separate out from the water in an emulsion and permanent emulsions may be formed. The presence of dirt and metallic particles tends to accelerate the formation of permanent emulsions and eventually cause deposits and sludge.

Emulsions impair the lubricating qualities of oil and, in extreme cases, rupture of the oil film will result with consequent scoring of bearings or gear teeth.

Sludge

All deposits in turbine oil circulating systems are commonly known as sludge, a slimy mass containing emulsions, oxidized hydrocarbons, and other impurities together with some good oil. Unlike an emulsion, sludge does not form suddenly but is only present after the oil has been in use for some time. Oxidation is the primary cause of oil sludge together with solid contaminants and emulsions. The useful life of a turbine oil therefore depends upon its resistance to oxidation.

Sludge is sometimes deposited when too much new oil is added to a system at one time because the chemical balance of the oil is temporarily disturbed. For this reason, it is considered good practice never to add more than ten percent volume at one time to the turbine oil system capacity.

OIL SAMPLING

For smaller engines, it is usually sufficient to replace the oil on a regular basis as determined by running hours. If engine usage is low as with backup generators (say, less than 50%), oil changing should be based on calendar time with a yearly change being the standard.

For large rotating equipment, it is common to maintain a systematic check on the oil condition by taking representative samples at regular intervals, normally every one to three months as part of a predictive maintenance program. Observation of these samples at site will give indications of major changes in the oil condition; and routine testing carried out in qualified laboratories will ensure an exact record. Oil is then replaced only if its condition requires it.

OIL TESTING

For testing of lube oil, the focus is on three basic areas:

1. Oil quality including viscosity, acid number, and effectiveness of the additive package

2. Contaminants in the oil that may consist of dirt (silicone) or glycol from cooling leaks

3. Wear metals indicating bearing wear or failure

The tests usually carried out on turbine oil samples include the viscosity, color, neutralization value or acid number, water content and any extraneous impurities such as wear metals. No single test determines the serviceability of the oil entirely nor, in fact, does one set of results.

Regular testing and recording, however, will show whatever trends are developing and give indications of conditions within the turbine and the future serviceability of the oil.

Generally speaking, the two most important indications of the oil condition are its appearance and its neutralization value or acid number. Visual inspection of the oil sample discloses whether water is getting into the oiling system or whether contamination by solid impurities is occurring. The sample is allowed to stand for 24 hours to precipitate out any solid impurities. It should then present a clear, bright appearance to show freedom from water content, sludge, and metallic impurities.

The neutralization value is the result of a test designed to ascertain the degree of acidity of the oil due to soluble (and therefore invisible) products of oxidation.

The sample of oil is treated with potassium hydroxide (KOH); the number of milligrams required to produce a neutral mixture per gram is known as the neutralization value of that oil.

As long as the oxidation inhibitors in a turbine oil are effective, the neutralization value will not increase. The exception to this principle is that it may be possible to have foreign acidic contaminants enter the oil and raise the neutralization value even though the oxidation inhibitor is still effective.

Laboratories use spectrographic analysis techniques that can accurately detect the levels of additives, contaminants, and wear metals in the oil and thus check its suitability for continued service. Condemning limits are usually determined by the manufacturer of the oil in conjunction with the manufacturer of the rotating equipment.